Electromagnetic Health

Making Sense of the Research and Practical Solutions for Electromagnetic Fields (EMF) and Radio Frequencies (RF)

By Case Adams, Naturopath

Electromagnetic Health: Making Sense of the Research and
        Practical Solutions for Electromagnetic Fields (EMF)
        and Radio Frequencies (RF)
Copyright © 2010 Case Adams
Copyright © 2012 Case Adams
LOGICAL BOOKS
Wilmington, Delaware
http://www.logicalbooks.org
All rights reserved.
Printed in USA
Front cover image: © Yaroslav Lazunov
Back cover image: © Donald Sawvel
Inside Illustrations: Virginia Callow

Publishers Cataloging in Publication Data
Adams, Case
Electromagnetic Health: Making Sense of the Research and
        Practical Solutions for Electromagnetic Fields (EMF)
        and Radio Frequencies (RF)
First Edition
1.   Science. 2. Health.
        Bibliography and References; Index

Library of Congress Control Number: 2010910561

ISBN Paperback: 978-1-936251-10-0
ISBN ebook: 978-1-936251-13-1

For the future of humankind.
Hopefully we will not screw this up any worse than we
already have.

Table of Contents

Introduction

Imagine you are a U.S. army soldier who has just parachuted into the jungles of Vietnam in the 1960s. You land on the ground and you are surrounded by dense jungle. The birds are whining and cawing with a deafening noise. Other than this, you hear nothing. You see nothing but massive bushes with Jurassic-looking leaves, and vines that wind around the trees like snakes. There is no sign of the enemy. Or is there?

As you look closely, in between the dense leaves, vines and trees, you think you see a little movement. Is the enemy hiding behind the trees and bushes? Are they going to ambush you at any time and machine-gun you down? Should you just start shooting at the bushes just in case? Or should you relax, knowing that you would have been dead by now if the enemy was in the bushes?

This situation is not unlike the situation many of us feel we are in at the moment when it comes to the barrage of synthetic electromagnetic fields (EMF) and electromagnetic radiation (EMR) surrounding us. It seems that wherever we turn now, we are being bombarded with blinking lights, radios, cell phones, power lines, appliances, technical equipment and much more.

Are they safe? Are we safe?

It is one thing to question one or two appliances that might emit non-ionizing doses of EMFs or radiofrequencies (RFs). But it is quite another thing altogether to consider the constant contact with appliances throughout the day, and sometimes multiple appliances at once.

Consider a modern family on a weekend drive. The car's instrument panel is loaded with different electronic appliances. The car has electronic ignition and much of the engine's operations are computerized. We sit back with our cell phone pasted to our ear (while our wife or husband drives). There is a TV blaring behind us for the kids to watch. We also might have the car stereo on, and even a GPS. The kids probably also have their various "pods" and "pads" to play games with, text with, or go online with. We probably also have a smart phone that can access the internet wirelessly or through WiFi.

Is that really a "smart" phone?

Let's find out. Here we will cover some of the history of how we developed all this electromagnetic stuff. We will then lay out the fundamentals of electromagnetic radiation. Then we will explain the sources of nature's electromagnetism and compare them to our synthetic versions. Next we will delve into the last half-century of health research on EMFs, and focus on the latest findings for each type of EMF and RF. We'll discuss what those findings mean to us on a practical level.

Finally, we will discuss practical strategies to reduce exposure and risk to unhealthy EMFs.

In other words, we'll get to the heart of the matter. We will do this without any axes to grind, and no ulterior motive to accomplish. We'll just use the hard facts, without a bias one way or another.

In addition, we will be straightforward. Anecdotal information is anecdotal, research is research, and clinical information is clinical information. Each have their failings, and each have substance to consider. Let's be clear about the information on EMFs and calmly approach the topic with a clear mind and careful review of the information. Above all, let's get the facts before we rush to conclusions, and figure out how to safely use the tools of modern technology for positive means.

≈≈ One

What is Electromagnetic Radiation?

The realization of the relationship between electricity and magnetism donned on Michael Faraday in 1831 when he coiled wire around an iron ring and demonstrated induction by passing a magnet through the ring. Faraday followed these demonstrations by calculating the relationships and proclaiming four formulas as the basis for what is now known as the *Field theory*. Faraday's proposed that a combination of current and magnetism formed a strange yet universal notion soon dubbed *electromagnetism*.

As many discoveries are, Faraday's theories were not accepted for many years. This didn't stop Faraday from further research into this strange substance. He soon developed the *homopolar generator*—still in use even today as the primary method of advancing direct current through a circuit. This is the most basic form of electrical generation—referred to as induction. Should it be directed through a circulating magnetic disk, the induction begins to alternate with the rotation. This phenomenon is was coined *Faraday's disc*.

Within a few years of Faraday's work, Heinrich Ruhmkorff developed a higher-voltage pulse from DC current. The *Ruhmkorff coil* consisted of copper wires coiled around an iron core—very similar to Faraday's disk. As a DC current was passed through one of his coils, current potential increased. When the pulse was shorted or interrupted, the immediate magnetic field decrease drove the voltage to jump into high gear onto the second coil. This could be arced out to an outlet line, producing a large spike in the voltage with a pulsed, alternating flow of current.

The distribution of this strange alternating current called electricity took a big leap when physicist and fire alarm designer William Stanley conjured a crude AC electrical installation at a New York Fifth Avenue store. Prior to that, direct current distribution technology had been dominated by the marketing and scientific genius of Thomas Edison.

The mid-1800s research of Scottish physicist James Maxwell cemented the notion that light moved through space in the form of waves. Maxwell utilized the notions of Faraday and Hans Christian Oersted to mathematically establish the relationship between electric and magnetic fields. Maxwell's equations also utilized the velocity of light as a constant, to establish what is now known as the *electromagnetic theory*. Maxwell, also given credit for producing the color photograph, should probably have the distinction as the father of electromagnetism. Maxwell published his research in a 1964 book entitled *A Dynamical Theory of the Electromagnetic Field.*

Albert Einstein, Max Plank, Niels Bohr and others followed Maxwell's mathematical approach as they further investigated the electromagnetic nature of atomic radiation, gravity, space and light. Maxwell was a mathematician by training, so his use of formulation assumed that a proof existed when each side of the equal sign was in fact, equal. This method of using *equations* to determine the properties of radiation became the standard: An equality between two or more conditions within nature. This of course assumes that nature is geometrically and harmonically balanced—a proposition famously presented by Pythagoras two thousand years earlier.

EMF refers to the fields that are created by electromagnetic radiation (EMR). The plural is used here because EMR actually produces two fields concurrently. One is an electric field (or vector), caused by the motion of electrons. The second field is a magnetic field, which typically moves perpendicular to electron radiation. While electric fields can "leak" from the flow of electric currents, most wires are insulated and grounded. This can significantly reduce electron fields. Magnetic fields are typically another story.

Electromagnetic fields are caused by the *waveforms* of the electronic and magnetic vectors of radiation. So what are waveforms? Here we will illustrate that not only are we surrounded by waveforms, but matter is quite literally made up of waveforms.

The Electromagnetic Atom

When we look around us, we see objects. What we are actually looking at are electromagnetic waves. Let's start with one of nature's smaller units.

Dalton's atomic theory, put forth by British John Dalton in the early nineteenth century, proposed that the tiniest indivisible piece of matter could be assigned a unit called the *atom*. He concluded that all matter must be made up of these indivisible units. Furthermore, he suggested that the indivisible atoms of different elements must each have a unique atomic weight—and compounds are made up of different combinations of atoms. These combinations, of course, came to be known as *molecules*.

Others had previously envisioned the existence of the atom—from the Sir Isaac Newton to the Greeks and even ancient Vedic philosophers thousands of years earlier. Dalton's theories—with his notions of atomic character—brought mathematical characteristics to these tiny portions of nature.

Radiation instrumentation further developed, due in part to the pioneering work of T.W. Richards—known for his work on the radioactive transformation of lead, which he called "radio-lead." This produced a better understanding of atomic reactivity, and the possibility of the existence of subatomic parts within the atom.

In the late nineteenth century, Joseph John ("JJ") Thomson—winner of the 1906 Nobel Prize for Physics—measured cathode rays passed through slits within a vacuum tube. Using magnetic fields, Thomson was able to bend the rays. This indicated to Sir Thomson that elemental matter must have both electronic charge and magnetic field characteristics.

Further cathode ray testing revealed the nature of these rays as subatomic particles. Thomson deduced that the rays must be produced by tiny particles that make up the atom.

Dalton's atomic number soon expanded to subatomic particles, with the notion of electrons, protons and a nucleus. These provided a semblance of balance and a rationale molecular combination.

Several theories of the atom were put forth in the mid- to late-nineteenth century. These ranged from Sir Thomson's *plum pudding model,* to Japanese physicist Hantaro Nagaoka's *Saturnian model.* This of course visualized electrons moving around the nucleus much as the rings of Saturn encircle that planet. This let to the *Rutherford-Bohr model,* which utilized the combined works of Niels Bohr and Ernest Rutherford:

The Rutherford Atom **The Bohr Model**

Continued research in the early twentieth century gradually eliminated the Bohr-Rutherford model as an acceptable description of subatomic particle motion. These subatomic 'particles' did not seem to maintain "particle behavior."

J.J. Thomson's cathode ray experiments led to the notion—elaborated on by Paul Dirac, John von Neumann, Max Planck, Louis de Broglie, Max Born, Niels Bohr, Albert Einstein and Erwin Schrödinger—that the reflective effects of the cathode rays indicated that subatomic particles were actually wavelike:

Cathode rays indicate that subatomic particles are wave-like

Subsequent subatomic particle experiments have confirmed that the smallest atomic parts contain electromagnetic properties. As the calculations of wave mechanics led to quantum theories, driven by the research and equations of Rutherford, Plank, Einstein, Born, de Broglie, Bohr, Schrödinger and Neumann, a new reality of the atom gradually came into view: Atoms maintain subatomic electrons in the form of *particle-waves*. The current picture of the atom is an immensely small nucleus surrounded by electromagnetic electron orbital clouds:

The electromagnetic atom's electron orbital cloud

Electromagnetic Waveforms

The notion that energy moves in waves has gradually gained scientific confirmation. The realization that light, radio and atomic energy were composed of energy pulsing at regular cycles led to the quantification of electromagnetic radiation using waveform mechanics. The basic waveform parameters are *frequency, wavelength* and *speed*. Furthermore, scientists have arrived at the following relationship between these three characteristics:

WAVELENGTH = SPEED divided by **FREQUENCY**

This formula has allowed scientists to calculate and categorize the various waveforms that surround us. Today, many of nature's energies—atomic energy, heat, visible light, radiowaves, color, cosmic rays, gamma rays and more—have been quantified in their respective frequencies and wavelengths. As a result, we can present the electromagnetic spectrum within waveform specification:

THE ELECTOMAGNETIC SPECTRUM

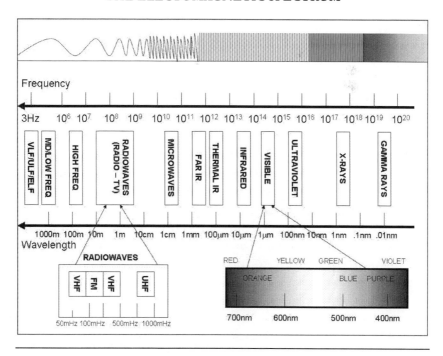

In other words, our universe is pulsing with waves of different types. So what is a wave?

While every electromagnetic frequency is a waveform, not every wave in nature is an electromagnetic wave. Throughout nature, we see repeating rhythmic occurrences. Each day we observe the sun's rise and set, establishing a cycle that is repetitious, adjusting slightly with every cycle. Seasonal changes with the rotation of the earth in respect to its orbit are also waveforms. We see this seasonal rhythmic rise and fall reflected in plant-life—waxing in the spring and waning in the fall. We see birds and other migratory animals move with similar rhythms, traveling periodically with the seasons to amazingly exacting locations.

We also see nature's waveforms pulsing through the oceans, causing waves and weather conditions. We see larger periods of ocean tidal rhythms bringing an exchange of ocean creatures and their food to and from the seashore. We see the rhythmic upwelling of cold waters from the ocean depths rotating and recycling the ocean's various biochemicals and marine life. Meanwhile, these surface waters are spun and rotated by the wind through a recycling temperature gradients. We see a similar rhythmic pulsing of waveforms throughout our atmosphere; recycling temperature, water vapor, and various gas mixtures with periodic precision.

These pulses of nature are waves from a macrocosmic and microcosmic view. The distinct and precise rhythms repeat and cycle, and their variances also repeat in a cyclical fashion.

Nature's waveforms extend to the electromagnetic spectrum. The waveforms pulsing through space in the form of electromagnetic light waves, radio waves, gamma waves, cosmic rays, infrared waves, ultraviolet waves, x-rays and other forms of radiation. These have been produced by the billions of suns of the cosmos for billions of years. Radiation is also produced by the earth, and by our own bodies. We also find geomagnetic field waves and proton storms from cyclic solar storms, and rhythmic magnetic influences around our planet.

The waveform order of nature is evident when considering the accuracy of the atomic clockworks. In today's standard for timekeeping—the atomic cesium clock—radioactive cesium provides a steady stream of radiative waveforms that pass through a magnetic field to routinely oscillate a crystal. The emission from cesium is so rhythmically accurate that we now quite literally set our clocks to these electromagnetic pulses.

When most of us think about waves, we think of the ocean. We think of waves pounding onto the beach. Stirred up by the forces of wind and weather, large waves will march onto the reefs and beaches, standing up with ferocious crests. The beauty and power of a large wave lifting and crashing onto the rocks or beach is often the subject of popular photography and film. What we may not realize is that each single wave is communicating an event that took place thousands of miles away: A particular mix of wind, temperature, atmospheric pressure and moisture combining in just the right way to instigate a weather system.

This weather system converts its potential into waveforms in the surrounding ocean waters. Should we look at a storm's confluence of elements from space, we will see nature's characteristic spiral. Harmonically, we see this same spiral shape within a cross-sectional view of an ocean wave.

A wave is a repeating oscillation of energy: A translation of information through a particular medium. Waves can travel through solids, fluids, gases and space. Waves are not restricted to a particular medium, either. Most waves will move through one medium and continue on through the next medium where those mediums intersect. A sound, for example may vibrate a drum skin first. Where the drum skin meets the air, it oscillates the air molecules to translate the sound information throughout the medium. Where the air connects with the tympanic membrane, the information waveform is translated through the malleus, incus and stapes of the middle ear. After vibrating through to the round window, the oscillation is translated through the cochlea into electromagnetic nerve pulses. This means that the original wave of the drum beat transversed several mediums before being converted to electromagnetic pulses.

A repeated oscillation or waveform through a medium against the backdrop of time is a rhythm. This repetitive and rhythmic pulse translates to a recurring waveform. It also translates to information. Any recurring result is associated with a causal event. In other words, a wave must be initiated by an original event. The waves in a pond originate from a pebble thrown in, for example.

Every movement in nature has a signature rhythm: The earth oscillates in specific types of seismic waves—some causing damage but most hardly noticeable. We each walk with a signature pace as our feet meet the ground. Our vocal cords oscillate to the reflection of our thoughts with a unique pace and timing. Our heart valves oscillate with the needs of circulation. Our lungs oscillate as we breathe in and out—unique to our lung size and cells' needs for oxygen. Even rugged, seemingly solid structures like rocks oscillate—depending upon their position, size, shape, and composition. A cliff by the seashore will oscillate with each pounding wave. A building in a windy city will uniquely oscillate with the movement of the wind through the streets. Each building will oscillate slightly differently, depending upon its architecture and location.

All of these movements—and all movements in nature for that matter—provide recurring oscillations that can be charted in waveform structure. Moreover, the various events within nature come complete with recurring cycles. While many cycles obviously repeat during our range of observation, many cycles have only recently become evident, indicating that many of nature's cycles are still beyond our current observation range.

Natural oscillations balance between a particular pivot point and an axis. The axis is typically a frame of reference between two media or quanta. An axis showing quantification may illustrate time in reference to height, time versus temperature, time versus activity or time versus other quantifying points of reference. Waves will also transist between media. The ocean wave is the transisting of waveforms between the intersection of the atmosphere and the water: the storm system. The water's surface tension gives rise to the ocean wave as it refracts the pressure of the storm system. The storm system's waveform energy will be radiated through the ocean to the rocks and beach.

Nature's waves are relational to the rhythms of planets and galaxies. These rhythms translate to electromagnetic energy and kinetic energy, which translate to the elements of speed, distance, and mass. Momentum, inertia, gravity, and other natural phenomena are thus examples of the cyclical activities that directly relate with nature's wave rhythms. Every rhythm in nature is interconnected with other rhythms. As a house is built with interconnected beams of framing, the universe's waveforms are all interconnected with a design of pacing within the element of time.

The most prevalent waveform found in nature is the sinusoidal wave or sine wave. The sinusoidal wave is the manifestation of circular motion related to time. The sine wave thus repeats through nature's processes defined by time. For example, the rotating positions of the hands of a clock translate to a sinusoidal wave should the angles of the hand positions be charted on one axis with the time on the other axis.

Sinusoidal waveforms are thus the typical waveform structures of light, sound, electromagnetic waves and ocean waves. Late eighteenth and early nineteenth century French physicist Jean Fourier found that just about every motion could be broken down into sinusoidal components. This phenomenon has become known as the Fourier series.

The cycle of a sine wave, moving from midline to peak, then back to midline, then to a trough, and then back to midline completes a full cycle. If we divide the wave into angles, the beginning is consistent with 0 degrees; the first peak is consistent with 45 degrees, the midline with 90 degrees and the trough with 270 degrees. The cycle repeats again, as we make another revolution around the sine wave circle.

Other wave types occurring in nature might not be strictly sine waves, yet they are often sinusoidal in essence. The cosine wave, for example, is sinusoidal because it has the same basic shape, but is simply phase-shifted from the sine. Other waves such as square waves or irregular sound waves can usually be connected to sinusoidal origin when their motion is broken down into composites.

We see so many circular activities within nature. We see the earth recycling molecular components. We see the recycling of water from earth to sea to clouds and back to earth. We see planetary bodies moving in cyclic fashion, repeating their positions in periodic rhythm. We see the seasons moving in cyclic repetition. We see organisms living cycles of repetitive physical activity.

While not every cycle in nature is precisely circular—the orbits of planets or electron energy shells for example—they are nonetheless linked within a grander cycle. Linked cycles often contain various alterations as they adapt to the other cyclic components. This modulation can be described as adaptation—a harmonic process between waveform matter and life.

This all should remind us of the notion of the circle of life, which has been repeatedly observed throughout nature in so many respects that it is generally assumed without fanfare. Circles recur in human and animal activity, social order, customs, and individual circumstances. The tribal circle is common among many ancient cultures—and for good reason. In modern society, we have circular conferences, round-table meetings, and cyclical ceremonies. The potter's wheel, the grinding wheel, and the circular clock are all examples of circular symbols in our attempt to synchronize with nature. Just about every form of communication and transportation is somehow connected to circular motion. For this reason, it is no accident that the wheel provides our primary and most efficient means for transportation. The motion of walking is also circular and sinusoidal, as the legs rise and fall forward, rotating the various joints.

In nature, we observe two basic types of waves: mechanical and electromagnetic. A mechanical wave moves through a particular medium: sound pressure waves as they move through air, for example. Mechanical waves can move over the surface of a medium. Ocean waves and certain earthquake (seismic) waves are examples of mechanical surface waves. Another type of mechanical wave is the tortional wave: This mechanical wave twists through a spiral or helix.

The electromagnetic wave is seemingly different because it theoretically does not move through a medium of any composition. Einstein assumed space is a vacuum and the ultimate electromagnetic wave—light—moved through this vacuum with constant speed. Dr. Einstein's theory supposed that time is collapsed within space: Instead of time and distance being separate, he supposed a singular element called space-time.

Yet in 2001, collaborative research led by Texas A&M University physics professor Dr. Dimitri Nanopoulos, Dr. Nikolaos Mavromatos of King's College in London, and Dr. John Ellis of the European Center for Particle Physics in Geneva confirmed that additional influences can alter the speed of light. Their calculations showed that the speed of light varies to frequency. Furthermore, in 1999, University of Toronto professor Dr. John Moffat calculated that the speed of light has actually slowed down over time. Space may actually be a bona fide medium after all.

Nature displays two basic waveform structures: transverse and longitudinal. Visible spectrum, radio waves, microwaves, radar, infrared and x-rays are all transverse waveforms. As these waves move, there is a disruption moving at right angles to the vector of the wave. For example, should the wave move along a longitudinal x-axis, its disruption field would move along the perpendicular y-z axis. This might be compared to watching a duck floating in a lake strewn with tiny waves. The duck bobs up and down as the waves pass under the duck's body. In the case of the transverse electromagnetic wave, the disruption field is the magnetic field.

In the longitudinal wave, pressure gradients form regular alternating zones of compression and rarefaction. During the compression phase, the medium is pressed together, and during the rarefaction, the medium is expanded outward. This might be illustrated by the alternating expansion and compression of a spring. Instead of the wave disturbing the medium upward and downward as in the case of a transverse wave, the medium is disturbed in a back and forth fashion, in the direction of the wave. Examples of longitudinal waves are sound waves and most seismic waves. In the case of sound waves, air molecules compress and rarefy in the direction of the sound projection.

These two types of waves may also combine in nature. An ocean wave is a good example of a combination of transverse and longitudinal waveforms. Water may be disturbed up and down as it transmits an ocean wave, and it may convey alternating compressions and rarefaction as it progresses tidal currents.

Waves are typically referred to as radiation when the waveform can translate ("radiate") its energy information from one type of medium to another. In this respect, ocean waves can be considered radiating as they translate their energy onto the sand. In the case of seismic waves, they translate through land to buildings and people. The classic type of radiation comes from electromagnetic waves such as x-rays or ultraviolet rays, which can travel through skin or other molecular mediums after transversing space.

Waves are typically measured by their wave height from trough to crest (amplitude), rate of speed through time (frequency) and the distance from one repeating peak to another (wavelength). Waves are also characterized by their wave shape. Examples of wave shape include sinusoidal waves and square waves, as we've mentioned.

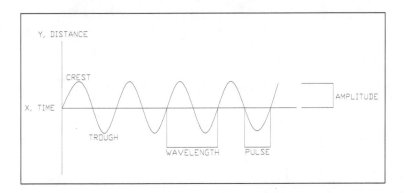

The frequency of a wave is typically measured by how many wave cycles (one complete revolution of the wave—a wavelength) pass a particular point within a period of time. Therefore, waves are often measured in CPS, or cycles per second. The hertz is named after nineteenth century German physicist Dr. Heinrich Hertz— who is said to have discovered radio frequency electromagnetic waves. Note that hertz and CPS are identical: Both identify the number of complete waves passing a given point every second. Other frequency measurements used include machinery's RPM (revolutions per second), special radiation's RAD/S (radians per second), and the heart's BPM (beats per minute).

When we describe a sinusoidal waveform, we can state either its frequency or wavelength, since the two will be inversely related. Wavelength is typically measured in meters, centimeters, or nanometers to comply with international standards. Each radiation type is classified by its wavelength. A wave's wavelength has an inverse relationship to its frequency. This is because a shorter wave's length will travel faster through a particular point than a longer length will. Note also that speed is the rate measured from one point to another, while frequency is the rate of one full repetition of a pulse past a particular point. Therefore, a wave's wavelength can be determined by dividing its speed by its frequency, and a wave's frequency can be derived from dividing its speed by its wavelength.

A wave's amplitude is also an important consideration, as this relates to the height of the wave—its magnitude. The amplitude is measured from the wave's baseline to its peak. Among sinusoidal waves, a larger amplitude will accompany a larger wavelength. A larger amplitude often lends to a wave of greater intensity as well.

Other considerations among waveforms include phase, medium of travel, and wave shape. These together characterize a particular wave's effect and conductance.

Waves travel with repetition or periodicity. The very definition of a wave describes a repeating motion. This repetition, occurring with a particular pace and particular time reference, forms a rhythm. Can waves be chaotic? To the contrary, it is their consistent rhythm that allows us to interpret light, color, sound, or warmth with duplicatable precision. All of these waveforms connect with the senses because they have consistent and congruent oscillations. In sensing the world around us, we do not perceive each wave individually. Rather, we sense waveform interaction.

When a waveform collides or interferes with another waveform, the interaction yields a more complex waveform. This creates information. As waveforms collide throughout our universe, they comprehensively present a myriad of information via their interference patterns. Our brains and minds translate those interference patterns that resonate with our sensory neurons.

Depending upon the characteristics of the incoming waveforms, wave interference can result in larger, more complex waveforms. These are *constructive interference patterns*. Alternatively, should interactive waveforms contrast each other; their meeting can result in a reduction of magnitude—creating *destructive interference patterns*.

The interactive quality of two waves as they collide often lies within their wave phase similarity. If one wave is cycling in positive territory while the other is cycling in negative territory, they will most likely destructively interfere with each other, resulting in a reduction of amplitude. However, if the two waves move in the same phase—where both cycle with the same points on the curve—then they will most likely constructively interfere with each other, creating a greater amplitude—and a greater magnitude.

As a result, interacting waves are identified as either in-phase or out-of-phase. In-phase waveforms will typically meet with superposition to form constructive interference and greater intensity. Out-of-phase waveforms will often conflict:, reducing their intensity. The canceling or reduction during destructive waveform interference is not necessarily bad, however. Depending upon the type of radiation, destructive interference can also produce healthy effects.

The degree that two or more waves will interfere with each other—either constructively or destructively—relates to their *coherence*. If two waves are coherent, they are either completely in-phase or out-of-phase. They will thus increase in intensity or undergo significant cancelation. Waves that are different but not completely out-of-phase are considered incoherent.

Waveform coherency might be loosely compared to speaking coherently. Coherent speaking refers to sounds that are better understood by the listener. Whether the communication is interpreted by the listener as positive or negative information is not relevant. The clarity of the communication indicates its coherence.

In the same way, coherent waves interact to produce significant results as they interact—either constructively or destructively.

Destructive Interference

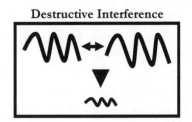

Resonance occurs when individual waves achieve a balanced state—one where amplitude and period is consistent and efficient for that waveform system. Thus, resonating waves typically occur when waves come together in constructive interference. This results in an increase in their respective amplitudes. This is illustrated when two tuned instruments play the same note or song together. Their notes will resonate together, creating a convergence with greater amplitude, typically resulting in a louder, clearer sound. We also hear this when we create the familiar whistling sound of blowing into an empty bottle: To get the loudest and clearest sound, we must blow with a certain angle and airspeed. Once we find the right positioning, angle and speed, we will have established a resonance between the shape of the bottle and our breath.

Constructive Interference

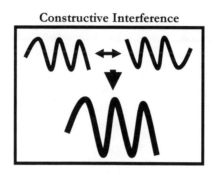

As waves move from one type of media to another, they will often reflect or refract. Reflected waves will bounce off the new medium, while refracted waves will move through the new medium with a different vector and speed. This of course depends upon the density and molecular makeup of the medium. Mediums are thus quantified by their index of refraction, absorbance or conductance levels when it comes to waveform interaction. Some mediums will reflect certain waveforms while refracting others. Thus, the media is as important as the waveforms when it comes to characterizing the positive or negative effects of a type of radiation.

Refraction (A) and Reflection (B)

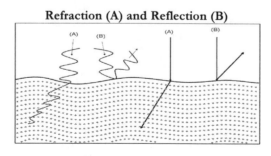

This is illustrated by the passage of UV radiation through the atmosphere. The stratosphere contains higher levels of ozone, which absorb and reflect ultraviolet-B rays in the 270-315 nanometer (NM) range. Ozone's filtering effects absorb or reflect over 98% of the sun's ultraviolet-B rays, as well as some far-infrared radiation.

Surface waves are typically seen at the surface of a particular medium where that medium interfaces with another medium. Surface waves are seen on the surface of mediums—for examples, on the surfaces of oceans and lakes. Surface waves are mechanical in nature and thus tend to respond to surface pressures from the interfacing medium. In the case of surface seismic waves, the collision of the wave with some soils may mute the waveform amplitude while other soils (looser, with more water content) may exaggerate the waveform amplitude.

Surface waves are divided into two basic types—the first being a capillary wave. The capillary wave is a carrier wave that forms during the beginning of the build-up process. Therefore, it is considered a low-amplitude wave—often seen as smaller ripples on the water as the wind freshens. The second type of surface wave is a gravity wave, typically having a larger wavelength and amplitude than the capillary wave has. It is the gravity-type rogue waves that seafarers respect for their shipwrecking abilities, for example.

In deeper water, a combination of transverse and longitudinal wave motions combine to form monochromatic linear plane waves. This forms a type of wave called an inertial wave. Inertial waves are typically moving within rotating fluid mediums. Inertial waves are common in not only the ocean and among lakes, but also within the atmosphere and presumably within the earth's core. The various currents and winds within the atmosphere all travel in inertial waves of varying lengths. Surface waves will interact with these inertial waves to move energy over the surface of their medium. This energy movement allows surfers to ride a wave from the outside to the inside of the tidal region, for example.

A *simple harmonic* is a recurring wave (in nature, usually sinusoidal or cosinusoidal) that repeats in rhythmic frequency. A *combined harmonic* occurs when different waveforms converge and their wavelengths become aligned—their wavelengths are multiples or integers of each other.

In other words, harmonic convergence is achieved when different waveforms with a multiple of the same wavelength-frequency proportions interfere. Other coherent interference among waveforms can also create a harmonic. Though the source waveforms might not be harmonic, a combined harmonic convergence can be created through a combination of natural waveforms and media.

As forward-moving waves interact with returning waves, both waves will become compressed and dilated. This effect is known as the *Doppler Effect*—named after nineteenth century Austrian physicist Johann Christian Doppler. If the incoming waves have the same waveform, frequency, and amplitude, this will create a standing wave. If they do not, either the incoming or the outgoing wave will divert the waves it meets, and distort those waves in one respect or another. This distortion would be analogous to the oblong or parabolic orbitals of solar systems and electrons, which are distorted by the interference created by surrounding fields or waveforms.

Standing waveforms will typically be created by interacting waves with precisely the same frequency, wavelength, amplitude, and shape.

As suggested by Zhang et al. in 1996, and confirmed by multiple physicists over the last decade, multiple electrons within shared orbitals (or valences) among multiple atoms situated within a close-range matrix are best described as multiple standing waves: These standing waveforms create structure. They also create some of the strongest forces in nature, as they produce the illusion of physical solidity. The convergence of multiple waveforms standing together in a harmonic resonating interference pattern over a period of time is best described as architecture.

In other words, standing waves among molecules interact with and reflect certain types of electromagnetic radiation. These reflected rays resonate with our retinal neurons to produce the illusion of a solid physical world.

Standing waveforms also continually undergo interference displacement. This alters their energy through convergence or interference with other waveforms. This is illustrated by the effect of certain types of radiation upon certain types of materials: The incoming waveforms may produce changes to the molecular structure of the material as they interfere with the standing waveforms existing within its atoms and molecules. As the architecture of the molecules changes, energy may be produced. Heat, for example, is often produced when the sun's radiation begins to interferes with the molecules within our skin cells. We've all experienced this as we've stepped outside into the sunlight.

This interference displacement conveys the energy and information traveling within radiation on to new media. New waveform interference patterns, energy and information are the result. These interference conveyances render the transfer of energy, motion and information within the physical universe.

As researchers have probed deeper into the nature of energy and matter, we have found that everything around us is oscillating at a particular waveform or rhythm. All information is conveyed within waveform interference patterns. It is these interference patterns that our bodies and minds utilize for sensory perception.

This might be compared to the bits and bites of computer code. A bit of computer data is an on state or off state. In itself, neither an off state or off state produces any information. But when a particular pattern of on and off states is put together into a byte, information is created. In the same way, waveforms in themselves do not produce information. It is their interference patterns with others that create the information.

We might consider this in light of the development of telecommunications. Radio wave signaling from the ingenious research of Gugielmo Marconi and Ferdinand Braun during the late nineteenth and early twentieth centuries led to the 1909 Nobel Prize in Physics for the wireless telegraph. This built upon the development of the cable telegraph more than a century earlier through the combined tinkering of Francisco de Salva, Alessandro Volta, Samuel von Soemmering and Johan Schweigger. These efforts began with simple electrostatics—the use of radiating pulses through conductor materials. Electostatics gave us the ability to manipulate currents and voltage to transmit information.

Heinrich Hertz introduced the methodology to measure electromagnetic radiation in the late 1880s. Italian physicist and university professor Augusto Righi investigated and published no less than 200 papers on the transmission of information via electromagnetic propagation. While Marconi developed methods of electronic wave propulsion, it was Righi who meticulously exacted the technology.

Through his research, Righi was able to increase the wave stability and the reception clarity of radio transmissions.

Edouard Branly, utilizing some of the work of Italian physicist Temistocle Calzecchi-Onesti, eventually assembled a crude radio wave transmitter. This became referred to as the *Branly coherer*. It utilized current resistance to transmit radiowaves across an electrode conductor through space. Englishman Dr. Oliver Lodge coined the term coherer—postulating that the coherent medium through which the radiowaves transmitted was the aether. Dr. Lodge is thought to have demonstrated wireless transmission prior to Marconi. It is also thought that Nikola Tesla demonstrated the first wireless radio wave communication in 1893—but this claim has proved to be controversial over the years.

Reception was still a missing link. This piece was introduced around 1898 by the German Ferdinand Braun. Braun invented the cat's whisker crystal diode rectifier. This formed the basis for the crystal radio receiver semiconductor. A naturally mined crystal was positioned to receive and conduct radiowaves through contact with a thin bronze wire—the cat's whisker.

Eventually a tuner was installed to fix the radio crystal and whisker upon a particular frequency—one matching the radiowave pulses emitted by the sender. The crystal semiconductor converted these waveforms into electrical pulses, driving a speaker. Marconi, the ultimate businessperson, assembled the various equipment— much of it under patent by the original inventors—and combined them with existing cable telegraph technology to send and receive real-time radiowave communication.

It should be emphasized that the signaling system on both ends must be grounded to the earth: Nature provides not only the facility for semi-conductance, but also the grounding for the electrical pulses to provide the right polarity. Early semiconducting devices were made from crystals of natural minerals such as galena or pyrite. Prior to the cat's whisker crystal radio, other minerals like silicon carbide and vitreous silicon were also used as crude semiconductors. All of these of course preceded the use of synthetic silicon crystals for the semiconduction of modern-day integrated circuits and microchip processors.

In other words, the ability to broadcast communications rides on the bandwidths of nature's radiowaves and the earth's semiconductors. The assembly of these natural components enabled humans to utilize natural radiation as a *carrier* for information communication. With various experiments and mechanisms developed through trial and error, inventors and physicists have been able to piggyback upon nature's technologies.

Electromagnetic technology is also utilized by nature for the transmission of vision, sound, heat, light, chemical reaction and atomic energy. If we examine the timeline of the equations and theories presented by Bohr, Einstein, de Broglie, Planck and others, the mechanical application of electromagnetic radiation thoroughly preceded humankind's understanding of the technologies. Furthermore, we are still trying to fully understand electromagnetic radiation. In other words, we still do not completely understand nature's electromagnetic technologies.

Radiation transmission is an innate rhythmic process natural to all living beings. Radiation communication can be compared to the barking of a dog, or the tapping of Morse code. The sending of a radiowave signal is no different in principle from the act of tapping or barking. The receiving of the signal is the act of sensing or hearing those pulses, followed by a translation of interference patterns into information. This allows the sender and receiver to have intentional communication by filtering out other interference patterns with a handshaking protocol. As long as each party agrees on how the rhythm is to be converted, communication can be pervasive amongst all participants.

A television camera, for example, converts visual radiation into a series of digital pulses. Those pulses are amplified with alternating current and converted into broadcast radiowaves. A television set is the receiver and converter of those radiowaves, translating the waves back into digital pulses. As long as the television receiver is set up with the same conversion pulse coding (or handshaking) used in the camera to broadcast signal conversion, it can convert the pulses into a facsimile of the original visual images.

If we were to analyze voice or even Morse code on a two-dimensional oscilloscope, we will see the same process: A series of pulses translating to information.

Photosynthesis is also a waveform transmission and conversion process. Ultraviolet radiation stimulates photosynthesis to produce the nutrition and energy needed by the plant. Chloroblasts within chlorophyll molecules utilize the sun's radiation to split water into hydrogen and oxygen atoms. The hydrogen atoms combine with carbon dioxide to form carbohydrates (such as CH_2O and $C_6H_{12}O_6$) while releasing oxygen. The carbohydrates make up the plant's sugars, starches and cellulose.

Each living organism has this capability of converting radiation through genetically driven biomolecular reactions. The conversion of the sun's radiation is a fundamental metabolic process common among most organisms.

All organisms are receivers, converter and transmitters of informational waveforms. Dolphins and many whales, for example, can not only code and transmit through sound, but they can utilize informational waveform signals to *echo-locate*—obtaining three-dimensional pictures of surrounding objects or creatures. This sense is typically referred to as sonar, which stands for SOund Navigation And Ranging. Sonar allows these intelligent creatures the ability to analyze an object's shape, movement and location from very long distances. While research has long confirmed that dolphins and whales use sonar, it now appears they may have the ability to sense the feelings and emotions of other creatures during these complex sound wave transmissions.

Other animals can broadcast reports and emotions over many miles. They can announce their proprietary territories along with their state of affairs with complex sounds. When a dog's domain is faced with a threatening situation, for example, he can broadcast that situation to many other dogs in that area. Those dogs can in turn broadcast the information to other regions if necessary. Theoretically, remote dog populations can almost instantly know a single dangerous situation through a relay of sound transmission. This is not unlike the broadcasting feature of radio or cell phone transmitting systems.

This illustrates how broadcasting and reception technologies are simply an extension of natural processes. Just as the ears are equipped with a converting mechanism in the form of the bones of the ear and the cochlear hair that translate sound frequencies into nervous impulses, our cell phones are equipped with antennas, crystals and digital circuits that receive and convert radiowave transmissions into sounds. The same basic operation is taking place, except that cell phone technology requires an external power source. This external power source also happens to be one of the causes of the synthetic radiation put out by these devices. The reception and conversion process is similar nonetheless.

The question, however, is whether these technological uses of natural waveforms interfere in the body's natural processes. Do cell phone towers interfere in the cells' ability to communicate with other cells within the body? Do cell phone radiowaves interfere with the brain's own wave signaling processes?

Different sense organs translate light, sound and tactile waveforms. These waveforms allow us to receive information from a variety of energy sources. These information waveforms provide the basic platform for structure within our universe. The information carried through waveforms of various types connects everything together with resonation and coherence—aligning molecular waveforms into sequential progression. This provides an environment designed for information exchange.

Humans are riding on the back of nature's existing technologies with our electromagnetic appliances. The technologies we are using are not new. The ability to broadcast intended information through waveform radiation is well established by nature. Our technologies deliver information utilizing radiowaves, lasers, x-rays, infrared and atomic energy. These waveform frequencies existed prior to our appliances.

The laser is one such example. LASER means *Light Amplification by Stimulated Emission of Radiation*. Nature's crystals (the ruby was used to initially develop the laser) are used to step up and duplicate light waveforms in a way that concentrates their electromagnetic intensity. This might be compared to shining the sun's light through a magnifying glass in order to produce fire. Today, lasers are being used for communications and for non-invasive surgery. These purposes present to us the positive effects of their waveforms. Just as the sun's rays intensified through a magnifying glass can light a forest fire that will burn down houses, it can also be used to light a campfire that will cook our food and give us light and heat for the night.

Radiowaves transmitted between cell phones and cell towers or from transmitters to television sets present similar possibilities. They present the ability to communicate information between humans located many miles apart. They also present some the ability to steal money from others (ergo, internet crime).

In other words, electromagnetic technologies can be used intelligently for the good of others—or not.

Our latent realization of the informational wave technology exhibited by nature is illustrated by the nineteenth century research of Oxford University physics professor Henry Moseley. Professor Moseley followed Mendeleev's chemical periodic table formulation with radiation emission measurements. Using x-ray diffraction, he determined that each element emits a unique frequency of radiation. These frequency relationships, he found, also correlate with their orbital valence relationships. As atomic number count increases among the elements, the wavelengths decrease and the frequencies increase. Moving along the elements of the periodic table, frequency measurements increase in a stepped fashion and taper with elements with completed electromagnetic valence shells.

Diffraction is a type of interference pattern created when one waveform interacts with another waveform or interacts with a medium (a body of waveforms). When a waveform diffracts, it splits up into sub-waveforms. Assuming there is no energy absorbed or released by the intercepted waveform (or medium), the diffracted set of sub-waveforms exhibit the partial characteristics of the initial interfering waveform. In other words, because energy is conserved, the sum of the energy of the diffracted waveforms must equal to the initial interfering waveform.

This brings us to the extraordinary arrangements displayed by nature resulting from the innumerable interference patterns produced by the electromagnetic waveforms surrounding us.

Spiraling Currents

As coherent waveforms of nature interact and interfere, spirals develop. For example, when we see the rhythmic spiraling growth of leaves or branches around the trunk of a tree, we are presented with an interference of radiation that result in a spiral of Fibonacci proportions. This spiral or helix pattern of leaves and branches growing upward and outward is produced by the interference patterns created by nature's conjunctive waveforms. Should we spread out the spiral orientation of a plant into two dimensions—x and y coordinates—we would find that the branching reflects a sinusoidal wave pattern.

Should we look down at the plant from its apex, we would see this spiraling or helical effect, depending upon the size and nature of the plant. Looking at a younger plant—where we could see the top shoots with respect to the bottom trunk—we will likely perceive a spiral. Should we look at a larger tree with a large trunk at the bottom with its branches swirling and widening to the top, we will likely perceive a helix.

These helical and spiraling forms provide the basic structures for function within the physical world. We see these structures present within nature's smallest elements to her largest, most complex organisms. From the double helixed DNA molecule to the spiraling galaxies of the universe, we see the spiral within all types of anatomical shapes. The nautilus shell is most famous, but just about every shell and sea formation also reflects this spiral—illustrated by the swirling of water spouts, hurricanes and weather systems.

Other displays of nature's spiraling waveforms include the biological spirals within claws, teeth, horns, irises, ear pinea, and fingerprints.

Our senses utilize these rotational spirals to channel and conduct information waveforms. Our cochlear anatomy utilizes a spiral to convert air pressure waves to neuron impulses. Our eyes are circular, with spiraling irises to the pupils through to the retina.

As illustrated on page 30, the nature of the electromagnetic wave is also spiraling.

Just as the sinusoid wave is derived from the circle, the classic spiral may be derived from the sphere. Beginning at any one of a sphere's apexes or poles, a spiral is formed if we move around the curvature of the sphere towards opposite poles. This most basic type of spiral is known as the *spherical spiral*. The spherical spiral is also known as the *arithmetic* or *Archimedean spiral*, named after the third century B.C. Greek mathematician Archimedes of Syracuse.

In this spiral, the distance between each layer (and spiral arm) is held equidistant. This creates an angular moment that is consistent throughout.

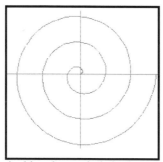

Archimedean spiral-single arm

There are various other types of spirals appearing in nature. The Fibonacci sequence is either helical or spiral, depending upon the relative perspective. *Fibonacci spirals* are close relatives to the *logarithm spiral*. *Fermat's spiral*—named after sixteenth century Frenchman Pierre de Fermat—is related to the arithmetic spiral. In 1979, Helmut Vogel proposed a variant of Fermat's spiral as a better approximation of nature's Fibonacci spiral. This is the spiral observed within *Phyllotaxis*, which include sunflowers, daisies and certain spiraling universes.

Rene Descartes revealed the *equiangular spiral* around 1868. This spiral reflects geometrical radii outward as polar angles increase. The relationship Descartes discussed (S=AR, which Evangelista Torricelli also developed independently during that era) has also been called the *geometrical spiral*.

Edmond Halley's seventeenth and eighteenth century work revealed the *proportional spiral*. Jacob Bernoulli developed its logarithmic basis, revealing the *logarithmic spiral* shortly thereafter. Bernoulli gave it the namesake of *spira mirabilis*, meaning "wonderful spiral." It is said Bernoulli's fascination of the spiral led to his request it be engraved on his tombstone.

As pointed out by Giuseppe Bertin and C.C. Lin in their 1996 book, *Spiral Structure in the Galaxies*, the spiraling galaxies may well be generated through a combination of density waves that rotate in a slower rhythm than the rest of the galaxy's stars, planets and gases. This *density wave theory*, first proposed in 1964 by C.C. Lin and Frank Shu, explains that the harmonization of the angular paths and the mutual gravitational attraction of the galaxy's components form areas of greater density: This allows the spiral arm formation without a *winding problem*.

Much of nature is arranged in helix or spiral shape. What may not appear to be spiraling is likely requiring us to peer through its cross-section. For example, an ocean wave breaking over a reef may appear to be a half waveform as it is looked at straight on from the beach. However, a cross-sectional view of the same wave reveals its spiral motion:

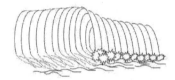

Ocean wave breaking (and spiraling) through to the beach

The combination of the forward movement of the wave to the beach and the sideways movement of water along the crest creates the surfer's classic spiraling *"tube"* or *"barrel."* To ride the tube or barrel requires the surfer to stay just ahead of the final eclipsing of the water with the trough. Should the surfer lapse into the center point of the spiral, the surfer will most likely be separated from the surfboard and experience the dreaded *"wipe out."*

The hurricane provides an additional example of this effect. Waves from two different pressure and temperature fronts interact to form the classic cyclone effect as seen from satellite.

The hurricane's spiral is only visible from above. This means that for thousands of years, humankind had little direct awareness of this spiraled form. Looking at a hurricane front from the land renders a view of the coming wall of rain and wind from the storm. This is why it has been called a 'storm front.' Many have speculated about weather systems as they experienced the 'eye of a hurricane.' They have compared this with other spiraling interactions of waveforms—the tornado. However, it was only when humans began to take to the air that these beautiful spiraling images began to unveil themselves.

This is the same dynamic we see when we flush the toilet or watch water draining a basin. The water's swirling motion reflects the interference pattern of multiple waveform forces. Because the earth is magnetically oriented with north and south poles, the direction of the spiral formed in the basin is clockwise when we flush the toilet in the southern hemisphere. In the northern hemisphere, the same flush rotates counterclockwise. This is caused by the earth's magnetic orientation; effectively "pulling" the water outward one way or another as it is being pulled downward by gravity.

D'Arcy Wentworth Thompson's 1917 classic *On Growth and Form* and Sir T.A. Cook's 1903 *Spirals in Nature and Art* illustrated the many examples of nature's spirals. Mr. Thompson detailed how elements and organisms within nature have a tendency to coil. These include hair, skin cells, tails, elephant trunks, roots and cordiform leaves among others. Other interesting helix and spiral movements include the spiraled burrowing of rodents and the spiraled swimming of dolphins and whales.

In 1973, Dr. Michael Rossmann reported the finding of a protein structure where multiple coiling strands are linked together with two helical structures. The connection between the strands and the helices were found to be alternating, forming an available structure for nucleotide bonding. This structure proved to be one of many important helical molecules: Nicotinamide adenine dinucleotide (NAD), a critical coenzyme involved in cellular energy production and genetic transcription within every living cell.

Numerous other biomolecular structures are helical when we are able to observe their *tertiary* structure. Various polysaccharides, polypeptides, hormones, neurotransmitters and fatty acids produced by metabolism have helical-spiral molecular structures.

We can't forget the king of spiral biomolecules, DNA. DNA and its related RNA are protein molecules known for the storage and dissemination of the programming of the body's metabolism. Their helical-spiraling structures have mesmerized the scientific community for nearly six decades.

As we look closer, we find that electron clouds (orbitals or energy states) have helical-spiral dimensions. This spiraling micro-universe of subatomic particle-waves is still beyond the grasp of today's leading physicists.

At the same time, some physicists have been disturbed by the *paradox of the spiral*. This issue was discussed by Dr. Einstein, who concluded this as a radial conductance in his paper on the Faraday disc problem: *"It is known that Maxwell's electrodynamics—as usually understood at the present time—when applied to moving bodies, leads to asymmetries that do not appear to be inherent in the phenomena."* He went on to propose *"asymmetry"* arises when the currents are produced without a *"seat"* of forces. As we have previously discussed, the magnetic field tends to exert a force vector moving perpendicular to that of electrical current. As this happens, angular momentum is inferred from the induction. When the torque of angular momentum arising from the conducting Faraday disc is considered together with coherently interacting currents and fields, the dynamic of the electromagnetic spiral becomes evident (Serra-Valls 2007).

These waveform forces are precisely mirrored by the classic electromagnetic structure: As the electronic vector pulses forward in one plane, the magnetic vector pulses outward into another plane. Consider a two- and three-dimensional representation:

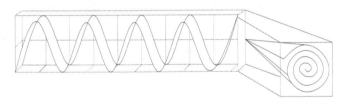

Electromagnetic wave in second and third planes

Electronic radiation is not that different from the motion of water. In both, we see a motion in three dimensions: Playing out the third dimension illustrates the magnetic field moving away perpendicular to the electronic vector of the electromagnetic wave. Because the electronic motion is radiating in an alternating fashion, the magnetic vector moves with a helical, spiraling formation around and outward of the electronic vector. This above representation of this effect shows the electromagnetic waveform from side and cross sections.

Regarding the apparent differences between the spiral and the helix, we point out that when cross-referenced with the axes of time and space, a helix will convert to a spiraled helix. This may require a cross-sectional view to complete the image, however—just as was illustrated earlier with the beach break wave. If we are looking at the wave breaking from the front view, we see a cylinder from the beach. It is the cross-sectional view of the wave looking down the length of the wave from the side that brings its spiraling motion into view. In the same way, as time and space accumulates helical motion along one axis or another, we observe that one end of the helix will be more relevant than the other end with time. This progression may also be perceived as spiraling arms expanding outward as the helix approaches.

The three dimensional wave presents a helical spiral when the relativity of motion towards the perceiver is considered. We can illustrate the effect of time and space in motion by observing a train approaching us. The front of the train as it approaches us is closer and thus appears larger than the rest of the train. Though the train size is consistent through all cars, our perception at that point of time is of a large locomotive and small caboose. In the same way, traveling through time within the motion of a spiral would arrive at a helixed perspective: And vice versa for the inverse. Likewise, a person caught in the eye of a hurricane or tornado will not perceive the funneling shape of the storm. The helical or spiral view would only be perceivable from a distance or from above, respectively.

As we peer deeper into the electromagnetic interactivity between electronic current and its reciprocating magnetic field, we unveil through analysis the potential disturbance they create. This implies a designed functionality between conduction and induction. All of nature's waves and spirals oscillate within this sort of cooperative context. The fields of one electromagnetic rhythm will affect surrounding electromagnetic rhythms. The inter-relationship between natural waveforms within the same environment indicates nature's harmonic organization on a grander level. A chaotic arrangement of replicating depth and organization would simply be an oxymoron.

We can ponder more deeply the nature of matter as we see the elements of multiple dimensions: The waveform and polar mechanics of molecules, combined with the waveform nature of their orbital subatomic content, produces interactive radiation vectors.

This helical-spiral relationship between time and motion also applies to polarity. As polarity bends the electromagnetic spiral motion in one direction or another, the helical orientation turns away or towards the polar application. Because this is a waveform interaction, this bending creates the facility for information flow along the intersection region. This intersection of pulses and polarity is how combined atoms provide bonding character and structural architecture among their molecular combinations.

As we've discussed, interfering waveforms are information carriers. Spirals, then, are simply a conglomeration of waveform interference patterns under a polar influence. This provides a complexity of information and the facility for resonance. We might compare a waveform to a letter, a waveform interference pattern to a word, and a spiral to a paragraph or even a book. We could pull a letter out of a book, but its context and meaning would be lost without the rest of the arranged letters and words of the book. While combined waveforms form interference patterns, spirals provide the platform for the flow of information and structure within nature.

In other words, information is conducted through spiraling waveform interference patterns. The medium or space-time may be disturbed by information waveforms, but the information does not move the medium. The information-waves *pass through the medium.* In *The Evolution of Physics,* Dr. Einstein and Dr. Infeld compared a wave to gossip that travels from one person to another over large distances, yet the people who communicated the gossip did not move. Only the gossip moved. In the same way, we can understand that the spiraling waveform interference patterns of nature serve to conduct complex information through the universe.

Dr. Einstein proposed we accept that the movements of nature are either moving relatively too fast or too slow for us to observe. We can apply this to our understanding of the universe's wavelike, spiraling interference patterns. For this reason, we find out that human research only gives us fleeting glimpses of the complex waveform harmonic existing within the universe.

How does this relate to the electron clouds we discussed previously? The interactions of nature's waveforms to form resonating and sometimes standing waves are harmonic with those of atoms and molecules. Like spirals, electron clouds are created by wave interference and confluence. The shape and angle of the cloud depends upon the confluence of reciprocating electromagnetic waveforms. How do we know that electron clouds maintain harmonic scale? The valence shells of twos and eights specify this sort of harmonic: Harmonic frequencies of standing waveform orbitals create interference patterns with spiraling frequency.

We also know that certain types of radiation can interfere with these complex spiraling standing electron clouds. This has been repeatedly shown with the bombardment of radiation in particle accelerators. As the resonation of polar interference patterns is disturbed by radiation, the molecule or ion undergoes structural change, and subatomic particles are released (or absorbed) with concurrent energy state changes.

Consider observing standing waves within a small pond of water caused by dropping a couple of small pebbles into the pond. While we see waves appearing to be standing in the same place as they meet each other, their motion is still reflecting the original pebbles that disturbed the water in the first place. In other words, whatever motion is on the water reflects the original cause of the motion. If we were to drive a car over a cliff into the pond below, the resulting large waves within the pond will also reflect the weight and volume of the car. These waves would reflect onto the basin at the side of the pond to form interfering wave patterns. These patterns eventually become standing waveforms as they resonate with each other and the edge of the pond over time. These standing wave patterns would 'memorize' and reflect the impact of the car upon the water for a period of time.

The 'solids' of nature are all standing, spiraling waveform interference patterns. Each part is made up of a unique combination of specifications which include waveform characteristics such as wavelength, frequency, amplitude, field, and phase—as well as spiral characteristics such as radius, loci and angular velocity. As spiraling waveforms interfere, complex interference patterns form among molecular electron clouds. The radiation they emit or reflect gives them the appearance of solid objects.

This might be compared to looking at the surface of the ocean from far away. From a distance, the ocean looks like a solid, flat object. But when we get closer to the coast, we begin to see that the surface is actually made up of a series of moving, spiraling and standing waves of water. They 'stand' in this case because while the water waves may be moving through the ocean, the waves themselves are contained within the ocean. When we look at repeating waves onto the shoreline, we are seeing an approximation of standing waves. The waves are vibrating virtually the same water molecules repeatedly.

As we get even closer, we find that these ocean waves are made up of water molecules, which also contain their own electromagnetic waveform interference patterns. These waveforms and interference patterns are harmonically resonating with the spiraling larger waveform interference patterns of the larger ocean waves.

This harmony is repeated throughout the spiraling waveform interference patterns of the electromagnetic world.

Our Electromagnetic Sun

The energy of the sun is primarily due to the sun's electromagnetic radiation, hurtling at us at 186,282 miles per second from a heated core estimated to be 93 million miles away.

The sun influences the earth's motion, warmth, spin, weather systems, tectonics, magnetism, ocean currents, air circulation, and many other qualities. Without the companion of the sun, the earth would simply not exist as we know it. A delicate balance exists between the sun's electromagnetic rays and the earth's atmosphere. The atmosphere shields and protects life on the planet by absorbing and neutralizing many rays that would likely delete life otherwise. Plants and trees also reduce heat. They absorb ultraviolet rays for photosynthesis and reflect other rays to produce an array of colors. In the oceans, plankton and various other algae also absorb the sun's rays on the water during photosynthesis.

The sun produces several types of radiation, many that significantly affect our metabolism in one respect or another. The sun's known waveforms are categorized (see also chart on page 7) as visible light rays (from 400 to 700 nm wavelength), infrared radiation (from 750 nm to 1 mm), ultraviolet rays (280 to 400 nm), x-rays (about 10 x -5 nm), gamma rays (10 x -11 to 10 x -14 nm), cosmic rays (10 to 12 cm) and microwaves (1 mm to 30 cm). The earth's atmosphere and the sun's geomagnetic fields block a good amount of the x-rays, cosmic rays and gamma rays and a significant part of the ultraviolet rays—depending upon the levels of ozone. This allows a good portion of the sun's visible, ultraviolet and infrared radiation to hit the surface. In all it is estimated that the atmosphere blocks about 40% of the sun's total radiation.

While many of the rays of the sun can cause damage to the body with over-exposure, ultraviolet radiation has probably received the most attention over recent decades. Ultraviolet-C rays are significantly blocked by the atmosphere. UV-B and UV-A will make it through, however. Between UV-B and UV-A, UV-A rays are more prominent, depending again upon the ozone layer. In most areas, UV-A rays make up over 98% of the ultraviolet radiation that breaks through the atmosphere. The majority of the remainder is UV-B radiation—known best for producing vitamin D.

The sun is might be considered a very large magnet. Its magnetic field fluctuates to up to 3,000 times its normal range. The sun also emits solar flares, which appear to our eyes and instruments to be massive eruptions spewing up to 20 billion tons of matter into space. On a mass basis, researchers estimate the sun represents 99.8 percent of the total mass of this solar system. The planets are quite tiny compared to the sun.

As a result of the sun's influence, our solar system is pervading with natural magnetic fields. One of the most powerful magnetic influences upon us is the sun. These are generated by intense streams of protons produced by the sun's solar storms.

Galileo is given credit for making the first correct interpretation of sunspots on the sun's surface. In the early nineteenth century, astronomers began to notice a periodic cycling of sunspot activity. This led to a correlation between solar storm activity and changes within the earth's environment. In the years following, sunspot activity was also correlated with human behavior. Over the past few decades, scientists have confirmed that birth rates, ice ages, wars, epidemics and many other events are associated with the sun's solar storm cycles and activities. (See pages 56-59 for more detail on this.)

Cyclical solar flares erupt on the surface of the sun, hurtling various forms of radiation towards the earth. These include x-ray flares and massive streams of protons. Some of these flares eject *coronal masses*, which appear like tentacles reaching out into space. These events hurl electromagnetic waves through the solar system. Their projections can create damage for orbiting vehicles and can penetrate the earth's atmosphere, causing power outages and radio blackouts.

Scientists believe that a sunspot is a region where strong magnetic fields shoot up through the sun's surface. Often a solar storm will follow, with an explosion above the sunspot. It is thought that the instability of the sunspot's magnetic field stimulates the explosion. This, however, has yet to be proven.

Solar storms propel magnetism in the form of proton sprays much as a sprinkler will spray water from the middle of the lawn. This sets up a regular magnetic field pattern in space, which naturally collides with the planets in a periodic fashion. In addition, solar storm activity is also periodic.

In 2005, a seemingly new kind of solar storm unleashed itself upon the earth. This is now referred to as *Sunspot 720*. Sunspot 720 is unique in that a coronal mass ejection produced a proton storm that hit the earth within minutes of its eruption. On January 20, 2005, the earth's atmosphere was inundated by a proton storm—produced only a half hour earlier on the surface of the sun.

The geomagnetic fields created by solar storms prevent damaging cosmic rays from intruding upon the earth's biosphere. This was discovered recently, as scientists correlated carbon-14 levels in trees and the atmosphere (through rock and ice core readings) with solar storm activity. Periods of higher solar storm activity were met with reduced carbon-14 levels. This indicated one of the many protective effects of the sun upon the earth. The ice core readings also indicated that solar storm activity has coincided with global cooling and heating trends.

German astronomer Samuel Schwabe first documented observations of periodic solar activity in the 1840s. Over many years of subsequent analysis by astrophysicists, it has been determined that sunspot cycles range from 9 years to 14 years, with an average of 11.1 years. Within this obvious cyclical behavior, astronomers have also noticed other cycles occurring within the period of each cycle. Advances in monitoring technology has revealed that solar flares or sunspots also cycle periodically with respect to their intensity. When sunspot and solar flare activity are graphed over more than a century, an amazing butterfly-shaped graph is revealed.

In the 1950s, the American astronomer Dr. Harold Babcock detailed the magnetic field distribution on the sun's surface. Using his invention, the *solar magnetograph,* Dr. Babcock determined that the sun reverses magnetic polarity on a periodic basis. He also found that stars also emit unique magnetic fields.

The Magnetic Universe

In 1175, English monk Alexander Neckam experimented with and eventually described how a magnet could be used to make a compass. In 1269, Petrus Peregrinus de Marincourt described the pivot compass. William Gilbert's sixteenth century *De Magnete* described many other uses for the magnet. He also proposed that the pointing of the magnetized needle of a compass in the downwardly north direction meant that the earth must have a *"magnetic soul."*

Polarity is the key ingredient of magnetism, and shifting polarity is a driver of alternating current. In any organism, the polarity of the molecules and atoms making up living cells are arranged in such a way that the poles of each molecule balance each other. This is driven by the reality that negative and positive poles tend to attract each other. Solid structures have latticed patterns founded upon this polarity balance. A polar balance creates stability between intercellular organelles, inner and outer cell membranes, organ tissues, and other cooperative components of the body.

Most biomolecules are either *paramagnetic* (attracted to a magnet) or *diamagnetic* (repelled by a magnet), depending upon which way their polarity balance is trending. In a lodestone or ferro-magnet, however, there is a little less balance in the structure. Groupings of magnetic atoms align together with their poles pointing in one direction or another. These aligned groupings tend to overwhelm unaligned atoms of the substance, rendering one end a polar negative and the other a polar positive. The ability of a magnet to attract or repel other materials works via this polarity difference on one end or another. As a result, the polarity difference on one side will produce a field that attracts the opposite polarity among other materials. This polar attraction of a magnet is strong enough to drive the rotors of an electric motor.

The strength of the field created by this polarity difference is typically measured in gauss or Teslas. A Tesla is 10,000 gauss.

When an electronic pulse moves through a magnetic field, the electron flow will be drawn either away from or towards the magnet, depending upon the polarity. The forward motion of the electronic current creates an arc. This arc is a representation or byproduct of angular momentum. As electronic currents and magnetic fields interact together in nature, this angular momentum effect creates the spiraling of orbital clouds and matter in general.

The dynamics of magnetic induction between the sun and the earth also creates a pathway for the arc of gravitational orbits.

Consider the trajectory of an arrow shot upwards. It would continue in a straight line until it was acted upon by gravity. Since an arrow's path typically curves upward, arcs, and then curves downward, we can see that the force of gravity was acting in a direction opposing the (upward) direction of the arrow. This interfering combination of vectors produces the perfect arc of the arrow as it heads back to earth. In the same way, the arcing of geomagnetism within the solar system adjusts the vectors of the electromagnetic waves pulsing from the sun.

The earth is a giant magnet, and so are all living organisms. Geologists propose that the earth is magnetic due to the motion of magnetic metals within the surface—a sort of liquefied magnetic core. The concept of a core in motion stems from the fact that the earth's magnetic fields are not static, but are changing. Findings from mountain and desert core samples show that the earth's magnetic north and south poles have varied from the current poles over the past few million years.

The magnetic North Pole is now near Bathurst Island—equidistant from the north geographic pole and the Canada's Arctic Circle. The magnetic South Pole is located close to Hobart, Tasmania. In the late sixteenth century, William Gilbert measured the north magnetic declination at 10 degrees east. By the early nineteenth century, it was 25 degrees west. Now the north magnetic pole lies about 6 degrees west. The magnetic north pole is by no means static.

The earth's physiology is intimately connected with the geomagnetic flows from the sun. This becomes especially apparent when considering the moon's relative effects upon the planet, and the *aurora borealis*—or northern lights. The later is caused by the interaction between atmospheric ions and the electromagnetic radiation from solar activity with the earth's magnetic fields. A glorious light show from nature's EMF arsenal.

Scientists have long thought the earth's magnetic fields rotated above the earth's surface like a band of atmosphere. However, anisotropic scaling has modeled and measured magnetic fields flowing both vertically and horizontally, cross-sectioning the earth's crust. It has also been proposed that these changing magnetic fields predispose movement of magma and/or tectonic plates (Moshe 1996).

The amount of the earth's magnetic field ranges from 45,000 to 60,000 nT (nanoTeslas) over the U.S. This huge variance is assumed to be created by the existence of "buried magnetic bodies" under the earth's surface. This is consistent with surface magnetic field variances found in areas where underground tanks or other fixtures are buried. Steel underground tanks, for example, will result in magnetic field variances of thousands of nanoTeslas.

Core samples with magnetometer readings have confirmed that the earth's magnetic flow has maintained the same approximate direction over the past 700,000 years. Before that, the magnetic field direction of the earth changed a number of times. More than once, the poles have completely reversed. Several times in the planet's history, the earth's major magnetic field has traveled from east to west. Measurements are now illustrating that there is an overall weakening of the magnetic field—some 16% since 1670. This indicates that there is a reversal or another abrupt change in progress. Some estimate a complete phase change—or reversal—could come as soon as 2000 years from now.

The moving core theory is not the only theory that attempts to explain the earth's changing polarity and magnetic fields. Some have proposed magnetic direction changes are caused by the motion of magnetic field loops circulating from east to west within the earth's interior. This rhythmic field looping has been compared to the rotating magnetism apparent between each side of a bar magnet as it changes polarity. Still others have proposed that an impact from a large meteor might be strong enough to change the earth's magnetic field. The emerging possibility is that the rhythmic geomagnetic fields created by solar storms produce the earth's magnetic changes. Certainly, the sun's solar storms are a contributing factor.

Research on animal migration has confirmed that migratory movement is directly related to the earth's magnetic fields. Cornell University research in 1974 disclosed migration's link to geomagnetism. Researchers tied magnets on bird's heads and let them fly. The birds became disoriented and could not navigate.

Further testing with other migrating species such as lobsters and turtles have since confirmed that all migrating organisms find their direction using tiny magnetic elements within certain cells. Magnetite metals within their cells orient with the earth's polarity to guide their migratory path—much the same way a compass might be used by a ship's navigator to steer a course over the sea.

Magnetic cells have been found in the smallest of species. Bacteria have been found to contain tiny magnetic metals, for example. In fact, many bacteria could very well be compared to a living bar magnets. Tiny pieces of magnetite material will line up within the center of the bacterium—approximating a rudimentary spine. This observation has led some researchers to speculate that the human spine is also magnetic. Indeed, researchers have recently discovered magnetic molecules such as iron oxide within certain human brain and spinal nerve cells. Thus, we might conclude that our bodies also contain little magnetic compasses.

✋Two

The Electromagnetic Body

As we emerge from the womb, our bodies begin their entrainment to the sun's electromagnetic pulses. This entrainment process takes a little time. Infants progress from almost all day sleep (with some feeding and crying in between) to sleep cycles precisely timed to the sun. This, of course, is a gradual process of adaptation.

Not randomly, mind you. Rather, a baby's sleep cycles decrease in daily frequency at a consistent pattern, influenced by geographical location (with respect to the equator) and the amount of artificial light present in the room. In other words, with each passing sunrise and sunset, our bodies slowly and gradually entrain their operations to nature's electromagnetic pulses and cycles. By the time our bodies reach adolescence, our clocks have become quite rigid, exhaustively trained by so many daily cycles of the sun.

The body's electromagnetic character is revealed throughout our metabolism. Practically every metabolic act is driven through electromagnetic activity originating outside and inside the body.

The Metabolic Circuit

A circuit consists of a closed loop of current running from one terminal point to another through appropriate grade wiring, often together with various switches, fuses, resistors and grounding mechanisms. The utility power grid is a network of electrical circuits connecting houses to power generating facilities. This is also a circuit—albeit a larger one. Once power is delivered from the grid to a house, it is led into a number of smaller circuits—each distributing power into the different regions of the house.

Each circuit is opened and closed with a circuit breaker wired into a main panel: The current for each circuit travels from the distribution panel through that area of the house and then back to the panel. Outlets and switches allow the electrical circuit to distribute current to electrical appliances. Assuming the appliance has the right capacity, resistance and conductance; it will utilize this incoming current to power its operations.

All electricity has a power source. Modern electricity is produced from nature's elements. This includes hydroelectric (water), solar (sun), or the combustion of carbon (coal or gas).

Many power generating plants will produce and send alternating current through their grid circuits. Transformers will step down the voltage as it enters houses and buildings. Alternating current has become the standard because alternating current can be fairly efficiently transmitted over long distances in higher voltages and stepped down through transformers. In more recent years, high voltage direct current has become the preferred method of long distance power transmission, because direct current produces less resistance within wire conductors. This allows power to be transmitted over longer distances with less power loss and smaller wires.

Because every conductor provides some resistance to a current, power loss is a critical issue. Alternating current produces a *skin effect,* which pushes its conduction outward. This utilizes less of the conducting material, producing more resistance. Nonetheless, alternating current is the norm for appliances and household currents. An alternating current's waveforms pulse in one direction before reversing direction. Direct currents pulse in one direction only.

As power moves through the electrical grid, it is stepped down in voltage using transformers, and eventually enters the house with a single-phase three wire circuit. This means a positive wire and a negative wire with a ground or neutral wire. Triple-phase transmission is typically used at generating plants, enabling greater voltages with more stability, as three conductors are placed around each other at 120-degree angles to cancel their magnetic fields.

Electricity is complicated by its magnetic fields. The magnetic field pulses in a direction perpendicular to the motion of the electrical pulse. This affects the local environment of a circuit. For this reason, electrical wires are double-stranded, twisted and shielded. The double stranding and twisting cancels a good amount of the magnetic fields as they destructively interfere with each other. Shielding further prevents leakage and loss of electrical current. These strategies are designed to increase safety and lower magnetic field production within the household environment.

If a circuit were to surge inconsistently, appliances on the circuit may be damaged. Spikes in electrical current can occur during a lightning storm or power interruption. Circuit breakers and surge protectors are often installed into a house circuit to reduce surging and prevent an overloading of current within the circuit.

Most appliances contain their own miniature circuits. Electricity will be filtered through these appliance circuits using a series of resistors, transistors and capacitors. Most of today's appliances use integrated circuits to bring a greater number of resisters and transistors together into a single compact chip. These are designed to modify the waveform qualities of the current, and translate them into the waveform requirements of the appliance. The integrated circuit is thus designed to modulate and translate waveforms from one type to another. Digital appliances convert alternating current into a series of pulsed digital waveforms using integrated circuitry. These digital waveforms contain unique patterns, which create the programming instructions (often called machine code) to operate the appliance. Meanwhile, power will also be channeled directly into the mechanical portions of the appliance to give it the power to execute its hardware operations.

An appliance may also bring other waveforms. A radio or television will use an antenna and a receiver to channel in broadcasted radiowaves moving through the air. For this reason, most radios and televisions have tuners that focus their receivers onto particular waveform frequencies. Once received, these waveforms will have to be modulated and converted as they are brought into the appliance. Once the waveforms are crystallized, integrated circuits will convert them into digital pulses. These digital pulses are converted into the informational pulses that drive the speakers and/or screen—giving sight and sound to our televisions and radios.

Modern electrical circuits conduct current through copper, gold, silver, aluminum or other metals. Various alloys have been created in recent years. Copper is one of the most used conductors in home circuits because of its stability and low heat production. This makes copper less likely to cause a fire. Aluminum was popular for home wiring in decades past. Electrical fires have been found to be more prevalent in aluminum-wired households. For good reason, insurance companies now prefer copper wiring.

Other materials are considered partial conductors of electrical potential. In other words, they allow for only a muted or partial transmission of electromagnetism: These are called *semiconductors*. Most semiconductors have a crystalline structure such as silicon or germanium—whose crystal structure compares to a diamond.

Other compounded elements like indium phosphide and gallium arsenide are also used to provide specific semiconductance. Silicon is probably the most popular semiconductor used today, primarily because of its relatively low cost.

The human body also contains circuits. The body circulates and modulates electromagnetic waveforms in much the same way a grid, house, computer, radio or television does. The circuitry of the body is infinitely more complex than any of these, however. The human body utilizes a huge array of conducting and semiconducting mechanisms to distribute and translate waveform information throughout its circuitry.

The crystals used by early radio receivers and the various semiconductor materials used in today's digital devices utilize a similar process that particular biochemicals provide in the body. The senses and their specialized neurons receive transmitted waveforms much the same way a radio or television antenna and receiver does. Once received, these waveforms are converted and translated from their generated source transmissions into electromagnetic pulses suitable for nerve transmission within the body's circuits. These converted waveforms are then transmitted through a vast array of cells and biochemicals, to eventually be viewed by a conscious seer—the self. Once the self within reviews the transmitted and converted information, the self responds with emotion.

The emotional response by the self also utilizes specialized cells to accommodate and translate the information transmitted. These responses utilize the facilities of nerves, hormones, proteins, neurotransmitters, enzymes and DNA as crystals and semiconductors, to convert and transmit intention into informational waveforms and physical responses.

The connection between electricity and the body was established in 1937. Harold Saxton Burr, Ph.D. and Professor of Anatomy at Yale University's School of Medicine, began his research on what he described as living organisms' *biomagnetic field*. Later he named these fields *L-fields*, or *fields of life*. Dr. Burr believed the electromagnetic property of living tissue provided its "organizing principle." This, he thought, prevented the cell from descending into chaos. Dr. Burr also established that physical disease in a living organism is preceded by particular electromagnetic changes.

To establish living organisms' electromagnetic properties, Burr developed an instrument and measurement system sensitive to very weak electromagnetic waveforms. From observations using his specialized equipment, he concluded that living organisms conducted and resisted electricity in the 10^{-6} volts range—small enough to be called *microvolts*.

In one trial, using specially designed microvolt meters with transistors, Dr. Burr suspended salamander eggs within a saline solution. To screen out the potential galvanic action of the solution, Dr. Burr inserted minimizing silver nitrate electrodes between the microvolt meter probe and the saline. He also set up a spinning disc with a measurable sinusoidal voltage waveform, which allowed him to establish a net increase in voltage when the egg was added. This design allowed Dr. Burr to accurately measure any subtle changes in electronic potentials. To provide some controls, Dr. Burr also tested and compared electric potentials of salamander unfertilized eggs. The results were compared with the readings of fertilized eggs and salamanders immediately after hatching. Using a control group of about 100 eggs, Dr. Burr's testing provided clear evidence that the salamander eggs possessed electromagnetic circuitry. Furthermore, he established that the eggs exhibited increasing levels of electromagnetic energy as the eggs matured.

Dr. Burr also discovered that a particular point on the equator of the eggs had a higher voltage than anywhere else on the egg. Points 180 degrees from that point on its equator had a significantly lower voltage. As the eggs matured and hatched, it became evident the higher voltage points corresponded with the salamander's head and the lowest voltage points corresponded with the salamander's tail. Dr. Burr duplicated these results with frogs' eggs and chick embryos. It became evident that a voltage circuit occurred along the alignment of the body's nervous system, with the greatest voltage differential occurring between the top and the bottom of the spine.

Dr. Burr's studies with the living bioelectrical field expanded into diverse areas in the following decades. He published or contributed to nearly one hundred scientific papers on the subject. One of the more fascinating studies Dr. Burr conducted was on the relationship between disease and the bioelectric field. Here he discovered that within about two weeks of contracting cancer, mice would experience an abnormal spiking of their bioelectric field. Confirmed with over 10,000 measurements, it became obvious that most organisms emit a bioelectric surge in advance of contracting disease (Burr 1938).

Another notable result from Dr. Burr's research on various animals and humans was the observation of abnormal bioelectric voltage changes during episodes of metabolic stress. For example, notable voltage changes were observed during wound healing, ovulation, drug use, and a variety of illnesses (Burr 1936; Burr 1937; Burr 1972).

The nervous system is not the only bio-electromagnetic system of the body. The entire body contains multiple circuits and conducting mechanisms. This has gradually become apparent to mainstream science with the discoveries of a multitude of various types of *ion channels*. These are tiny *gateways* lying within cell membranes, consisting primarily of proteins. These protein ion channels reside within the phospholipids of cell membranes. They provide the primary passageways through which the cell's electromagnetic balance is established. The ion channel gateways are stimulated through voltage potential changes, which can take place through the conductance of minerals such as sodium, calcium, magnesium, potassium and others.

In other words, voltage potentials are negotiated through these ion channel gateways. As an ion channel gateway is stimulated with a particular ion polarity, it will open or close. As it opens, it conducts specific information into the cell. The process compares favorably to the opening of an electrical circuit to power an appliance. Once we switch on the power to an appliance, we open its circuits. Then we can tune it to the proper frequencies in order to channel in the information we desire. In the same way, ion channels within the body can be opened or closed. Once open, informational signals (or nutrition) can be channeled in. Typically, mineral ion polarities open or close these gateways. These polarities are networked through the body to open many ion channel circuits at once.

The metabolic importance of these ion channels located throughout the body cannot be overstated. Should these channels fail to respond or react appropriately to a particular voltage parameter, or should they close or open at the wrong times, they can signal the wrong action, or perhaps even signal cells to shut down. This would undoubtedly result in a diseased condition.

Ion channels function very similarly to circuit breakers, resistors and capacitors. They are the gateways for the informational electromagnetic currents running through our body. These electromagnetic currents utilize minerals as conductors. Just as copper conducts electricity through our house wiring systems, the various mineral ions like calcium, sodium, potassium and others conduct information and energy through our bodies. They provide the means through which electromagnetic information is passed from one part of the body to the other.

Ions, however, provide only a subsystem of many levels of bioconductance. Along with ions, *neurotransmitters* provide the conductors for the legions of neurons tied together with synapses and ion channels. These linked neurons create the pipelines that make up our nervous system. The nervous system utilizes synapses and ion channels to conduct information from one neuron to the next.

Other complex molecules such as *enzymes* and *coenzymes* also facilitate the exchange of electromagnetic information throughout the body. Like integrated circuits, these specialized biomolecules conduct and transmit information by stimulating and catalyzing biochemical reactions within the body. Hence they act as the body's resistors and transistors for electromagnetic information.

The body also conducts complex information through the broadcasting mechanisms of *hormones*. Hormones fall within a grouping of specialized proteins called *ligands*. Ligands have molecular structures that transfer unique waveform combinations. These unique waveform combinations provide specific information. Information is transmitted from ligands to specialized gateway biomolecules called *receptors*. Within the body are innumerable types of receptors and ligands, each equipped to send and receive different sorts of information. Receptors are very similar to ion channels. Like ion channels, they are responsive to electromagnetic conductors. By stimulating receptors, ligand 'conductors' can switch on metabolic activities within cells, discontinue metabolic activities, or significantly alter metabolic activities.

For example, on the surface of most cells are insulin receptors. These will respond to the information communicated via the ligand hormone, insulin. As part of a vast array of mechanisms including glucose reception and surtuin instigation, insulin receptors are stimulated and 'switched on' by insulin. When insulin receptors are switched on, the cell becomes receptive to glucose. This will allow the cell to readily absorb glucose molecules for energy utilization. Should the insulin receptors become altered over time as a result of a poor diet, the receptors can become less sensitive to insulin. They won't be switched on as easily, in other words. This insensitivity can contribute to the condition of adult-onset diabetes—which is increasingly being seen among modern children. As a strategy to prevent the surging of insulin into the bloodstream, high fiber foods can be eaten with every meal. These high fibers slow the absorption of glucose into the bloodstream—giving the blood somewhat of a timed release of glucose and insulin (as nature intended). This timed release of insulin and glucose can gradually increase the sensitivity of insulin receptors, thereby smoothing out the cells' utilization of glucose.

Innumerable ligand-receptor transmission circuits conduct information throughout the body. These range from thyroid hormones, growth hormones, cortisol, melatonin, dopamine, serotonin, epinephrine, and so many others. Some ligands communicate specific instructions to cells from endocrine command centers, while others facilitate cell-to-cell communication. Neurotransmitters are examples of the latter. Through neurotransmitters, particular waveforms are transmitted from nerve cell to nerve cell. Neurotransmitters and hormones are functionally the same in that they broadcast information signals. However, hormones tend to broadcast a tighter range of instructions. Neurotransmitters appear to provide a broader range of waveform conductance.

Hormones and neurotransmitters are extremely complex biochemical molecules. Most are proteins, consisting of hundreds of amino acids joined with other elements. We might compare them to miniature radio stations because they will broadcast received information, while filtering and even sometimes distorting the information to fit their particular design and situation. Within each hormone or neurotransmitter lie semiconductors and integrated circuits. They also have their own broadcasting beacons—the ligand portion of the molecule. These ligand portions conduct electromagnetic information. Prior to conductance, information is modulated, filtered or regulated as it is processed through the molecule. This translation function gives these molecules tremendous power within the body. Incidentally, most of these larger biomolecules are crystalline with helical or spiral molecular shapes. This would compare favorably with some of our integrated circuits with semiconductor crystals such as silicon and germanium.

The complexity of these *integrated bio-semiconductors* reflects the programming involved within the various circuits of the body. Digital appliances use a system of 1s and 0s compiled together into bytes, which translate information. The on and off gateway states of ion channels, hormones and neurotransmitters create groups of on-off states. These provide complex instructions in the same way a gathering of computer bytes in machine code can instruct hardware operations.

Consider again the pulsing—the rise and fall—of a waveform. An on state would be equivalent to the peak of the wave, and the off state would be considered its trough. As different waveforms *interfere* with each other, however, they can form a more complex pattern of on and off states, depending upon how waveforms collided. This combination of waveforms (the interference pattern) provides a larger array of information—comparable to the byte.

As computers have progressed, their byte length systems have increased. Only a couple of decades ago, computer processing programs worked on an 8-bit byte. This meant that a combination of eight 1s or 0s could fit within a particular byte. The 8-bit byte has now been replaced by 64-bit and 128-bit bytes. The increased byte size increases the productivity of the computer by requiring fewer bytes to process complex information.

The intersection of multiple waveforms within the body creates an tremendously larger 'byte size'. This allows for an almost limitless opportunity for information complexity. Suffice to say that our bodies are not limited to 8- or even 132-bit processing. The body has multifarious gateway switches at different levels, with a multiplex of variances at any level. Thus, comparing the 1s and 0s on-off states of digital computer processing with the body's metabolic processing circuitry might be like comparing a game of checkers to a combat war covering multiple continents and millions of soldiers.

The electrical nature of the body was illuminated by the controversial work of Russian researcher Semyon Kirlian. In 1917, Kirlian attended a presentation by Nikola Tesla, who at the time was experimenting with a new phenomenon called *corona discharge*. Working as an electrical equipment technician later, Kirlian noticed a light flash between an electrotherapy apparatus and a patient's skin. This gave Kirlian another type of flash. For the next few years, he and his wife Valentina worked to develop an oscillating generator. This allowed an observer to look through an optical filter at the electrical activity arising from the skin's surface. This is dramatically similar to the sun's coronal effect as seen during an eclipse through telescopic equipment.

The ability to photograph the body's *corona effect* was developed by the Kirlians shortly thereafter. They began to notice several interesting correlations as they compared coronal images between different people in different circumstances: The color and activity of the corona seemed different between healthy people and diseased people. They also noticed relationship between the corona and the Chinese *meridian* points.

Observations of *auras* have also been recorded in ancient texts, some thousands of years old. Halos and illuminations have been described in various circumstances throughout Biblical texts. The ancient Vedic literature of the Indus Valley described the *pranic aura field* surrounding the body and the observations of certain personalities with significant bodily effulgence thousands of years ago. In addition, the outward effects of *chi* as an effulgence surrounding the body was also described in ancient Taoist texts. Pythagoras recorded the notion of an outer human energy field around 500 B.C., and Paracelsus described it in the sixteenth century as the *"vital force"* that *"radiates round him like a luminous sphere...."*

More recently, Romanian physician Dr. Ion Dumitrescu had a startling discovery in the late 1970s. His discovery illustrated that the living electromagnetic aura also has a holographic nature. Dr. Dumitrescu utilized an electrographic process with a scanning mechanism to photograph leaf images before and after portions of the leaves were removed. Interestingly, the leaf's corona, despite the removal of a section of leaf, would remain in the shape of the entire leaf as if the section were never removed. The phenomenon was even more dramatic when a hole in the center of the leaf was cut out. Through this hole, the electrographic photo revealed a tiny leaf shape, identical to the outer leaf, which also had a hole in it (Gerber 1988).

Western medical science avoided the role of electromagnetics in living organisms for many years. This was despite the research of Burr and others. For example, in the mid-twentieth century, Dr. Robert Becker proved that salamander limb regeneration accompanied millivolt potentials (Becker 1985). This and other research has showed the proliferation of electromagnetism throughout the body.

Continuing studies of *electrotherapy* have confirmed the body's electromagnetic qualities. Electrical stimulation for pain relief is now well established, and today hospitals and pain centers regularly implant *electrostimulators* into the spinal cord region to relieve pain. Current theories regarding the process of pain relief now center around the *gate control theory* first proposed in 1964 by Melzack and Wall. This theory states the closing and opening of pain-relay gates located in the spine determines the level of electronic transduction of pain signal communication to the brain. Apparent confirmation of this theory has been the successful treatment of lower back neuropathic pain and pain elsewhere. In addition, electrostimulation has proven successful in bone healing. Veterinary surgeons report success rates in the 75% to 80% range for healing fractures and nonunions with electrostimulation (Clark 1987). Healing rates of almost 65% with an 85% effectiveness rate in human patients have also been observed (Heckman *et al.* 1981).

A number of other studies confirm these. Neurostimulation has been proven successful in a variety of human applications. Pathologies have included urinary and bladder issues (Tanagho 1990, Dalmose 2003, Banyo 2003, Kennedy *et al.* 1995); tachycardia arrhythmias (Volkmann 1991); spinal cord injuries (Beckerman *et al.* 1993, Meinecke 1991); low back pain (Shutov 2007); gastric issues (Deitel 2004); pain (Devulder *et al.* 2002, Siegfried 1988); smoking cessation (White *et al.* 2002); and many other conditions.

The research of Dr. Ronald Melzack and Dr. Patrick Wall eventually led to the famous McGill Pain Questionnaire and other gate control applications. These in turn led to the discoveries of some of the body's feel-good biochemical conductors such as endorphins and enkephalins.

The gate control theories also led to hypotheses regarding the *phantom limb* phenomenon. This curious event—in which an amputee continues to feel pain in an area of an amputated limb—is congruent with Dr. Dumitrescu's *phantom leaf theory* mentioned above.

Observation tells us that the body derives energy from food, sunlight, water, and air. However, there is significant evidence to conclude that these are actually different forms of radiative inputs translated from an upstream generating source. A hydroelectric plant—generating electricity for millions of homes—is not actually producing power. The power is being converted from one energy source to another. This is also stated in the conservation of energy law of thermodynamics.

The body's energy sources—food, sunlight, water and air—are more appropriately identified as conductors. Their waveform potentials carry nutrients into the body. Nutrients include amino acids, minerals, vitamins and oxygen. As discussed in the first chapter, these molecules are made up of atoms, which are made up of electromagnetic electron clouds. These electromagnetic waveforms provide the information our body requires to conduct its operations. This is illustrated by the damage a free radical (the anti-nutrient) can do within the body. Free radicals damage arteries and other tissues, producing disease. A free radical is essentially a molecule with an 'free electron'—an unstable electron cloud that damages other molecules as it seeks stability.

Our Magnetic Physiology

The body is full of polarity differentials. This makes the body a magnet. Most of our cells, organs and tissue systems are also independently magnetic. As electromagnetic biochemical reactions cascade through the body, magnetic fields are generated. These magnetic fields are dispatched through our local environment with polar results. Some fields are by-products of electronic processes, while others maintain polarities that affect metabolism directly.

The anatomical effects of magnetism are not readily addressed by modern medical science. This is odd, noting the extensive use of diagnosis using magnetic resonance technologies. MRIs (magnetic resonance) utilize the body's inherent polarity to visualize its anatomy. Just as electrical currents moving through appliances generate magnetic fields, the currents running through the body's ionic mechanisms utilize magnetic fields.

Magnets were named after the lodestone—a rock found by the Greeks in the province of Magnesia. This was a curious stone, and it was found by early Greek physicians to have healing properties. The Greek philosopher-physician Aristophanes explored this mysterious rock for many years. Hippocrates utilized the magnet for many treatments. Chinese and Vedic physicians had used magnets for healing centuries earlier. Ancient texts show that everything from heart disease to gout was treated with magnets in Chinese, Greek, medieval European, and Ayurvedic therapies.

After suffering from avoidance, the concept of magnetism within the human physiology arose again when the late-nineteenth century Julius Bernstein proposed that nerve impulses transferred through polarization. This *membrane polarization* model became the basis for the conclusive research of Otto Loewi in the early 1920s, which led to a 1936 Nobel Prize for synaptic transmission. Loewi's experiment—which apparently occurred to him during a dream—was to extract two frog hearts and retain each in a separate bath of saline. Some of the solution surrounding the faster heartbeat was extracted and put into the bath of the slower heart. This made the slower heart beat faster. The experiment effectively provided the evidence for biochemical synaptic transmission.

The polarity exchange between ions and biochemicals is unmistakably magnetic. Magnetism is, after all, a polarity issue of ions or atoms aligning in one direction or another. The irrefutable link between magnetism and biological response has been confirmed by study and clinical application during the last half of the twentieth century, as the existence of ion channels has been clarified.

Furthermore, the link between intention and magnetism has become evident. This was illustrated by Dr. Grad's research at Canada's McGill University in the late 1950s and early 1960s, when growth rates of barley sprouts were stimulated by the focused intentions of particularly gifted individuals. Further studies indicated these growth rate effects were similar to the influence magnetism has upon plant growth.

The central subject of these investigations was a Hungarian refugee named Oskar Estebany, who appeared to be able to exert intentional effects with his hands. A number of tests confirmed that magnetism was involved in Mr. Estebany's abilities. In one, Dr. Justa Smith at the Rosary Hill College (1973) compared Mr. Estebany's ability to increase enzyme reaction rates to those of magnetic field emissions. After Mr. Estebany affected an increase in reactivity among enzyme reaction rates, Dr. Smith applied magnetic fields and compared the rates. It turned out that the increased growth caused by Mr. Estebany precisely matched the growth caused by a 13,000 gauss magnetic field. The results indicated that somehow, intention can produce magnetic fields within the body.

Dr. Smith had spent a number of years studying these effects prior to and after her tests with Mr. Estebany. She authored a book on the topic—*Effect of Magnetic Fields on Enzyme Reactivity* (1969). While this research was considered radical at that time, other scientists soon confirmed her findings. In the 1990s, a flurry of research was published around the world showing magnetic fields in the 2,500-10,000 gauss range affecting reaction rates of various enzymatic reactions. By 1996, more than fifty different enzyme reactions were found to be influenced by magnetic fields. In two linked studies by University of Utah's Charles Grissom, (1993, 1996), single-beam UV-to-visible spectrum and rapid-scanning spectrophotometers with electromagnets built in were applied to two different cobalamine (B12) enzymes.

One enzyme (ethanolamine ammonia lyase) had significantly different reaction rates in response to magnetic fields, while the other enzyme (methylmalonyl CoA mutase) had no apparent response. It could thus be concluded that some biochemical processes are sensitive to magnetic field influence and others are not. This effect is still mysterious, but it has become increasingly evident that within the body exists a driver of magnetic fields.

There have been a number of controlled studies showing that major body centers respond to magnetic stimulation. Amassian *et al.* (1989) stimulated the motor cortex with a focal magnetic coil, which rendered movement to paralyzed appendages. Maccabee *et al.* (1991) stimulated almost the entire nervous system with a magnetic coil. This particular stimulation instigated responses from the distal peripheral nerve, the nerve root, the cranial nerve, the motor cortex, the premotor cortex, the frontal motor areas related to speech, and other nerve centers.

Dr. Howard Friedman and Dr. Robert Becker studied human behavior and magnetic fields in the early 1960s. They found *extremely low frequencies* (ELF) such as .1 or .2 Hz affected volunteer reaction times (Becker 1985). This paralleled work by Dr. Norbert Weiner and Dr. James Hamer with low-intensity fields—described as "driving" waveforms existing within the body.

Dr. Jose Delgado's research illustrated that ELF magnetic fields influence sleep and manic behavior.

Furthermore, a substantial amount of evidence demonstrates that magnetic fields generated from power lines and transformers can modulate physiology. This has been especially noticeable in power line and transformer effects upon plants. Research linking cancer and power lines has been controversial. Still, enough evidence enables a conclusion that magnetic fields can alter certain physiological processes, as we'll discuss in more detail later.

The magnetic nature of the body is revealed through *nuclear magnetic resonance* (NMR). Its application of *magnetic resonance imaging* (MRI) is now one of the more useful diagnostic machines used in medicine when a true cross-sectional analysis of the body is required.

The NMR scan is performed on the human body by surrounding the body with strong magnetic fields. The body is guided underneath magnetic fields ranging from about 5,000 to 20,000 gauss (the earth's magnetic field is about .5 gauss by comparison). These fields polarize the hydrogen (H+) proton ions in water (as the body is mostly water). As these ions' north poles align, they emit a particular frequency. Radio beams positioned around the body (tuned to this frequency) are shot through the body. As the polarity-altered hydrogen protons become excited by radio signals, a computer calculates the water content differences to form the image. Were it not for the magnetic nature of the body's molecules, the three-dimensional images produced by the MRI would not be possible.

Our entire metabolism is magnetic. Every cell and every tissue system utilizes and produces polarity during instructional transmissions. This is illustrated in the behavior of ion channels, neurotransmitters, hormones, enzymes and ligand-receptors as we've illustrated. While magnetic metabolism is symptomized in migratory travel, it is further demonstrated in our metabolic responses to the sun's geomagnetic fields produced during solar storm activity.

The awareness of a correlation between human behavior and solar cycles is due largely to the research of Russian scientist Alexander Chizhevsky. Chizevsky is also known for his groundbreaking research discovering the properties of ionized air during the earlier part of the twentieth century.

In the early 1920s, Chizhevsky analyzed the timing of wars, battles, riots, and revolutions among the histories of 72 countries from 500 BCE to 1922. He discovered that 80% of these critical events took place close to a sunspot activity peak. In an attempt to explain the data, Chizhevsky proposed that strong magnetic fields might be emanating from these intense solar storms. He suggested that magnetic influences from magnetic solar storms could trigger mass behavior changes among large populations simultaneously. These magnetic stimulatory effects, he thought, could affect mental propensities, predisposing aggressive or violent behavior.

Chizhevsky's studies demonstrated similar patterns between solar sunspot cycles and mortality rates caused by epidemics and spikes in births. This research was considered novel and controversial during Chizhevsky's lifetime. However, continued research over the decades since Chizhevsky has confirmed a number of significant effects caused by what is now referred to as *geomagnetism* upon behavior and disease.

The relevance and conclusions from Chizhevsky's research have received confirmation in new research by Musaev *et al.* (2007), which studied solar activity and demographic data specific to infectious disease mortality between 1930 and 2000. Disease and mortality statistics related to cardiovascular, neurological, oncological, bronchi-pulmonary, and infectious pandemics proved to be instructive. The data indicated a clear relationship between these pandemics and solar storm cycles.

Recent research has uncovered many other disease associations resulting from the geomagnetic influence of auroras, sunspots and solar storms. The Cardiology department of Israel's Rabin Medical Center (Stoupel *et al.* 2007) studied the occurrence of acute myocardial infarction together with the timing and measurement of solar activity. This study differentiated the effects of higher cosmic ray activity from periods of higher geomagnetic activity (sunspots and solar flares). It was found that myocardial infarction rates inversely correlate with monthly solar activity, and positively correlate with increased cosmic ray activity. Low geomagnetic activity days and higher cosmic ray days are linked with significantly greater rates of fatalities due to myocardial infarction.

Marasanov and Matveev also reported in 2007 that among lung cancer patients having surgery, complications occur more significantly during geomagnetic solar storm periods than during geomagnetic "quiet" days.

In 2006, Stoupel *et al.* calculated immune system strength by measuring levels of IgG, IgM, IgA, lupus anti-coagulant, clotting time, and autoantibody blood levels among a group of subjects over time. Their levels were correlated with solar activity patterns as measured by the U.S. National Geophysical Data Center. This research found that these immune system levels move with solar geomagnetic activity—reducing with more activity and increasing with less solar activity.

Stoupel's research was confirmed by studies done at Canada's Laurentian University (Kinoshameg and Persinger 2004). Here, rats exposed to induced geomagnetic activity suffered immunosuppression, resulting in higher rates of infection.

In 2006, Yeung analyzed pandemic influenza outbreaks from 1700 A.D. to 2000 A.D. Significant correlations were found between flu outbreaks and sunspot cycles.

Vaquero and Gallego (2007) confirmed the connection between immunosuppression, infectious outbreaks, and sunspot cycles in research studying pandemic influenza A.

A 2006 study from Kyoto University (Japan) researchers (Otsu *et al.*) reported that a strong correlation existed between sunspot activity, unemployment rates and suicides between 1971 and 2001. Both unemployment and suicides were inversely proportional to sunspot rhythmic periods.

Another study from 2006 (Davis and Lowell) using the birth dates of 237,000 humans, found a positive correlation between the births of children with genetic mental diseases like schizophrenia and bipolar disorder with solar activity. They also found similar correlations between solar activity cycles and 'genetic' diseases like multiple sclerosis and rheumatoid arthritis. These diseases were also closely correlated with being born in a particular season.

In another study done in Israel (Stoupel *et al.* 2006), 339,252 newborn births over a period of seven years were compared to monthly cosmic ray and solar activity. Significantly more babies were born of both genders during periods of greater cosmic ray activity. In other words, fewer newborns were born during high solar activity periods as compared with periods of reduced solar activity.

The Rabin Medical Center (Stoupel *et al.* 2005) also studied Down syndrome cases among 1,108,449 births together with solar activity. With 1,310 total cases of Down syndrome in the data, a significant inverse relationship between solar activity occurred. In other words, Down syndrome—long considered a genetic defect—occurs more often during periods of reduced solar activity, and less often during periods of increased solar activity.

Researchers at the Universidad de Chile's Clinica Psiquiatrica Universitaria (Ivanovic-Zuvic *et al.*) presented a study in 2005 that compared increased hospitalizations of depressive patients and manic patients to solar activity periods. In this study, depressive hospitalizations correlated with periods of lower solar activity, while manic hospitalizations positively correlated with higher solar activity periods.

A study at the Augusta Mental Health Institute in Maine (Davis and Lowell 2004) established that excessive ultraviolet radiation from the sun combined with solar flare cycles correlated positively with mental illnesses resulting from DNA damage.

It also appears from other research by Davis and Lowell (2004) that human lifespan correlates with solar activity. This research illustrated that chaotic solar activity (as opposed to typical pattern cycles) coincide with increases in mutagenic DNA effects. Further exploration into lifespan and birthdates around solar cycles found disrupted solar cycles correlating positively with shorter lifespan.

In an Australian study (Berk *et al.* 2006) of suicides between 1968 and 2002, both seasonal and geomagnetic solar storm activity were investigated using 51,845 male and 16,327 female suicides.

Suicides among females significantly increased in the autumn, concurrent with increased geomagnetic storm activity. Suicides were lowest during autumn for males and lowest during the summer for females. The average number of suicides for both males and females were the greatest during the spring.

This connection of seasonal and geomagnetic activity with suicide was also confirmed in research on 27,469 Finnish suicide cases between 1979 and 1999 by Partonen *et al.* (2004).

Biotransmission

Anyone who has taken a polygraph will report that the examination is complex and requires some technical training in physiology and psychology. A polygraph examiner is thus typically expert in physical-emotion expression. The equipment utilizes primarily *galvanic skin response* (GSR) and electrocardiography equipment to monitor the physical reflections of specific emotions. What polygraph examination techniques have taught scientists over the years is that the skin, heart and many other parts of the body will reveal heightened emotions with particular physical responses. One of the most noticeable physical responses results from the emotion of fear.

Lie detection has thus become recognized as a verifiable science after over thousands of polygraph examinations and hundreds of studies. Even with the occasional variance in specific results, there is undeniable evidence that the body reflects heightened emotional response. Polygraph research has revealed that some people have the ability to cheat the polygraph, assuming they understand how to control certain emotional and physical responses. Here again, this underscores the connection between intention and physical response. Whether cheating the polygraph or not, intention is being expressed through the various responses of the body.

In 1966, Cleve Backster, a former CIA employee and licensed polygraph examiner, began experimenting with polygraph equipment connected to plants. His first plant was a dracaena cane plant. After connecting the polygraph's electrodes, he immediately began to notice that its galvanic skin response readings were not so different from human examination charts. What surprised Dr. Backster was that the plant's exam also registered emotional responses that reflected fear. Furthermore, these responses were highest during moments where an intention to harm the plant came to mind. A simple thought by a nearby human of harming the plant produced a precise fear response in the plant's skin response.

The prospect of a plant responding to a threatening intention was certainly incredible to Dr. Backster—then an owner of a polygraph school and research laboratory. Following this incident, Dr. Backster spent the next thirty years carefully conducting controlled experiments to study conscious mechanisms within plants, eggs, and then human cells. Dr. Backster published two scientific papers on the subject, along with a number of popular magazine articles and a book documenting his years of study (Backster 2003).

Dr. Backster carefully conducted hundreds of experiments on emotional intention, devising automated research equipment to remove extraneous influences. Many of these studies were reviewed by well-known scientists, and some even took part in the research. His results were clear, and many were replicated by other scientists—although this also proved to be difficult to the spontaneity required by consciousness research. Dr. Backster discovered that plants were not the only living organism to sense intention. Through exhaustive tests using various subjects and perspectives, he found that human leukocytes separated from their host and kept *in vitro* somehow had the ability to sense and respond to emotions of fear and excitement that occurred within their former host *remotely*. Furthermore and amazingly, he found this effect can occur at a distance of up to fifty miles.

The human polygraph examination focuses upon our fear of detection. The fear of harm through discovery is the typical emotion being tested. This is also controlled in Dr. Backster's research on plants, eggs and human cells. Because the fear of detection is closely related to the fear of harm, the physiological results of the two emotions are practically identical.

One of the dramatic findings of Dr. Backster's research with plants was that once a person consistently begins caring for a plant, that plant becomes emotionally connected to that person. Dr. Backster discovered that even when the person has traveled miles away from this plant, emotionally charged circumstances occurring in the life of the person would affect the plant. In other words, the plant becomes emotionally tied to the person taking care of it. This sort of emotion is typically referred to as *empathy*.

In vitro cells separated from a human responded very similarly in Dr. Backster's research, but only with their host. Living cells being incubated and electroded with the equipment responded to the heightened emotional activity of their former host, even when the host was located rooms or even miles away from the cells. This indicated the separated cells somehow had the ability to receive remote communication transmissions from the host. How is it that cells have this ability? Furthermore, Dr. Backster's research demonstrated that the cells were able to prioritize their responses specifically for their host, even amongst emotional controls set up to distract the response.

Dr. Backster's research controls were thoroughly vetted by a number of scientists. Still, it is regarded as controversial, and has been difficult to duplicate in some cases. Nonetheless, communications between a remote ex-host is not altogether different from the cell's known ability to instantly receive instructions from the brain and other remote locations in the body—located many feet away, amongst trillions of other cells. Medical researchers recognize that the body's nervous systems and various biochemicals such as neurotransmitters and hormones conduct waveforms from one location of the body to another. This begs the question: How do billions of cells instantly become orchestrated into a particular activity? Nerves are certainly high-speed, but all cells are not innervated. So how do all the cells instantly respond?

Every cell making up a living organism is a waveform receiver. Each cell has the ability to receive instructional waveforms just as any radio can receive a local broadcast. In addition, groups of cells can align and organize to receive and respond to specific types of waveforms. Just as a radio broadcast will reach millions of radios at once, the body's waveform broadcasts reach a multitude of cells simultaneously.

Our entire metabolism is set up to send and receive multi-spectrum waveforms. Groups of cells called the senses have organized around receiving specific types of waveforms. We can perceive waves in the visible spectrum with the eyes, infrared radiation with the skin, air pressure waves with the ears, and subtle electromagnetic waveforms with the tongue and nose. These are only a few of the multitude of waveforms that are received and translated throughout the body. This is compounded by the fact that the cells also conduct various waveforms via ion channels and receptors.

The body's cells pick up waveforms beyond our current technologies. This is the only explanation for cells being able to receive precise information from remote locations. Dr. Backster's research illustrated that these communications are received through insulated and even metal walls.

Waveform communications outside our range of recognition is not a new paradigm to science. The past few hundred years of research have continuously revealed previously unperceivable waveforms.

The body's cells have the ability to perceive a variety of waveforms considered outside the visible wavelengths. There is evidence to the contrary. Wavelengths shorter than violet such as ultraviolet, x-rays, and gamma rays have been observed visually under extraordinary circumstances such as a darkened room penetrated with radiation leakage. Both x-rays and gamma rays have been observed on occasion with the naked eye, as a yellow-green glow. Meanwhile, some have identified nuclear leakage in flashes of blue. As the rods of the eyes sensitize for night vision they also become sensitive to other waveforms. Longer and less damaging radiowaves have also been received by humans in extraordinary circumstances. Hearing radio stations through dental fillings, bridgework, and even bobby pins has been a rare but well-documented occurrence.

The body's cells translate radiowaves into electrical brain impulses just as a radio crystal translates radiowaves into electronic pulses. The senses illustrate this well. Once received through the antenna mechanisms of the eyes, ears, nose, tongue and so on— waveforms are converted through the crystalline structures of nerve cells.

Individual cells have these same antenna systems. Radiowaves influencing single cells and single-cell living organisms is well documented. In 1958, for example, *The New England Institute for Medical Research* published articles documenting that radiowaves could influence red blood cell movement and bacteria motion. Murchie (1978) observed amebas, euglenas, and paramecia aligning their movement with radiating field lines of five to forty megacycle radiowaves. Many other studies have documented similar effects.

The reception and translation of ultraviolet radiation by skin cells is obvious and well understood. The sun's ultraviolet B waveforms stimulate the production of vitamin D_3 when wavelengths of 270-290 nanometers enter the epidermal layer. The *conrotatory electrocyclic reaction* cycles 7-dehydrocholesterol to pre-vitamin D, and eventually to 1,25 dihydroxyvitamin D, or 25-OHD. During this cycle, melanin production is stimulated to provide a filtering and buffering mechanism for additional rays from the sun. Vitamin D is an essential nutrient to the human body. It is important for immunity, cardiovascular health, nerve health and bones and teeth health. Our primary source is through the sun, although a limited number of foods contain small amounts as well.

For many decades, researchers have been studying the effects of light upon other human cells. We all know about photosynthesis—where plant cells utilize light, water and carbon dioxide to produce starches, sugars and oxygen. The molecular structure of chlorophyll acts as a semiconducting crystal, absorbing some ultraviolet waveforms from the sun while reflecting others. With these absorbed waveforms, the unique biochemical reaction of photosynthesis is stimulated among special chloroplasts—specialized proteins embedded inside chlorophyll.

This process illustrates the intimate connection between waveform conversion and living organisms. The complex transformation of light waveforms to plant nutrition is a conversion related to the intention to survive—a conscious act. This intention creates the impetus for energy transformation. We see a similar transformation process occurring through the human cellular production of energy from oxygen and glucose. Cellular energy production occurs through a waveform transition process called *electron transport* (reminiscent of the characterization of electricity as electron movement). ATP and NADPH are created and water is split, releasing oxygen. Part of this process uses an interesting exchange of phosphorus ions called *phosphorylation*. This process is one of transferring waveform energy through a transport chain to create an NADP+ molecule, after which an additional transformation takes place through a process of *redox* to create an energized NADPH. Some have theorized that the continuing process of ATP conversion and glucose takes place without UV. Further research has revealed that light is at least indirectly involved, as it stimulates the production of some of the enzymes used as catalysts.

In the 1920s, a Russian scientist Alexander Gurwitsch picked up a weak photoemission from living tissue. The emissions appeared stronger during mitosis, so he termed these UV-range wavelength rhythms *mitogenetic rays*. The presence of living radiation emitted from dividing cells was confirmed shortly thereafter by some German researchers. Even still, their conclusions were overshadowed by doubts from skeptics. Nonetheless, ongoing biochemical experiments have continued to confirm that cellular division produces radiation emissions.

The topic did not gain much additional research attention until after World War II. Research teams from Italy, Germany and Britain independently worked on the living photon research. Each confirmed waveform observations from living cells, which they named variously. Two names have stuck: *low-level luminescence* and *ultraweak chemiluminescence*. We'll discuss this research on biophotons in more detail later.

As we survey the empirical evidence, we arrive at the reality that throughout the body—through every cell, tissue system, circulatory system, organ system and nerve center—flow a variety of different waveforms. As we will discover in detail, every type of body waveform has a specific function, and affects metabolism in a distinctive way. Furthermore, the variety of different waveforms are all interacting within the body. These interactions result in the facilities we have come to understand as physiology. For this reason, we will utilize a new descriptor for the body's variety of internal waveforms that stem from consciousness: *Biowaves*.

Ion Pathways

Cells might be compared to smart radio-driven generators with multi-layered reception and transmission communication systems. As physiologists have delved deeper into the activities of the estimated trillion cells in the human body, they have continued to see increasingly deeper levels of biocommunication activity amongst the electrolyte ions within and around the cell.

The ion channel is an informational device because it establishes an on-off state in the form of an open or closed gateway. Actually, the gateway of most ion channels is a bit more complex. Research has indicated that one of three possible states is produced within the typical ion channel gateway: deactivation, activation or inactivation. Both the deactivated state and the inactivated state are closed, while the activated state is open. The difference between the two closed states is that a deactivated gate is blocked by an opposing open gate, while the inactive gate is simply closed in process after activation. In other words, the latter produces a rhythmic opening and closing adherent to voltage potential changes.

As we've discussed, these ion channels interact intimately with mineral ions such as sodium, potassium and other electron-transporting mechanisms like ATPase. The electro-chemical aspects of mineral ions led to early discoveries of electricity and its magnetic field qualities. This is because ions are electromagnetic conductors. Ions are activated with pulsed electromagnetic fields. This provides a means to carry and exchange waveform information. As the ionic waveforms interact with biowaves from other sources, an interference pattern results. This creates a mapping system that conveys information.

Ion channels have been observed transferring chemical charges and communicating processes such as glucose utilization and immune response between cell membranes and intercellular tissues. These electro-chemical pathways have been correlated with biophoton emissions, illustrating the reality that information-signaling systems exist on more than a chemical basis.

One of the most prominent potential conductors in the body is the sodium ion. Sodium ions negotiate electromagnetic waveforms efficiently. *Sodium channels* thus lie within cell membranes of the most active cells in the body, including muscle and nerve cells. These protein complexes are activated by the voltage potentials provided by sodium ions as they cycle through their biochemical processes. In response to ionic state changes, many sodium channels will generate a change in electric potential inside the cell by conducting sodium ions through the cell membrane. By changing the cell's electrical potential, the cell's inner polarity and reactive potential with various nutrients and biochemicals will change. This will stimulate particular types of biological processes within the cell. Among sodium channels are various sub-types—specialized for a particular cellular activity, organ or tissue system.

Potassium channels exist in almost every cell in the body. They are involved in regulating the secretion and reception of various types of hormones. Potassium channels lie primarily within the cell membrane. Much like the sodium channels, they provide voltage gates through which potassium ion charges can travel. Potassium channels are activated by various means with specific response ranges. A newly discovered type of potassium channel system is the double-pore system, contrasting with the primarily single pore system of other known ionic channels. This double-pore potassium channel is thought to be a complex regulator in vascular cells—it stimulates tone and flexibility to the artery walls.

Calcium channels provide another type of voltage circuit. Calcium ion channels are found among various specialized cells in brain, organ, and nerve tissues. The calcium gateways have been linked with an informational depolarization process. This turns on and off the release of various neurotransmitters and hormones. Like the sodium and potassium channels, calcium channels have various sub-types. These will produce specific results within specialized cells.

Chloride channels appear to be related to regulating the cell's nutritional contents. No less than thirteen different types of chloride channels have been discovered. Each type regulates different nutrients and informational functions within different types of cells.

These are merely the tip of the iceberg. There are likely billions of ion channels located throughout the body. Information flows through each and every one constantly. Other types of channels have been isolated by research over recent years. *Cation channels* are activated through a combination of ions. They predominate within sperm cells. Cation-selective double pore channels provide both inward and outward voltage potential changes. *Rhodopsin channels* are activated open through the reception of light. Another type of voltage channel is the *cyclic nucleotide channel*. These are thought to regulate the entry of ions and nucleotides that drive energy use and cellular clock activity. The heart's pacemaker neurons function extensively with cyclic nucleotide channels, for example. *Transient receptor potential channels*—also called TRPs—have so far been observed among fruit flies, but many scientists suspect that these also exist within humans. TRP channels respond to photoelectric waveforms. There are a number of different types of TRPs with various functions. To the billions of channels of the types mentioned above, we can add the cAMP and IP3 channels, along with many others.

There are about 80 known macro and trace minerals in the body. As nutritional research into macro minerals has progressed, we have gradually come to understand that every mineral plays an important role. Should the human body be lacking in any of these elements, imbalances in metabolism begin to occur. Some of the more prevalent macro minerals include, among others, calcium, potassium, magnesium, sodium and phosphorus. These are called macro because they exist in larger quantities in the body. These minerals contribute to the ionic informational activities of the vast legions of catalysts, proteins, enzymes, cell walls, artery walls, and so many other structural elements of the body's anatomy. And of course, they also facilitate communications between cells through ion channels.

All the trace and macro minerals are subject to ionization within the polarity of the body's metabolism. Ionization produces conductivity, as ions can connect and pass on electron waves. This also explains why negative ions in the atmosphere appear to increase well-being. Positive atmospheric ions—in advance of storm fronts or accompanying Foehn winds—will often bring about an array of health problems such as inflammation, headaches and allergies.

Ions are also produced by the body's trace minerals, including fluorine, cadmium, copper, chlorine and even uranium. In larger quantities, these elements can be toxic. They become ionized during metabolic reactions. They are each involved directly or indirectly in innumerable enzyme functions, protein sequencing, immune cell composition and many other functions. Without a consistent supply of trace elements, our body's ion operations quickly become handicapped.

Each mineral ion provides a specific polarity and covalence for subatomic bonding. Each also provides a unique facility for waveform conductance. Conducting ions provide a bridge for information transmission throughout the body. Mineral-conducting biowaves converge through a variety of ion bridges and channels into interference patterns. From these interference patterns, instructional signals emerge.

Just as 110 household current is conducted through copper wires to be received and manipulated by appliances connected to the circuit, electromagnetic currents pulse through the body's mineral ion bridges, transferring electron energy to cellular and tissue operations.

During cellular reactions, tiny electromagnetic waveforms work to define which reaction will occur when. The specific assembly of minerals provides the basis for the molecular combinations that create the appropriate electromagnetic interference patterns.

Illustrating our need for ions for proper metabolism, several World Health Organization-sponsored studies have determined that people who drink water with low hardness—with a lack of calcium, magnesium and other ions—there is a greater risk of heart attack (Bernardi *et al.* 1995).

The respective interference patterns created by the biowaves transferred through an assembly of ion bridges form the instructional signals that turn on and off specific biochemical reactions. Without this instructional signaling system, there would be no operational control over the body's reactions. They would simply begin randomly; and after beginning, they would run indefinitely and likely out of control.

These is on-off state functions are starkly illustrated by the inflammatory pathway. The body responds to an injury with a number of inflammatory repair cells such as plasmin and fibrin to patch up the injury. Blood will usually coalesce around the injury to deliver these and other nutrients required to repair the wound. At some point in the process, signaling molecules will stop the inflammatory process, and initiate a clean out of the area to allow for the next steps of the healing process.

Cortisol is one of these switching conductors. As cortisol levels increase, inflammation is reduced. Pharmaceutical medicine has discovered this link, prompting the success of cortisone-based pharmaceuticals.

Cortisol also so happens to modulate both sodium and potassium concentrations within the body. It also modulates insulin levels and stimulates gastric juices, and stimulates copper-based enzyme functions such as superoxide dismutase. All of these functions are driven by the transmission functions of the cortisol molecule. Cortisol's molecular structure is made up of a combination of carbon, hydrogen and oxygen, just as are many of the body's molecules. It is the unique combination of standing electromagnetic bonds between the hydrogen and oxygen ions that facilitate cortisol's transmission capabilities. The commingled arrangement of its electromagnetic electron cloud waveform interference patterns enables cortisol's unique information structure.

In traditional chemistry, acids and bases are defined in hydrogen atoms—or proton proportions. An acid is typically described as a substance with an excess of hydrogen atoms (H+), which acts as a net proton donor. A base, on the other hand, is considered either a hydroxide (OH-) donor or a proton acceptor—a substance often described as having excessive electrons. Net charge is also used to describe these solutions. An acid solution is one with a net positive charge, while a base solution has a net negative charge. An acid is often referred to as *cationic* (with cations) because it has a positive net charge, while a base will have a negative charge and thus is referred to as an *anion*.

We can also describe this in the more suitable context of electromagnetic waveforms. The imbalance between units of positively oriented waveforms and units of negatively oriented waveforms creates the measure of its acidic or basic state. This "orientation" is purported to compose of quantum mechanical elements. We can summarize these as containing multi-dimensional magnetic fields with unique spin directions. As mentioned, every electronic wave is accompanied by a perpendicular magnetic field. This field also relates to the spin orientation and magnetic field direction of the molecule.

A measurement of the level of acidity or alkalinity using a logarithmic scale is called pH. The term pH is derived from the French word for hydrogen power, *pouvoir hydrogene,* which has been abbreviated as simply pH. pH is measured in an inverse log base-10 scale, measuring the proton-donor level by comparing it to a theoretical quantity of hydrogen ions (H+) in a solution. Thus, a pH of 5 would be equivalent to 10^5 H+ *moles* worth of cations in the solution. (A mole is a quantity of substance compared to 12 grams of the six-neutron carbon isotope.) Put another way, a pCl (chlorine) concentration would be the negative log of chlorine ion concentration in a solution, and pK would be the negative log of potassium ions in a solution.

The pH scale is 0 to 14, for 10^{-1} (1) to 10^{-14} (.00000000000001) range. The scale has been set up around the fact that pure water's pH is log-7 or simply pH7. Because pure water forms the basis for so many of life's activities, and because water neutralizes and dilutes so many reactions, water became the standard reference and neutral point between an acid and a base. In other words, a substance having greater hydrogen ion concentration characteristics than water will be considered a base, while a substance containing less H+ concentration characteristics than water is considered an acid.

Of course, a solution concentration may well be lower than log-14 or higher than log-1, but this is the scale set up based upon the typical ranges observed in nature. Using this scale, any substance measuring a pH of 7 would be considered a neutral substance, though it still has a significant number of H+ ions. In humans, a pH level in the range of 6.4 is considered a healthy state because this state is slightly more acidic than water, enabling alkaline ionic current flow through the body. Better put, a 6.4 pH offers the appropriate currency of energy flow because there are enough negatively oriented waveforms present for the passage of positively oriented waveforms. The earthly minerals like potassium, calcium, magnesium and others are typically positively oriented—or alkaline in nature.

The proof to these points is provided by conventional science: pH is simplified in conventional chemistry as the level of proton donor capability. Yet we know from emission measurements that the higher the electron orbit, the higher the energy emission. Energy release is measured by waveform emission characteristics such as frequency. If we remove the concept of electron particles from the equation, and replace with this the understanding of wave mechanics, we can then realize that the charge is *traveling through* a particular medium, and the pH of the substance simply quantifies the type of waveforms able to be conducted through that medium. This is why pH meters are voltage meters.

This concept of current traveling through a medium is understood when we consider how an electric charge can be maintained by a battery. A lead battery is set up to perform two reactions (stated conventionally): One reaction oxidizes lead—in a solution of sulfuric acid—to lead sulfate. During this reaction, energy is given off as electrons are emitted, along with hydrogen protons. The other reaction is a reduction, which converts lead dioxide to lead sulfate. This also releases energy, but this is accomplished as hydrogen protons and electrons are being absorbed to create the lead sulfate. Meanwhile, two types of lead plates attract and adhere to the resulting lead sulfates. The positive plates are filled with lead dioxide to drive the oxidation side, while the negative plates are made of lead to drive the reduction side of the battery. These two processes combined are called *electrolysis*—the utilization of ions to conduct current through a particular medium.

We note in this discussion the obvious: Batteries—between their positive and negative poles—exchange an electrical current. This current is used in an automobile to start the engine, after which a generator will create enough electromagnetic energy to recharge the battery. This event reverses the changes to the lead, lead dioxide and sulfuric acid. We must also note that the initial flow of electricity out of the battery is not a spontaneous reaction, nor is the recharging of the battery. Both of these processes have been designed and assembled by humans with the conscious intention to draw a flow of electricity for a specific purpose: To start our automobile for example. If our car were not in use for a while, the battery would gradually lose its charge, requiring a charge.

As we examine the currency properties of the living body, we recognize the same general features of the battery. The living body performs a number of reactions, some oxidizing and some reducing. In these reactions, energy is often converted from one type to another—a conversion of electromagnetic bonding energy into different forms of kinetic energy such as movement via muscle cells. The exact utilization of the energy is steered by consciousness, which steers usage.

For example, the principal energy conversion of glucose and oxygen into the energies mentioned is a complex oxidative reaction called the Krebs cycle. This Krebs cycle will utilize the waveform bonds of ADP to ATP to generate a transport mechanism, which results in kinetic energy, heat, and ion release. The body also has similar energy conversion mechanisms such as the NADP transport system. These are only two of the billions of ionic conversion systems working within the human physiology.

All metabolism operates on this waveform conversion process. Our sensory nerves all conduct impulses through waveform ionic exchanges. Taste is driven by the acid or alkaline nature of our foods. Acidic solutions taste sour while alkaline solutions taste bitter. As we taste food, waveform characteristics set off a chain of ionic signals through the nervous system. Our taste buds, retinal cells, olfactory bulbs and tactile nerve endings all have similar waveform sensing electrodes with ionic gateways. The different types of waveforms emitted by physical matter simply stimulate these gateways, setting off an ionic charge relay within the body's sensory nervous systems. This relay results in interference patterns within the brain, effectively producing perception.

Electromagnetic Brainwaves

Over the past 150 years, researchers have tried to understand the electrical nature of physiology. The electric quality of the body was hard to deny even in the early days of electricity exploration. Gradually the apparatus for this probing were refined. Though crudely applied, Dr. Hans Berger is credited to be the first researcher to use the *electroencephalogram* (or EEG) to record brainwaves in the early 1920s. These efforts gradually gave brainwave testing credibility in psychological research. Today the EEG is utilized for medical diagnostics, psychological testing, biofeedback testing and polygraph detection.

Several types of brainwaves, each with unique frequencies, were discovered using EEG testing. Further testing using the later-discovered *magnetoencephalograph* indicated that a variety of subtle magnetic pulses also pulse through the body. First used by Dr. David Cohen in 1968, the MEG picked up another dimension of magnetic polarity among waveform transmission. MEG technology was further developed using superconductors. This equipment has been referred to as *superconducting quantum interference devices* (or SQUID).

The multitude of EEG and MEG studies over the years has confirmed the existence of several major brainwave pulses, ranging from one to sixty cycles per second. Our neurons pulse with waveforms with frequency bandwidths that correspond to particular moods, stress levels, and physiological status. As we focus on the complexities of daily life, our brains reflect and emit shorter-frequency *alpha* or *beta* brainwaves. A relaxing mood tends to accompany the deeper *delta* or even the more meditative *theta* waves. The greater the stress, the higher frequencies tend to get. Just as higher-pitched sounds tend to indicate intensity or urgency, higher frequency brainwaves reflect a mind hustling to keep up with life's details. Because initial EEG and MEG research predominantly focused upon the brain, these waves were tagged as *brain*waves. Actually, we find these waves resonating throughout the body. They tend to be more predominant among the central nervous system and the brain because the brain and spinal cord tend to be the main collection foci for these waves. As will be detailed further, the central nervous system provides freeways for high-speed wave transit.

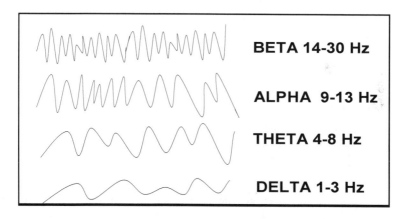

BETA 14-30 Hz

ALPHA 9-13 Hz

THETA 4-8 Hz

DELTA 1-3 Hz

Researchers have divided the millions of possible brainwave combinations into five general ranges. Alpha waves are the typical dominant cycle during dream states and light meditation. The alpha waves are oscillations with between eight and thirteen cycles per second (same as hertz). Beta brainwaves are dominant during normal waking consciousness, and range from fourteen to thirty cycles per second.

Theta waves range from four to seven cycles per second and dominate during normal sleep and meditation. On the lower frequency side are the delta waves, which range from less than one cycle per second to about three cycles per second. These slow waves tend to be dominating during the deepest sleep and meditation states.

On the other side of the spectrum, some of the fastest rhythms recorded in the brain are the gamma waves. The high-energy gamma waveforms typically dominate during periods of advanced problem solving or critical thinking. They oscillate at between thirty and sixty cycles per second. Over the past decade, researchers have discovered the existence of even shorter-wavelength and faster brainwaves. Ranging from sixty to two hundred cycles per second or more, these high-speed waves are referred to as *high gamma waves*. The high gamma waves are thought to accompany critical thought processes and brain functions.

Multiple brainwave types occur simultaneously in our body. One type will often predominate, however. Just as multiple tuning forks will align to one dominate tone, the body will typically tune—harmonically—to the predominant waveform driven from the pervading consciousness.

A recent neuroscience study—done jointly by researchers from the University of California at Berkeley and the University of California at San Francisco (Sanders *et al.* 2006)—has concluded that it is likely these brainwaves are conduits for signaling between the various regions of the brain. Dr. Robert Knight, professor of neuroscience at the University of California at Berkeley, and a director of the research observed that some regions of the brain emitted waves, others reflected waves, and still others modulated waves. Meanwhile, a confluence of these waves corresponded with particular activities, indicating different brain centers were using brainwaves as a sort of information exchange system.

As these respected researchers correlated the type of wave with the part of the brain involved in some functions and thought processes, they began to see longer-wavelength theta waves synchronizing or *coupling* with shorter-wavelength gamma waves. They considered this coupling as part of a hierarchical signaling process. Regions of coordinated neurons produce resonant coherent wave patterns, which provide the means for one group of neurons to communicate with another group. Synchronizing waveforms between neurons appear to coordinate firing patterns. The brainwave synchronization provides a process for ranking between brain regions in operational order. Theta waves appear to provide an executive control mechanism, which bridge the operations of various neuron groups.

Using epileptic subjects, the researchers found consistent relationships between cognition and the occurrence of coherent theta and gamma waves. These two types of waves provide a locked resonation process. As cognitive processes change, one wave from one region first couples with, then transitions into the next type of waveform. A congruent harmonic becomes apparent between these brainwave transitions.

Biofeedback therapy has focused on the relationship between stress and brainwave types for a number of decades. Biofeedback research has confirmed that stress directly influences brainwave activity and vice versa. Researchers have tested brainwave activity with patients in a number of different circumstances. Stressful conditions are linked to higher beta wave levels and lower alpha and theta wave levels. Consequently, a person who feels more relaxed and less stressed will produce more alpha and theta waveforms.

Many of us are aware that certain sounds influence relaxation. Most of us have experienced greater relaxation as we listen to soothing music or the songs of birds for example. Melinda Maxfield, PhD (2006) determined that slowly beating a drum at 4.5 beats per second readily brings about a state of theta brainwave activity. In 2006, Stanford University's Center for Computer Research in Music and Acoustics held a symposium with a purpose of *"interdisciplinary dialogue on the hypothesis that brainwaves entrain to rhythmic auditory stimuli, a phenomenon known as auditory driving."* This symposium brought together some of the nation's leading sound researchers. Many discussed the implications of auditory driving as it relates to our mental and physical wellbeing. The implications of the research, reflected by the consensus at the symposium, were that we are merely at the tip of the iceberg of this research.

The applications of brainwave entrainment through auditory driving are numerous. Successful auditory driving and brainwave entrainment treatments have contributed to resolving psychological trauma, chronic pain, stress, and weakened immune systems. Research comparing normal subjects with schizophrenic subjects (Vierling-Claasen *et al.* 2008) has illustrated how gamma and beta waves interface and guide cognitive processes. Normal subjects will tune to a 40 Hz wave in response to either 20 or 40 Hz driving frequencies. Schizophrenic subjects will typically respond with 20 Hz waveforms. The study's authors comment that these results illustrate *"how biophysical mechanisms can impact cognitive function."* This research confirms that brainwaves provide a mechanism for signaling specific information throughout the physical anatomy.

Biofeedback testing has further demonstrated that with practice and proper feedback access, human subjects can consciously change their brainwave levels. As a stress-reduction technique for example, a person can decrease their beta wave activity and increase their alpha and theta activity. The procedure entails the subject sitting down in front of a computer screen visually displaying rates from an electroencephalograph, photoplethysmograph (PPG—heart rate and blood flow), and/or possibly an electromyograph (EMG—muscle tension) to read waveform activity feeding back from different body parts connected to a variety of electrodes. Electrodes may be placed around the head, typically either on the scalp or in some cases around the cerebral cortex. Skin electrodes may also be applied to the arm, and PPG electrodes may be connected to the chest. The computer will monitor the waveform output of these different locations—displaying the results on a graphic display screen for the subject and therapist to monitor.

Most of us will generate brainwave signals reflecting our mental or emotional state—be it anxious, focused, relaxed, tired, angry or asleep. A good biofeedback machine will register several of these waves and their relative strengths around the body. Using a good biofeedback machine, most people can gradually learn to significantly lower or increase their alpha and theta wave strengths. For a few people, there will be an almost immediate ability to influence their waves as soon as the monitoring begins.

For most of us, it will take a bit of practice—a number of sessions usually—to be able to effectively modulate our brainwaves. Researchers have found that most everyone is able to modulate their brainwaves at one point or other. Researchers have yet to understand why there is such a variance among people's ability to control their brainwaves.

Nonetheless, once people do learn to change their brainwaves using the biofeedback, they can usually transition successfully into being able to adjust their brainwaves without the biofeedback equipment. Bringing about a relaxed mental state through visualizing relaxing situations or hearing relaxing sounds are probably the most effective techniques used for this result. Auditory driving with rhythmic sounds has been increasingly used in biofeedback therapy.

Biofeedback therapy illustrates that our brainwaves are expressions of the role of consciousness within the body. An alteration of brainwaves from primarily beta to theta waves will almost invariably result in a lower heart rate, a slower, deeper rate of breathing, and a lowering of blood pressure. Conversely, a lower heart rate, and slower breathing—as long as there is no mental disruption—will also tend to induce a theta brainwave state. We thus have an intersection between consciousness and the cascade of brainwaves with physiological states.

Physicians specializing in the central nervous system have observed another wave associated with the circulating spinal fluid: Aptly named *cerebrospinal fluid pulse waves* (or CSF waves). The data have suggested this wave is composed of five different harmonic waves, ranging in pressure from .25-1 mm Hg range, and averaging .72 mm Hg (Nakamura *et al.* 1997). This is a pressure wave. In comparison, the standard atmospheric pressure at sea level is equal to 760 mm Hg. It has not been completely ascertained as to the exact source of the CSF waves. One theory says that the pulse waves are due to the pressure gradient between arteries supplying the spinal cord and the spinal fluid. Another says they are based upon brain pulses sent through the spine's subarachnoid spaces. Many osteopaths, chiropractors, and cranial practitioners believe the cerebrospinal fluid pulses are due to the tiny movements of the cranial bones during breathing. Some research has linked breathing with these pulse waveforms. Correlations with ventricle pressure have also been made.

An interesting connection is made when CSF pulses are measured for wavelength: Beta-frequency waves seem to dominate the CSF pulse. Further EEG testing in controlled environments has demonstrated an interference relationship between the CSF pulses and the neural biowaves exhibited during memory retrieval and cognition. It seems these CSF waves play an important role in the orchestration of brainwave interference patterns.

From the research we can also understand that each cell produces a unique collection of coherent electromagnetic emissions. Because each type of cell function has been connected with different types of emissions, it is safe to say coherent emissions by groups of brain and central nervous system cells should yield resonating patterns through constructive interference. The collection of weaker emissions should yield larger biowaves, just as thousands of stadium fans may each make unique sounds, but their confluence together creates a single sound of the crowd. Most of us have heard someone mimicking the single sound of a large stadium crowd full of cheering and jeering fans.

As subtle waveforms traveling in from our sense organs interface with internal biowaves feeding back from around the body, they combine to form a compounding of interference patterns reflecting our body's inner and outer environment. This is accomplished because these biowaves interfere in different ways with each different waveform. The collection of interference patterns create a combined picture that resonates within our brain's cortices—predominated by the prefrontal cortex. The combined collection of interference patterns provides our unique perception of physical reality.

Neurotransmitter Conduction

Information waveform transmissions travel from neuron to neuron as they travel through the nervous system. Neurons stretched end to end make up the nerves—and the nerves are the pipelines for neural transmission.

Waveform transmissions pass between neighboring neural cell bodies through arms called *dendrites*. The dendrites of neighboring neurons do not touch, however. Rather, between them exists a space called the *synaptic cleft* within a region called the *synapse*. This region contains a special fluid called the *neurotransmitter fluid*. The chemistry of this fluid provides the medium for the specific waveform signals that travel between neurons.

CNS neurons can range in dendrite and synapse count. Large neurons might have several thousand while others have significantly less. Through these synapses, each neuron may be firing up to 100,000 electromagnetic pulse inputs into this fluid at one time.

This tiny sea of neurotransmitter fluid contains various biochemical components, most of which are ionic in nature. These ions combine with the protein neurotransmitters to create a medium that can buffer, accelerate or malign transmissions. The overall conducting ability of the neurotransmitter fluid is considered its electromagnetic *synaptic potential*.

The neurotransmitter fluid chemistry facilitates particular waves of different frequencies, wavelengths and amplitudes. At the same time, the fluid chemistry provides filtering mechanisms to buffer and screen out some transmission elements. Depending upon its particular makeup at the time, the fluid will provide a combination of *excitatory potential* and *inhibitory potential*. This balance serves to escort or conduct waveform information from one nerve to another, while at the same time dampening or filtering these waveforms to prevent overload and over-stimulation.

This process might well be compared to the process of transistors and resistors we see in integrated circuits. Neurotransmitters are tremendous semiconductors. Their precise molecular structures allow them to buffer and/or amplify waveform transmissions within a particular spectrum.

Two examples of active neurotransmitters are acetylcholine and adrenaline (or epinephrine). These two biomolecules conduct and/or magnify waveforms that relate to autonomic function and physical response. Acetylcholine will accelerate instructions to muscle fibers to contract, while adrenaline will amplify internal conditions that perpetuate the 'fight or flight' response: Causing a quickening of heart rate and blood flow, immediate motor muscle response, visual acuity, and so on. These two biochemicals are interactive throughout the body. They impact the functioning of digestion, the secretion of mucus, defecation, the immune system, and many other processes around the body. They occupy the neurotransmitter fluid chemistry, but they also interact with processes outside the confines of the synaptic fluid. For example, acetylcholine also stimulates skeletal muscle cells directly. This means the body's autonomic response programming is facilitated through these chemicals, much as a key might facilitate the unlocking of the front door and our passage into the house.

Neurotransmitters and hormones have similar actions in the body, and some hormones are also neurotransmitters. By definition, a neurotransmitter is released by a nerve cell into the synapse, while a hormone is produced by an endocrine gland. For example, when epinephrine is secreted by the adrenal gland, it is a hormone. When it is secreted by the synapse it is a neurotransmitter. Most hormone secretions of the body follow a chain of command. Their secretions are stimulated by other secreted conductors, produced in turn by the pituitary gland. The pituitary gland is the master gland stimulating most of the various hormones. Neurotransmitters, on the other hand, are produced through waveform-nerve reception. While hormones will stimulate a variety of responses in cells throughout the body, neurotransmitters are typically associated with the effects of the nerves.

At the same time, both hormones and neurotransmitters are waveform conductors. They both facilitate the transmission of electromagnetically-generated information from location to location around the body. The pituitary gland is considered the master gland for hormone productivity. The pituitary is about the size of a cherry. It is located behind the eyes in a depression of the sphenoid bone, just behind where the optic nerves cross. It is also lying within the region of the sixth *chakra*.

The pituitary produces master hormones that directly stimulate the body, such as growth hormone (GH), vasopressin, oxytocin and others. The pituitary gland connects to the hypothalamus by the *infudibulum*, a stalk of portal veins and nerves tracts. It is through this stalk that the pituitary gland's activities are regulated by the hypothalamus. The hypothalamus sends *releasing hormones* to the pituitary. These stimulate the releases of the pituitary.

The hormone's chemistry provides a conductor for the body's instructional signals. Hormones are in essence tiny crystals that resonate particular types of waveforms. These resonations are passed on to cells and organs by stimulating the gateways of tiny receptors that sit on the surface of cell membranes. We'll discuss this interaction between ligands and receptors in more detail shortly.

We must be careful not to confuse chemicals with waves, however. Waves are informational, and conduct *through* chemicals. Their interference patterns can be stored within biochemicals in the form of standing waves between atoms. This is why biomolecules have unique properties. Biochemicals serve primarily as echo chambers, reflecting the informational waveforms being transmitted around the body. We might compare this to hearing a radio playing a song broadcast from a distant station. The radio does not contain the song, nor is it the source of the radiowaves that are being broadcast to millions of radios from the same radio station. The radio does not contain the singer either. Rather, the radio is simply a conducting vehicle, which temporary crystallizes and transforms the radiowaves into the speaker sounds that we can hear. In the same way, biochemicals reacting throughout the body during metabolism are merely vehicles of wave conduction. Waves and their informational interference patterns are being broadcast in multiple bandwidths as they are released and move through the body.

Neurotransmitter and hormone conduction also might be compared to opening our eyes under water. Were we to dive into a river during a rain storm and attempt to open our eyes and look through its murky, muddy waters, we would not see much. We would be lucky to see our hand in front of our face underneath the muddy brown waters. That same river during a warm summer day might be so clear that we could see the bottom ten feet down. The difference between seeing within the two rivers is due to the muddy river mud being stirred up by the rain and stormy weather. It is not that our vision has gotten worse.

In the same way, an imbalanced chemistry among the neurotransmitter fluid and/or hormones within the bloodstream will alter the transmissions passing from neuron to neuron. Some chemicals will interfere in the waveform transmissions. Others will facilitate them, while still others may subdue or distort the transmissions.

Case in point: When we drink alcohol, the alcohol will affect the chemistry of the synaptic junction—the neurotransmitter fluid—in such a way that distorts the electromagnetic signals that travel from one neuron to another. This produces an altered synaptic state that affects how nerve cells control motor functions. The motor cells may receive slow or even inaccurate signals. The same ethanol neurochemistry will distort sense and feedback signals as they are sent to the brain. The distortion can cause disorientation, coordination impairment, irrational behavior and mood swings: A potentially disastrous combination we often refer to as being drunk.

The key role of the neurotransmitter is to create a potential for the electromagnetic transmission. This creates a bridge of sorts for the waveforms to transverse. The type of neurotransmitter also dictates which type of channel gateway will be opened on the post-synaptic nerve—the receiving nerve. The type of ion channel will typically dictate what kind of information will be transduced through the linkage of neurons.

One of the more interesting players in neurotransmitter biochemistry is GABA, which stands for *gamma-aminobutyric acid*. GABA is considered an inhibitory neurotransmitter in that it slightly slows down wave conduction. This actually has a positive effect upon the synaptic transmissions, allowing nerve signals to pass through without as much distortion. As a result, GABA is known for producing feelings of relaxation and alertness. Research has indicated that various mood disorders such as depression, anxiety and even insomnia are related to the body having lower GABA levels within neurotransmitter fluids. Epileptics typically have insufficient amounts of this neurotransmitter as well. Many of the popular anti-depressant pharmaceuticals increase GABA levels. It should be noted, however, that these drugs also produce various side effects as well.

Healthy amounts of GABA in the neurotransmitter fluid are also associated with an increase in alpha brainwaves. L-theanine (a GABA precursor) directly was given to thirteen subjects in one study (Abdou 2006). Electroencephalography examinations were conducted, and each subject given L-theanine had heightened levels of alpha waves and reduced beta waves. Remember that beta waves are associated with nervousness and anxiety while alpha waves accompany increased concentration.

Dr. Abdou's research also demonstrated the effect chemical neurotransmitters have upon the biocommunication of fear around the body. Two groups of eight volunteers were divided into a non-GABA (placebo) group and a GABA group. Both groups were monitored for IgA immunoglobulin levels following the crossing of a suspension bridge. Because IgA levels tend to shut down during anxious or fearful moments as the adrenal gland prepares for 'fight or flight,' this test illustrated GABA's effects upon fear-based immune response. The GABA group had normal IgA levels while the non-GABA group experienced significantly lower IgA levels. It was thus concluded that GABA levels are associated with reducing inappropriate fear responses as well as facilitating alpha waves.

As we assess this last trial, we can conclude that GABA's effect upon the neurotransmitter fluid allowed the subjects to realistically assess the dangers involved. Using the senses to realistically assess the strength of the bridge and the likelihood of the bridge actually collapsing would be considered a clear-headed response. On the other hand, a heightened fear of falling simply by looking down (acrophobia) would not be considered a realistic assessment of the situation, simply because the bridge could be easily crossed and obviously was strong enough to handle all of the walkers.

A normalized neurotransmitter environment at the synapse (including GABA) allows for a clearer broadcasting of waveform information through the neural pathways. Just as clear water allows us to see the bottom of a stream, normalized neurotransmitter fluid produces less resistance and distortion along the conducting synapses placed along the transmission pipelines of the neural network.

Tubulin Transmission

During the 1970s, Dr. Stewart Hamerhoff from the University of Arizona, and Dr. Kunio Yasue and Dr. Mari Jibu from the Okayama University began researching the pathway of transmission between neural cells. One of the mysteries they probed in independent research was how anesthesia agents such as chloroform and nitrous oxide could disable the consciousness of a patient. Through their respective research, they independently discovered that conscious activity within the body had to do with a curious matrix of twisted spiral filaments they called *tubulins*. These tubulins are arranged into networked pathways that wind through the neural cells in three-dimensional protein spirals called *microtubules*. The research showed that these microtubules are conducting tracts for electromagnetic transmission. Microtubules make up a previously unseen network for subtle waveform biocommunication through-out the neural net (Hameroff 1974; Hameroff 1982; Hameroff *et al.* 1984; Hameroff 1987; Hameroff and Penrose 1996).

The nerve tracts are pathways for lower-frequency reflexive biowaves, while the microtubules broadcast higher-frequency, com-plex information waves. As the larger waveforms are processed and transmitted through dendrites, they conduct through the neuro-transmitters between the synapses. As they are conducted through this medium, the waveforms meet with other waveforms traveling within the neural network. This convergence creates coherent inter-ference patterns. The resonating results of these interference pat-terns are 'stepped up' to higher frequencies. These high frequency waveforms contain more information, and they create holographic wave patterns. These hologram patterns are ultimately reflected (or mirrored) onto the 'screens' of the cortices. Once on the screens, these holograms interact with others to create a organized view of the body and the world around us. The inner self interacts with these cortices through the frontal cortex and pre-frontal cortex to view this holographic 'picture.'

Within these microtubules also travel the various subtle bio-waves that conduct the emotional responses of the self through the body. The discovery of these microtubule pathways confirms much of the ancient wisdom of the *nadis* and *meridians,* which we will dis-cuss later in detail. The ancients described these channels as path-ways for the flow of living energy.

We might compare the microtubular process of projecting wave interference patterns onto the mind to the recording of a musical composition in a modern studio. The studio producer will record the guitar onto one track, the piano onto another track, the drums onto another and the voice onto another track. The producer may even overlay background singers' voices onto other tracks. Then using these various individual sounds, the producer will assemble all the tracks together at particular sound levels to form the entire piece of music. This is often referred to as a *composition*. Each track makes up a piece of the total song. To listen to each track alone without the other tracks will sound weird. In much the same way, the mind captures the various waveform frequencies coming through the microtubular network, neural net and biochemical conducting system—combining them to form unified holographic images of the outside world.

One of the basic principles of holography is that each part mirrors the entire image. This is accomplished through a splitting of waves as they interfere, creating a multitude of waves, each containing all the information via the composition of waveforms. Using waveform interference, the mind orchestrates holographic assembly in both directions. The mind reflects its images semiconducted through particular neurons. The mind also stimulates effector neurons to act reflectively by transmitting the emotional responses of the self.

Each cortex assembles biowaves from different locations. The mind projects the whole image, drawn from the various cortex images. This collection of images is broadcast through crystallized neuron pathways. Each cortex consists of a grouping of crystalline neurons with common genetic structures, ion channel systems and microtubule networks. This gives each cortex the ability to combine with others to create an broader waveform interference pattern.

Cellular Reception

Otto Loewi's research illustrated the involvement of biochemistry with metabolic signaling mechanisms. Biochemical information pathways have since been clearly established. Different biochemicals conduct different waveforms because of their unique subatomic bonding orbitals. These orbitals (or energy states) are either excited or stabilized by waveforms being conducted through their medium.

Ever since Dr. Morgan Hunt discovered a protein existing within the cell membrane—part in and part out, researchers have been convinced that inter-cell signaling requires that a ligand (e.g., hormone or neurotransmitter) must "physically" touch a receptor.

Receptors are cell membrane switches understood to receive ligand instructions. Once received, the instructions are translated to the cell's nucleus and/or organelles for activation. For this reason, they've been called *transmembrane protein receptors*.

Dr. Hunt's protein ligand system was called the *notch* transport system. Notch information biocommunication has since been observed among cardiac cells, neurons, bone cells (osteocytes), glandular cells and many others, progressing and stimulating some of their most critical functions.

Intercellular communication is often referred to as *paracrine* activity—signals being translated from one nearby cell to another. In comparison, *intracrines* are considered the cellular conductors within the cell, while *intercrines* are cell-to-cell conductors. Note in this respect that *endocrines* are biochemical conductors produced by specific glands, which are circulated around the body. The question is whether conduction requires a "physical" chemical binding between the ligand and its particular receptor.

Two cells are also thought to have what is considered a direct nucleus-to-nucleus interaction. This occurs through a type of direct-nucleus receptor called a *connexin protein*. When six of these proteins come together within a group, they form a pore or tube within the membrane called a *gap junction*. This allows cells to exchange genetic instructions, or one cell to inject instructions into another cell.

Many receptors lie on the surface of the cell membrane. Most are connected to ion channels between the cell membrane. These provide a transduction channel for the information to pass from the receptor to within the cell. Many neurotransmitters and hormones utilize this pathway to transmit their information. The assumption is that the ligand (hormone or neurotransmitter) *binds* with the receptor on a chemical basis, creating an electrical signal, which is transmitted through the ion channel.

These assumptions come from seeing ligands in the area of physical responses. Since they are in the vicinity, they must be involved in a binding reaction, right? It has been justly assumed that these neurochemical molecules must be intimately involved in the dissemination of metabolic signals. However, the notion that a chemical binding is required in all cases and among all endocrine transmissions appears unlikely, given the evidence we will present here.

A physical molecular connection between hormones and receptors on each and every cell membrane—even with some cells communicating with paracrines—would require circulation time for the master hypothalamic hormones, pituitary hormones and endocrine gland hormone pathways to execute simultaneously. It would require enough hormones to be secreted fully into the bloodstream, and physically be pumped from the endocrine glands—sometimes halfway around the body—to chemically and physically touch the appropriate receptor on *every* cell involved in the metabolic change.

Let us consider this scenario carefully. A receptor is a protein with an electromagnetic affinity. This requires either a polarity match, or even a constructive combination of spin or angular momentum between the ligand and receptor. In the human body, it is estimated there is one protein molecule for every 10,000 molecules in and around the cells of the body. Furthermore, there are about 200 trillion cells in the human body, and billions if not trillions of them are activated immediately in fearful or stressful response. Every cell in the toes must be activated immediately to break into an immediate run for example. According to the physical ligand-receptor theory, not only does each hormone molecule have to connect with each and every cell membrane, but each hormone must also locate an open, active receptor on every cell membrane.

Observation and *in vitro* testing has shown receptors to have four basic scenarios: They can be *agonized,* or stimulated. They can be *partially agonized* of partly stimulated. They can be *inversely agonized,* and their response lowered. They can also be *antagonized,* whereby they are blocked by a molecule and thereby not be stimulated. So we ask: How is it these hormones can intelligently weave through every tiny capillary and dense maze of tissue systems to bump into the right receptor on every needed cell instantaneously?

Now if we perceived parts of our body being activated first and then other parts, corresponding to the circulatory routes these hormones or neurotransmitters take, we might be able to agree with this hypothesis. Consider circulatory restrictions such as atherosclerosis and other artery diseases restricting blood flow. In addition, consider that many tissue cells are reached only through tiny micro-capillaries—some barely large enough to be able to allow a single red blood cell through at a time within the diameter of the lumen (the opening). If a response required the blood to deliver a hormone molecule to a receptor on every cell within a particular tissue system before that tissue system could respond, we would really be in trouble if we needed to run from an attacker.

We could only imagine the situation where we were frightened by a tiger in the woods, only to find that our upper hamstrings were ready to take off but our toes were not—leaving us stuck while the tiger pounced. Rather, the toes, hamstrings, knees and every skeletal muscle cell, along with the eyes, lungs, brain, and vocal cords all respond at the same moment as we scream and run instantaneously.

The body's process of stimulating metabolic activity has been a mystery to researchers for thousands of years. In modern research, the process of discovery has been to identify hormone presence using radiography with dye markers to trace the flow of chemicals. This physical 'snap-shot' process is combined with harvesting and analyzing organ chemistry with spectroscopic analysis. Via these two methods, researchers figure that since the hormone/ligands are in the proximity of the response, they must be physically setting off the response of each and every cell. This is often confirmed with the techniques pioneered by Loewi to provide the conclusion. While conferring biochemical presence, finding biochemicals in the region offers no conclusive mechanism. We might compare this to finding a gun near a murder victim. We can assume the gun was involved, but this fact alone does not tell us who shot the murder victim.

For example, we know the thyroid gland is one of the central endocrine drivers of metabolism. Researchers have linked cellular metabolic rates and thermogenesis to the presence of thyroid hormones thyroxine and triiodothyronine. These are also referred to as T4 and T3, respectively. The chemical makeup of these conductors are not that exciting—a combination of the amino acid tyrosine and iodine. However, these rather simple molecular structures T4 and T3 somehow charge trillions of cells throughout the body—increasing the speed and output of their various metabolic processes. Without enough of either T4 or T3 (T3 is considered to be the more active of the two, but T3 is derived from T4) the body begins to cool down. A feeling of fatigue will overwhelm a thyroid hormone-deficient body. Suddenly the most basic tasks become difficult in TSH (thyroid stimulating hormone), T3 or T4 deficiencies. The thyroid also produces calcitonin, which works with parathyroid hormone to balance bone calcium levels.

Once the blood contains enough thyroid hormones, the body becomes almost suddenly energized. This is evidenced by the oral intake of synthetic and analogous thyroid hormones. How again do all those trillions of cells become energized from a pill or two? Again, the theory of cell reception requires that each cell has a set of little chemical receptor 'locks' on its cell membrane, and these ligand chemicals provide the 'keys.' Thus, each cell receptor must be physically touched and unlocked with those chemical ligands. Are there enough moles of chemicals in one or two pills to circulate through the blood system and basal membrane to reach every cell's receptors and energize them? Or perhaps the paracrine system provides a mechanism for filling the gap for cells the chemicals do not physically bind to?

This problem is complicated by the fact that thyroid hormones are hydrophobic—they are not water-friendly. They are not water-soluble. Since the blood, the cells, and their basal surroundings are mostly water, this makes their journey to every cell difficult. Perhaps thyroid hormones require thyroxine-binding globulins, transthyrein and albumins for adequate circulation. It is thought that these may provide a carrier mechanism to each cell. Somehow, these chemical conductors T3 and T4 manage to instantly and simultaneously make their way around the body to stimulate and energize each cell. In other words, the neck does not warm up first, and then the arms warm up, and so on. All the body parts will become energized simultaneously with some exception for diseased tissue systems.

The cell membrane is composed of a variety of lipids— cholesterol, phospholipids and sphingolipids—specialized proteins and glycoproteins. The lipids making up most cell membranes are structurally double-layered and arranged to prevent unwanted molecules from passing through the membrane. The lipid wall is also hydrophobic—keeping water from penetrating the surface without passing through the cell membrane's complex ion channels.

Some cell membranes—particularly in nerve cells—are *myelin*. Others are *inner mitochondrial* in nature. Mitochondrial inner membranes are made up of electron transport proteins, while a myelin membrane will be composed primarily of plasma with less protein. The lipid cell membrane is negatively charged. This sets up an ionic gradient between the inside and the outside of the cell membrane. Crossing the cell membrane is not a physical experience for most molecules—it is primarily an electromagnetic crossing.

Water and nutrients are escorted through the membrane through ionic diffusion. This is complicated by the various proteins that electromagnetically identify substances as they pass. Mineral ions pass through the cell membrane via *ionic transport chains*. Ionic transport chains made from protein are similar to ion channels except they allow entry to key nutrients and minerals needed in the cell—particularly sodium, potassium and calcium but also many trace elements.

These ions provide just the right electromagnetic environment to set up channels for ionic instructional signals to pass through the cell membrane into the cytoplasm, where they can stimulate RNA, mitochondria and other organelles into action. Thus, the cell membrane's ionic transport mechanisms escort appropriate nutrients in and out of cell, while receptors receive and transmit the signals of hormones like thyroid hormones, insulin, and acetylcholine through ion channels into the cell.

Some might contend that some biochemical conductors are delivered through tissue spaces and ion channels. Yes, certainly there are basal channels that provide access. Still we must remember that the adrenal gland is a very small gland in the abdominal region of the body. The thyroid gland is a tiny gland in the neck. To assume that cortisol, epinephrine, acetylcholine, and thyroid hormones must jettison from these tiny organs to every cell—even in fingers and toes—to stimulate the correct cellular and tissue responses should these appendages come under attack is a stretch. Certainly, a strictly physical chemical delivery system would result in a lot more missing fingers and toes than we generally see.

It is interesting that we can accept that informational signals can travel instantly throughout the body via the nervous system. The nervous system can stimulate a particular skeletal muscle system to activate instantly. The ability of all the support systems to come into play, however, is the result of these biochemical informational messenger systems. A perfect example is vasopressin's ability to concentrate urine in the kidneys and constrict artery walls.

Environmental drivers of hormones include light, temperature, gravity, the changing seasons, and cellular metabolism. Internal drivers, however, stem from emotional consciousness. Hormones are complex body chemicals, made of either glycoproteins or steroids. Among other functions, hormones turn on cellular switches for many metabolic functions:

Growth hormones encourage cellular growth. Thyroid hormones regulate cellular metabolism speed and temperature regulation. Follicle stimulating hormones and luteinizing hormones stimulate reproductive mechanisms. Insulin stimulates the clearing and attachment of glucose into cells for energy production. Vasopressin decreases urine volume, constricts blood vessel walls and stimulates certain memory functions. Cortisol counteracts insulin, inhibits immune system processes such as inflammation and lymphocyte function, stimulates increased circulation and blood pressure, helps regulate potassium/sodium balance, stimulates stomach acids, and increases glucogenesis to name a few.

These are just a few of the hundreds of signaling hormones that make up the complex waveform broadcasting system working within the body. Hormones are directly and indirectly involved guiding all of the physical body's various mechanisms. Hormones turn on and shut off genetic switches in particular cells, typically through stimulating the transmembrane receptors. Hormones work primarily within pathways often referred to as *cascades*. As in the 'domino-effect,' a cascade is the progressive stimulation of one activity, which in turn stimulates another. These cascades fire at tremendous speeds, as ligand-receptor triggers initiate pathways of stimulating mechanisms.

An example of a cascading signaling system is the emotional response to feedback received from the sensory system and transmitted through the neurons to the brain. The pre-programmed sympathetic response (the reflex arc) is typically accompanied by conscious reception of the sensation via the limbic system. The focal point of this stimulation is the thalamus, which acts as a waveform signal translator and decoder. Waveform-transmitting neurons deep within the thalamus are engaged, stimulating waves that combine with others to form an interference pattern—also referred to as a neural mapping. As these waveform interference patterns are decoded, some are reflected back to the cerebral cortex.

Here an exchange of waveform patterns takes place. A relay of information is conducted between the cerebral cortex and the thalamus, reflecting the information back onto the prefrontal cortex. The information is responded to, followed by a return of pulses that stimulate the hypothalamus gland to secrete biochemicals. These biochemical conductors either stimulate endocrine or cellular function directly, or stimulate the pituitary gland to in turn secrete biochemical conductors that precisely activate endocrine glands and physical response.

The hypothalamus, located at the base of the brain under the thalamus, encapsulates part of the third ventricle. The body's autonomic responses are processed here, some of which stimulate the pituitary gland to release key master hormones. These master hormones signal responses that control the critical phase cycles of metabolism, body core temperature, appetite, thirst and so on.

The hypothalamus responds to waveform inputs from the brain centers and limbic system. These brain centers provide the platforms for conscious interaction with waveform signaling. Waveform interference patterns are created from the various sensory nerve transmissions and response neurotransmitter biochemicals. These interactive interference patterns form the basis for information. This facilitates perspective, and allows a sorting process to prioritize the information within the limbic system. Stresses on the body such as infection and immune response also feed into the limbic system for response. For these waveforms, the hypothalamus activates immediate response cascades using the limbic system's programming.

The hypothalamus and limbic system thus respond to a wide range of stimuli, and construct biochemical responses by activating an orchestrated flow of biochemical conductors to stimulate particular physical responses around the body. Dispatched conductors include dopamine, melatonin, somatostatin and others.

The hypothalamic hormones are sent through the hypophyseal capillary beds before they are delivered to the pituitary gland. Once arriving at the pituitary, these biochemical conductors instruct the pituitary gland to secrete specific 'master' hormones. These in turn stimulate particular endocrine glands around the body to produce yet another level of biochemical conductors. These instructional biochemicals include growth hormones, adrenocorticotropic hormones, luteinizing hormones, follicle-stimulating hormones, prolactins, estrogens, testosterone, thyroid stimulating hormones; as well as neurotransmitter-hormones like adrenaline, serotonin, acetylcholine and others.

Amazingly, the subsidiary endocrine glands and tissue centers receive the master hormone signals, and react instantly by initiating the release of even more specific informational biochemical conductors. These are hormones that precisely and directly affect the body's cellular metabolism, organ function and tissue mechanisms. As we all have experienced, the signals stimulate action at tremendous speeds—perhaps at speeds at or above the speed of light. So not only does the limbic system and master glands respond instantly to sensory stimuli, but the entire cascading system responds instantaneously with biochemical messenger cascades that broadcast precise instructions throughout our body's physiology.

Adrenocorticotropic hormone or ACTH is a good example. ACTH is produced by the anterior pituitary gland. Its function is to stimulate the adrenal cortex to release cortisol, and to a lesser degree androgens such as testosterone. The adrenal cortex also produces aldosterone, which stimulates the retention of urine and heightened blood pressure, involved in the renin/angiotensin cycle. The adrenal medulla is also stimulated by sympathetic nerves into producing epinephrine and norepinephrine. Epinephrine is considered a fight-or-flight hormone because it stimulates glycogen and fat breakdown while increasing the heart rate. It dilates the pupils and stimulates awareness. Epinephrine also constricts some blood vessels while dilating others. A gated pathway through the liver using inositol and liver enzymes activates glucose release to help coordinate this. Epinephrine's selective combination of constriction in particular blood vessels effectively diverts blood and nutrients from unnecessary tissues to those deemed necessary for a well-coordinated fight-or-flight response. How does a chemical—a combination of hydrogen, carbon, oxygen and nitrogen—produce this sort of complex selectivity? How does it select which way to divert circulation? How does it know which muscles will be needed?

Can a simple chemical structure make these sorts of selections—instantly?

Medical researchers believe this is driven by epinephrine's ability to stimulate multiple receptors, most notably the alpha-1 and beta-2 receptors. The alpha-1 tends to stimulate a liver signaling process affecting insulin, while the beta-2 tends to stimulate the process of converting glycogen to glucose. However, this simplistic version of the process can hardly explain how this hormone can instantly gear the body up for fight or flight mode while concurrently coordinating which tissue groups are fed and which tissue groups are starved.

The pituitary gland also produces follicle-stimulating hormone, which stimulates the ovarian follicle to produce estrogen in women. It also stimulates the testes to produce sperm in men. Estrogens are complex because they will assist in the development of female sex organs and female characteristics like breasts, while they also stimulate the uterine environment by expanding the endometrium at the early part of the menstrual cycle. Indeed, the rhythmic cycles of menstruation and ovulation, and of pre- peri- and post-menopause tell us that estrogens also have complex signaling pathways within various tissue mechanisms—some significantly affecting moods and nerve activity. Testosterone is also complex, as its levels relate not just to prostate health in men, but also to general vitality and overall health among both men and women.

Although modern medical science has assumed a physical proximity particle-molecule receptor binding mechanism for hormone effects within the body, it is a rather academic debate because at the same time, science is thoroughly aware that there is no touching within the subatomic atmosphere of atoms and molecules. Quantum mechanics and the law of uncertainty tell us that subatomic units are particle-waves, which rotate around the nucleus at dramatic relative distances. As atoms merge to become molecules, a sharing of particle-wave orbitals takes place. These orbitals do not have the ability to come into physical contact with each other within the molecule. So even in the paradigm of a ligand bonding with physical proximity to a receptor to create a new molecule, there is only a sharing of electromagnetic energy states (orbitals) involved, which are of course waveform in nature.

Logically, while we can say that close proximity orbital binding can and does occur with some signaling, the nature of the electromagnetic exchange of information logically should not require physical proximity to transfer the signal. We might compare this with two people standing next to each other exchanging information. They conduct this exchange through speaking. The nature of speaking is such that the two people could easily stand further away from each other and still exchange the information through speaking. They may have to speak a little louder, but the passing of the information would suffer no deficiency between standing next to each other and standing several feet apart.

The biochemical signaling process comes without the merit of observation, albeit indirect. Scientists cannot open up a human intercellular process and analyze the process to determine the exact mode of biocommunication. However, lab researchers can isolate a complex metabolic process requiring a signaling event, and run a chemical analysis on the whole region to see what chemical changes occurred. Before and after chemical analyses (typically via centrifuge followed by mass spectrometry, or possibly electron microscope) will illustrate a chemical change within the region. A change in the composition would infer that the biocommunication coincided with the ligand-receptor exchange. However, this does require an initial assumption that the biocommunication process is indeed biochemical-driven.

We cannot deny confirmed research indicating that chemical reactions in some cases coincide with biocommunication. The question that arises, however, is whether the chemical reaction causes the biocommunication event or the biocommunication event causes the chemical reaction? It is altogether possible that one of the byproducts of the biocommunication transmission was a chemical reaction. Chemical changes often coincide with waveform transmissions. The microwaving of food will likely create a chemical change in the food, for example. The sun's rays often spark composition reactions in soil and water as well. In fact, most electromagnetic waveform transmissions result in chemical reactions of some sort, because the waveforms interfere with the electromagnetic bonds within molecules of the substance being struck, creating a chemical response.

This basic question of which comes first might be compared to seeing some blood in a hungry shark's tank and assuming the blood made the shark hungry. It is quite possible (and probably more likely) that the shark was hungry before the water was bloody. It is more likely that the shark's hunger drove him to eat, making the tank bloody from the fish he ate. This is also logical, noting shark behavior.

This is not such a fantastic supposition. Every type of communication signal we receive externally is transmitted via waveforms. The most basic signaling event, vision, is produced via an electromagnetic reception of the visible spectrum. When we look at a star billions of light years away, we are seeing waveform transmissions that may have traveled for several days or even years before reaching our eyes. Hearing is also a waveform-stimulated process, as our inner ears convert air pressure waves to electromagnetic pulses. If the body conducts its most basic communication events via waveform signaling, why should we assume cells should not share those capabilities? Do we feel our cells are any less technical than the rest of our bodies?

This does not necessitate us completely abandoning the *lock-and-key* mechanisms theorized between ligands and receptors. Waveform communications can also be compared to a lock-and-key mechanism. The concept of the receptor simply has to be expanded to include waveform communications. It is also altogether possible that ligands can stimulate biocommunication through the lock-an-key biochemical basis in addition to remote biocommunication signaling.

We might justly compare this mechanism with our ability to turn on and off a television. We can either walk up to the television and turn it off by pressing the on-off button "manually," or we can use the remote control to achieve the same purpose. In the same way, hormones may make biochemical contract or utilize waveform transmissions to stimulate receptors. Furthermore, just as we can walk around our living room with our remote and control our television volume and channel, hormone-signaling molecules can move around the body and stimulate multiple cells into action simultaneously. Just as we are more assured of accurate channel changing when our remote is within close proximity of the television, the body is assured of more accurate responses among the cells when the signaling hormones are within close proximity of the cells and their receptors. It is for this reason that conductors are dispatched. Information exchange can begin instantly using radio signaling between these ligands and their receptors.

These mechanisms were proven by over two decades of research headed up by Jacques Benveniste, M.D. and several other research teams. Dr. Benveniste was one of the foremost experts in the study of ligand-receptor mechanisms within the immune system for many years. He was the research director for the French National Institute for Health and Medical Research (INSERM) for a number of years. Dr. Benveniste's career was very distinguished. Several years earlier, he was credited with the discovery of the platelet-activating factor.

It was during his rigorous immune system research on the action of basophils that Dr. Benveniste and his research technician Elisabeth Davenas accidentally discovered that an allergic response in solution took place even though the tested allergen was effectively diluted out of the solution. Because the allergen was responded to without an apparent molecular basis (as the substance was diluted out), Dr. Benveniste began a search for what actually caused the immune response.

This discovery led to a four-year study on the immunoglobulin IgE response. The research included joint trials and confirmations with five laboratories in four countries. The combined studies using independent laboratory teams concluded that even at dilutions of 10^{120} (one part to ten parts with one hundred and twenty zeros behind it), and no probability of available molecules, the same immunoglobulin immune responses would occur as with significant concentrations. After confirming this variously, Dr. Benveniste and his team proposed that water somehow acts as a carrier for immune system signal transmission.

After eliminating alternative causes for transmission conduction, Dr. Benveniste and his research associates began to focus on the potential for a radio signaling process of some type. After much experimentation, the right technology and equipment led to the understanding that cells respond to low-frequency electromagnetic waves. Remarkably, certain biochemical conductors like acetylcholine produce unique electromagnetic waveforms. The question was now whether these waveforms played a role in the immunoglobulin communication.

Dr. Benveniste eventually developed sensitive audio equipment to record the frequencies of these biochemicals. In the early 1990s, using his digital sound equipment with computerized technology, Benveniste and his associates recorded thousands of these low-frequency waves from various biochemicals. Amazingly, by playing back these recordings in the midst of cells and tissues, the recorded frequencies were able to stimulate the exact same responses the biochemicals had stimulated. After several years of testing, Benveniste and his associates built up quite a library of biochemical waveform recordings. Frequencies of established biochemical conductors such as heparin, ovalbumin, acetylcholine and dextran were digitized and recorded. Unbelievably, these digital recording files were then put on CD and mailed—or even emailed—to other labs. The other lab would play back the recordings onto various cell tissues—producing the same responses that the physical biochemicals stimulated within the tissues!

This proposition more accurately fits with the body's ability to bridge consciousness with external stimuli. An advanced signaling process using low- and extra-low frequency electromagnetic radiation creates a signaling system to elicit instantaneous responses simultaneously from billions of cells, just as radio broadcasts will bridge a single radio disc jockey with millions of remote listeners simultaneously.

This model also supports the observation of some ligands coming into close proximity with cells in certain regions. These ligands may require close proximity to their receptors in order to elicit a response. Others, however, are designed to elicit responses from further distances. This might again be compared to the radio-to-radiofrequencies used for communications. A CB-band, walkie-talkie system, remote telephone, or television remote may have a relatively short range of reception, depending upon the power of the signal. Therefore, remote telephones that transmit with greater power can be used at greater distances. Radio station broadcasting is also based upon the strength of the waveform signals. For this reason, some radio stations can be heard at much greater distances than others can. In contrast, other radiofrequencies, such as short-wave or ham radios, can transmit over thousands of miles, even at lower power.

We can apply this same signal strength issue to the intracellular biocommunication process. Different hormones or ligands within the body have different purposes. Therefore, they each broadcast with different signal strengths, and at different frequencies. Just as we choose different types of communication devices for different communication priorities, the type of electromagnetic conductor and signal strength used in the body would relate to the need and timing required.

Consider for example our use of modern communications. For some communications, we are likely to use email. For these, we will not usually expect a response for several hours or even days. In a more urgent situation, however, we will likely pick up the phone and call the other person. In this case, we are looking for a more immediate response.

As we examine signaling broadcasting and reception within the body, the cell's transmembrane receptors must *resonate* with the particular frequency emitted by the ligand. This follows the logic of any radio broadcast. Radios utilize not only a receiver but also a tuner, so the radio can synchronize with the broadcast's frequency. This is also a form of resonation. As we turn the tuner on a radio to find the right station, we are locating a point where the radio's receiver is resonating with the waveforms of the broadcasting station's signals. This process was developed using the radio crystal to receive and semiconduct particular waveforms into particular electronic pulses. In the case of the body, the crystals being used for semiconducting are the biochemical structures of hormones and neurotransmitters.

Arranged to these crystalline-like structures are programmed waveform signals being broadcast through the channel pathways of synapses and receptors. As we trace this programming process back further, we find the various brain cortices like the prefrontal cortex at the apex of these arcs—at the seat of consciousness. We might compare this to a song we hear playing on the radio being traced back to a particular radio station broadcast, and eventually back to the musician who originally wrote and performed the song.

Indeed, when we consider every response and movement within the physical body, we are seeing a relayed broadcasting process. These broadcasting pathways stimulate physical activity through the network of endocrine glands, the bloodstream, the nervous system, the basal membranes, transmembrane receptors and of course an army of semiconducting hormones and neurotransmitters. Every beat of our heart and every hunger pang or skeletal muscle twitch is the result of one of these conducted signaling processes. Waveform broadcasts relay information from one biochemical conductor to another. We can thus compare the transmembrane protein receptors to antennae, the neurotransmitter/hormone broadcasting systems to radio stations, and the paracrine and microtubule systems to integrated circuitry.

Biochemical conductors are not dumbwaiters. They each have unique informational fingerprinting and translation processes. They translate signals specific to the particular body and situation. In other words, each signal is unique to a circumstance, emotion, event, personality, fear, and so on. A person injected with hormones from a donor might have a physiological response generic to that hormone, but the specific signal-response being carried through the donor's hormones will not be translated specifically through the body of the recipient. The signal is the specific information that stimulate particular muscles, dilate particular arteries, and so on. We can test this by injecting epinephrine donated from one person into another person. The injected person's tissues might still be stimulated in a non-specific way, depending upon the location of the injection and the physical state of the injected subject. However, the injection will not stimulate the precise emotional response occurring in the body and person the hormones were extracted from. This is observable. The injected person simply will not engage in the exact same physiological responses.

The injection of vaccines has the same affect. Each body receiving the injection will respond slightly differently to the vaccine. The injection will stimulate to different degrees, the body's own immunoglobulins to fight the same antigen. Furthermore, none of the responses will match the response of the organism source of the vaccine.

Consider for a moment the translation of a United Nations speech given by a foreign diplomat into a number of foreign languages concurrently. The translating technology (and/or live interpreters) works to translate each word and each phrase from the speaker's language into these other languages. This allows each UN representative the opportunity to hear the speech in his or her native language simultaneously. It was simply translated in real-time into their respective languages.

As a particular waveform is sent via one part of the body to another, the signal is also being translated in real-time into the various functions necessary for the body. When the hypothalamus sends hormonal signals to the pituitary, they are encoded with the needed response for that event. They are also accompanied by brainwave and nerve cell signaling for additional support information. The pituitary translates this combined signal into a multitude of responses to each part of the body. These are broadcast out for processing to each endocrine gland through secreted hormones. Each endocrine organ receives this translated signal, and each one of these organs translates the signal into more specific biochemical signals in the form of hormones.

This broadcasting and translation system is specific and intelligent. If the translation system at the United Nations incorrectly translated any of the words spoken by the speaker, the speech could be grossly misinterpreted. This could be dangerous. It could theoretically start a war. Therefore, the speech must be translated using an intelligent and impartial translating system.

The signals sent through the endocrine system must also be intelligent. Imagine our endocrine system sending out the same signal regardless of whether we were being chased by a tiger, or were in danger of a head-on car collision. We simply could not react to these two situations with an identical physiological response.

Specific and complex signals are being broadcast from the intelligent centers of the neural network, whether on a purely sympathetic process or autonomic bandwidth. These signals travel within biowaves just as our radio and television communications travel within broadcast radiowaves. The body's waveform broadcasts utilize crystallized amplification mechanisms called hormones to set the stage for the response. Each endocrine organ—or relay station—receives the signals and translates them into a more specific waveform broadcast. This more specific broadcast is meant to stimulate activity with increased specificity for a particular organ or tissue system. As the signal is translated at the endocrine organ, it is broadcast throughout the body, using the hormone molecule-crystals to regulate, amplify, boost or even restrict the signal in some way. This enables a transmission to resonate with and appropriately instruct specific cells or tissue systems.

The use of these receptors and ligands are quite analogous to the functions of semiconductors and resisters among electrical circuits. Resistors and semiconductors—depending upon their positioning and makeup—will slow, redirect and in general modulate the flow of electrical pulses while providing an insulation process. This dampening affect allows the semiconductor or resistor to prevent the pulse from overloading the appliance or shocking its user.

The signaling biochemicals of the body—the hormones and neurotransmitters—must damper, modulate and sometimes even reverse the instructional flow in order for the signals to be properly and precisely engaged. We want to *just* outrun the tiger without killing the body with a heart attack, for example.

The broadcast signals of these relayed signals come with a *continuous flow* of waveform sequences. This continuous flow allows the same semiconductors to broadcast a response to a changing situation. For example, we might need to increase our running speed to stay in front of the tiger. This changing need is translated through the same semiconductors. The endocrine system does not produce one type of epinephrine molecule for five miles an hour, and another type for 10 miles an hour. The same molecule is used, but the biowaves being conduced *through* those molecules change in response to the changing situation.

These biowaves resonate with specialized receptors on the cell membranes. The receptors on the cell membranes then *translate* and *reflect* those continuous signals though the cytoplasm to mitochondria, RNA, and other organelles of the cell, depending upon the signal. These biowaves impart *specific* instructions to stimulate or modulate certain activities. These instructions serve to coordinate each cell's metabolic activity with the needs of the situation and the needs of the rest of the body.

In the case of T3, the information is sent to the cell's ribosomes—responsible for increasing the rate of ATP transport chain processing—which directly increases the metabolic processes. In the case of insulin, the signaling initiates the preparation of micropores to absorb glucose for energy use, together with a stimulation of mitochondria. This will also be signaled to other cells—such as liver cells that convert glycogen and adipose cells to store up fatty acids from glycogen.

The receptors on the cell membranes are the smart receivers for this intelligent signaling system. It might be comparable to having a satellite dish set up on a house. The dish is designed to pick up particular signals from particular satellites, and not others. The size of the dish and its positioning is established to pick up the specific waveforms emitting from that particular satellite. In the same way, particular receptors on the cell membrane are tuned to particular waveform signals sent from specific biochemicals. Whether those biochemicals are in close proximity or at a distance, their reception can be instantaneous.

Bioluminescence

In 1958, Harvard's Dr. Woody Hastings and Dr. Paul Mangelsdorf illustrated how the marine species *Gonyaulax polyedra* (now named *Lingulodinium polyedrum*) lit up the night's ocean timed to the sun's path. Exposing the tiny plant to various light pulses at different times, Dr. Hastings concluded that some internal biological mechanism within the organism must be responding to the sun, switching on and off its illuminating appearance and quite possibly reflecting the sun's light. Over the next decade, various other organisms—including humans—were observed for their biological response to light.

This research began a focused hunt to corner the body's biological connection to light. Researchers assumed that plants and animals possessed cell-switching mechanisms sensitive to light.

In 1972, University of Chicago professor and researcher Dr. Robert Moore discovered the existence of two small clusters of neurons deep within the hypothalamus. These pinhead-sized clusters of about 10,000 nerve cells were named *suprachiasmatic nuclei* (or

SCN) cells. It was discovered that SCN cells are implicated in the body's response to light along with the body's biological clock.

Over the next few years, Dr. Moore, together with Dr. Nicholas Lenn and Dr. Bruce Beebe, confirmed that the body's SCN cells responded specifically to the reception of electromagnetic radiation in the visible part of the spectrum. SCN cells were found to be the conducting means that initiated the body's responses to the rhythms of the sun and the passage of light within the retina and optic nerve (Lenn *et al.* 1977).

For the next two decades, Dr. Moore and many other researchers, including Dr. Charles Weitz, Dr. David Welsch, and Dr. Eric Herzog, investigated these SCN cells. They found that without the SCN cells' synchronization to the sun, an animal's body rhythms would collapse into chaotic patterns.

Initially, SCN cells were observed within the hypothalamus. This rendered the assumption that the body's clock was located within the hypothalamus as well. Furthermore, SCN cells connect the hypothalamus with the activities of the pineal gland—a small conical structure lying above the hind side of the third ventricle. The pineal gland receives waveform impulses directly from the optic nerves.

SCN cells are implicated in the secretion of most if not all the major hormones and neurotransmitters within the body. Their switching system appears to be related to the mechanisms of double-neuron oscillation guided by a combination of light and genetic expression (Ilonomov *et al.* 1994, Fukada 2002).

Further research has concluded that SCN cells are not only responsive to light. They also respond to selected mRNA and prostaglandin molecules. It was also found that every cell seems to have its own independent clock genes, and groups of cells synchronize their clocks to a common setting. The genomes of SCN cells indicate that they provide this synchronization facility (Buijs *et al.* 2006).

In 2005, Dr. H. Okamura from the Kobe University School of Medicine confirmed that SCN clock cell genes are located throughout most of the body's major tissue and organ systems. Apparently, the genetic expressions of SCN cell oscillations are coupled with the independent clock genes in these locations. This coupling (or resonating) of genetic expressions appears to synchronize the pacing of the SCN-stimulated activities within the cell.

A larger mystery is how the SCN cells and clock genes communicate throughout the body. In 2004, Dr. David Welsh and a team of researchers observed individual fibroblasts under various conditions. Fibroblasts are cells that will differentiate into connective tissue cells, bone cells and other types of cells. It turns out that fibroblasts also contain self-regulating circadian clockwork genes. These apparently synchronize their differentiation with the genetic clocks inside SCN cells.

Cave studies like Kleitman (1963), Siffre (1972), and Miles *et al.* (1977) have indicated that the human body's daily revolution without the resetting mechanism of daylight is about 24.9 hours. This exact period has been debated to some degree, but many studies have confirmed this range.

In a study done by Folkard in 1996, a woman was isolated for twenty-five days without daily light cues. While her temperature cycle was close to twenty-four hours long, her sleep cycles were closer to thirty hours. This study indicated that over time, the clock tends to stretch out without any sun. It also indicates some individuality among responses to a lack of daily sun waves. Without the daily resetting mechanism of the sun, we might be going to bed later and later each night, and after a few days, we might be doing all-nighters and sleeping during the daytime.

Consistently, the studies on the body clock illustrate how predictably the body's clockworks mechanisms reset with sunlight. For example, Dr. Czeisler performed studies (1989) with the Naval Health Research Center on Trident nuclear submarine crewmembers. Sub operation schedules required crew to attempt to maintain an 18-hour body clock. Dr. Czeisler's results found this just was not possible. The onboard lights were simply too weak to entrain their body clocks to that schedule. Dr. Czeisler and others had previously established that bright light from between 7,000 and 13,000 lux (daylight) was necessary to produce such a dramatic resetting of the body clock (Boivin *et al.* 1996).

The human body does respond to lower intensities of light, however. In another study, Dr. Czeisler and Boivin (1998) studied eight healthy men with eight control subjects. They found that a mere 180 lux of light (typical office lighting ranges from 200-400 lux) had the ability to shift the circadian body clock and increase body core temperature. In another test, Dr. Czeisler found that 100 lux of indoor light has about half the alerting response as 9100 lux of outdoor light (Cajochen *et al.* 2000). In a study of twelve adults, Dr. Czeisler and his associates (Gronfier *et al.* 2007) found that 100 lux is sufficient to slightly shift the clock, but 25 lux was not enough to shift or reset the body's clock.

Body core temperature, or thermoregulation, appears to be a little less sensitive to the body's reception of light as other rhythms are (St Hilaire *et al.* 2007). Studies of people tested in isolation without light have confirmed that if the body is deprived of light, the body clock will stubbornly maintain thermoregulation cycles long after other cycles fall off.

After a couple of weeks in *temporal isolation* chambers—meaning with only artificial light and no time signals—subjects will sleep highly irregular hours. Some days a subject might sleep up to 19 hours a day, while other days the sleep length might be as few as four hours. Interestingly, on days with as little as four hours sleep, subjects did not recognize that they had too little sleep. They might even remain awake for as many as 30 hours in a row without apparent sleepiness. Furthermore, these subjects' body temperature cycles—together with their melatonin and cortisol cycles—would remain constant despite drastic swings in sleep and waking hours.

Circulating melatonin levels in the blood have been shown to increase into the evening, proportionate to the level of darkness. Melatonin is a hormone/neurotransmitter that helps us fall asleep. Melatonin alternates with cortisol to time our sleeping and waking cycles.

Deficient melatonin levels have also been linked to lowered immunity and heightened risk of cancer and other diseases. A number of pro-inflammatory cytokines are produced when the body is not sleeping enough or is operating on an irregular cycle. Pro-inflammatory interleukin-6 is one of these, and its release correlates with irregular sleep patterns. Another pro-inflammatory trigger, *tumor necrosis factor* (or TNF), is observed higher in persons with inadequate or irregular sleep cycles. Heightened levels of these cytokines have been particularly evident during daytime sleepiness episodes and low levels of nighttime melatonin (Vgontzas *et al.* 2005).

Light and its absence are key triggers for a number of hormone/neurotransmitters. Dopamine and serotonin levels are also related to the reception of sunlight. Light stimulates the pineal gland. The pineal gland in turn stimulates the hypothalamus. The hypothalamus releases neurotransmitters that stimulate the anterior pituitary with releasing hormones. These releasing hormones stimulate the pituitary to release master hormones that drive the endocrine system. For example, ACTH hormones stimulate the adrenal gland to release glucocorticoids. The pituitary's release of TSH hormone stimulates the thyroid to produce secondary hormones T3 and T4, which help maintain metabolic balance. All of these and more are due to the reception (or absence) of the electromagnetic wavelengths of sunlight into the optic nerve.

Our bodies also produce light. In the early 1970s, German researcher Dr. Fritz-Albert Popp was focusing on cancer cell treatment at the University of Marburg. In one particular trial, he discovered weak emissions coming from living cells and multiplying tumor cells at wavelengths of 260-800 nanometers. Fascinated, Popp and his associates confirmed this phenomenon over repeated assays. Over the years, Dr. Popp conducted many studies and wrote many scientific papers on the topic. He called these weak emissions *biophotons* because of their resemblance to the waveform properties of light radiation. As for his cancer research, Dr. Popp was able to correlate greater biophoton emission levels in expanded cancer cell growth, and lower emissions during slower growth. His tests also indicated that anti-carcinogenic therapies had the effect of lowering emission levels during tumor reduction and remission (Popp 1976, 2003; Chang *et al.* 2002).

Dr. Popp, Dr. Chang and fellow researchers (1976, 1997, 2000) found that different frequencies were emitted from healthy cells as compared with diseased cells. He also found that cells positively responded to specific frequencies of light by increasing repair mechanisms. Especially productive were emissions from other cells. There appeared to be low-level radiative communications occurring between cells in response to cell damage.

The strange new ultra-weak radiation produced by cells was termed bioluminescence. Research by Gisler *et al.* in 1983 and Dobrowolski *et al.* in 1987 confirmed Dr. Popp's observations of distinctive bioluminescence effect among healthy and cancer cells.

Dr. Popp's research confirmed that every living organism emits unique frequencies (Popp and Chang 2000); just as each body has a unique fingerprint. The use of identification methods soon led to the description of *cellular fingerprints*—using signature frequencies and amplitudes to differentiate one from another. This concept correlates with differentiated DNA sequencing among cells as demonstrated by researchers like O'Brien *et al.* (1980) and Thacker *et al.* (1988).

This effect was confirmed variously using different types of cells. Dr. Popp's equipment was also able to distinguish conventionally grown tomatoes from organically grown tomatoes. Their ultraweak emissions were measured using another device he developed called the *photon detector*. In 1991, Dr. Barbara Chwirot and Dr. Popp co-authored a report confirming light-induced luminescence during mitosis among yeast cells. His biophoton device was able to predict the relative germination rate of barley seeds prior to sprouting as well. Apparently, biophoton emissions are increased during cellular growth and reproduction (Lambing 1992).

Research led by Professor Franco Musumeci at the Institute of Physics of Catania University in the early 1990s confirmed the existence of these weak emissions. Professor Musumeci studied cancer tissue systems and confirmed these ultraweak waveforms among growing tumor lines (Grasso *et al.* 1991). He and his associates also compared normal tissues with cancer tissues, confirming consistent variances between the two (Grasso *et al.* 1992). In 1994, Professor Musumeci and his associates analyzed food for biophoton emission, finding higher emission levels in freshly picked food. Older, storage-bound food had significantly lower emission levels. While early-picked tomatoes might have had the same red color as ripe-picked tomatoes, they were distinguished by lower biophoton emissions (Triglia *et al.* 1998).

Professor Musumeci's research also focused upon yeast growth and soybean germination: Measuring weak photon emissions during growth and sprouting. In his yeast growth studies, he discovered a consistent increase in photon emission levels with increased yeast growth. His soybean germination studies yielded some very interesting results as well. Both active soybeans and devitalized soybeans were tested together, and their photon levels were measured over time and against mass increase (growth). Consistently, the active germinating seeds displayed higher sustained photon emission levels than the devitalized ones. The devitalized soybean seeds had higher initial emission levels however. These decreased over time, while the vital germinating soybeans had increasing emission levels through germination until they leveled off as they matured (Grasso *et al.* 1991).

Cohen and Popp (1997) eventually conducted human trials, testing 200 subjects for biophoton emissions over a period of several years. These trials showed consistent emission levels among the test subjects. Some tests measured levels of a particular subject daily over an extended period. In one of Cohen and Popp's human trials, human biophoton emission was measured daily for several months. These longer-term measurements demonstrated correlations between biophoton emission and human biowaves. Rhythms estimated at 14 days, one month, three months, and nine months were evidenced by rising and falling emission level rates.

These human biophoton trials also revealed a number of other whole-body trends. These include left-right symmetry among biophoton emissions throughout the body. This symmetry was found to become disturbed in diseased states. Various biophoton channels appeared to be functional within the body, appearing to transfer information between different anatomical regions. They found these corresponded closely with acupuncture *meridians.*

Cohen and Popp proposed that these biophoton measurements could be useful as non-invasive diagnostic techniques. Emission levels were studied before, during, and after the application of skin therapy on psoriasis patients, for example. This confirmed that biophoton emissions tend to rise with therapy and an improvement of symptoms.

Other research also correlated biophoton emission with the human immune response. It was determined that during immune activity or wound healing, blood will reflect higher biophoton levels. Biophoton levels increase with greater neutrophil levels, which also happen to be active redox conductors. The blood is naturally extremely sensitive to immune threats, and biophoton levels appear to reflect the rise with immune cell response (Klima *et al.* 1987).

Other studies have demonstrated that fibroblasts (cells that participate in injury repair) have greater photon emission levels following mitosis. This provides additional confirmation that the body's healing and immune responses yield greater photon emission levels (Niggli 2003).

Biophoton measurements have also been closely studied by a number of other researchers from other disciplines. Among them, bioluminescence was observed by Edwards *et al.* in 1989 using electrotherapeutics. This research again confirmed a connection between acupuncture *meridians* and biophoton emissions.

Between 1986 and 1991, Dr. Humio Inaba, a professor at the Research Institute of Electrical Communication at Tohoku University, led a research project focused on these ultraweak emissions. Dr. Inaba's work utilized a single-photon counting device with an amplification system to enable photon-counting images with narrow photon ranges approximating single waveforms. His research demonstrated that these biophotons occur coincidentally with biochemical reactions within cells. The possibility that this effect was a response to external light was also eliminated. Although external radiation has been shown to prompt a delayed photon response within the body, these ultraweak biophoton emissions were unique and independent. Using his equipment, Dr. Inaba's research also measured similar biophoton emissions in the germinating seeds of various plants, soybeans, spinach chloroplasts, sea urchin eggs, and mammalian nuclei (Inaba 1991).

In 2003, Dr. Michael Lipkind noted higher photon emissions from cell cultures infected with viruses when compared with healthy cell controls. Virus-infected cells not only had higher but also more peculiar ranges than the more standardized ranges coming from healthy cells. The peculiarity of the virus emissions also closely correlated with the virus' replication cycles. These results closely corresponded with the tumor-cell growth studies done by Professor Popp.

In a study by Dr. Chwirot and associates published in 2003, colon lesion cells were measured for biophoton activity after their surgical removal from diseased patients. The biophoton levels significantly differed in colon lesion cells as compared with healthy colon mucosal cells. This has led some to suggest that photon emission testing could be an effective tool in diagnosing colon cancers and lesions.

Studies conducted by Russian researchers V.P. Kaznachejew and L.P Michailowa have confirmed and quantified the transmission and reception of these ultra-weak biowaves within the body. These results show that organs also produce and receive ultra-weak light emissions, and translate this information into metabolic processes (Schumacher 2005).

Further biophoton investigations have determined that greater toxic loads in living cells result in greater photon emission. As toxin levels or stressors increase, emission levels increase. This has been confirmed in other studies of plant responses to stressors. Higher lipoxygenase and peroxidase levels in plants have correlated with higher emission levels.

Biophoton research indicates that although each cell and each individual appears to emit unique waveforms, a significant level of coherence is observed between photon emissions of various cells. More significantly, coherence is observed as these emissions are broken down into their respective spectra. Coherent biowaves create informational interference patterns—either destructive (reducing) or constructive (expanding). The coherency factor became relevant to Dr. Popp and his fellow researchers as it provided a rational holistic model for information transmission within the body (Popp and Yan 2002; Li 1981; Popp 2003).

Communication signaling systems indicating biophoton activity were demonstrated with *dinoflaggellates* by Chang and Popp in 1994. A dinoflaggellate is a single cell organism that typically lives in the ocean or fresh waters of the world. Many plankton species are dinoflaggellates. Though single-celled, they have tremendous complexity, yielding cellulose armor plates for defense, and the ability to change structural shape to give them tremendous propulsion for escape. They also convert sunlight to nutritional energy. Dinoflaggellates thus provide the foundation for the nutrient content of the marine habitat. They also emit bioluminescence.

Most of us have seen the nighttime phosphorescent sparkling of the ocean's surface during plankton blooms. This bioluminescence is a biophoton event, occurring at a wavelength perceivable by human retinal cells. When *Lingulodinium polyedrum* blooms in red tide events, the billions of dinoflagellates will turn the seashore waters phosphorescent blue. It is quite an awesome scene.

Biologists now understand that these single cell dinoflagellates are communicating on a grander level during these bioluminescence events. These communications are referred to as *quorum sensing*. Quorum sensing is created when small organisms biocommunicate a general consensus between each other to effect an action on a mass population basis. Pathogenic microorganisms also have this capability within the body. This is why common yeasts like *Candida albicans* can exist in small colonies within the body without any detriment, but once they their populations grow, they can overwhelm the immune system. Not unlike what is seen among dinoflagellates, *Candida* microorganisms coordinate with waveform signaling to expand their colonies to take advantage of times of weakened immunity within the host.

While cells are not independent living organisms, quorum sensing illustrates the extent that electromagnetic signaling mechanisms occur within and around us. Every cell within our body is involved in electromagnetic signaling. These mechanisms provide the basis for synchronization among our metabolic processes. Biophoton signaling systems provide only one dimension of this. Others include neurotransmitters, hormones, ion channels, brainwaves and nerve conduction. We can conclude that the basic signaling systems of the body are multi-layered and multi-dimensional. Together, they provide a network and smart map that answers the mystery of how every cell in the body seems to know its precise place and function among so many other cells.

Most of us have observed how easily the reception of a radio station can be interrupted by an intruding hillside or building. Because electromagnetic radiation is dependent upon its medium and lack of destructive interference, it is quite easy to empirically establish that the introduction of synthetic electromagnetic radiation should certainly interfere—at least subtly—with the body's orchestrated and synchronized flow of hormones, neurotransmitters, biophotons, brainwaves, neurons, and so on. As we've shown, the interruption of these should effect metabolism, reproduction, digestion, and so many other processes within the body. Depending, of course, on the extent of the interference. What we can conclude is that at the very least, synthetic electromagnetic radiation is a potential stressor to the body.

We would see this interference as not so different in character from the metabolic responses of removing sunlight. As we've shown, removing sunlight can have a dramatic effect upon metabolism, sleeping patterns, energy and so on. However, we should also understand that the waveform interference needs to be extensive enough to have a measurable effect. In our radio station analogy, we can still drive through a variety of landscapes and building canyons and receive the radio station just fine. So the question is one of extent: How great is the effect and where is the line between a harmful interference and an ineffectual one? Or are most synthetic EMFs simply stressors that our bodies can adapt to and possibly even conquer?

We also must ask whether or not our bodies are designed to withstand some or much of the radiofrequencies and electromagnetic fields created by our modern appliances. Are our bodies impervious to these frequencies? Can radio wave transmissions disturb our electromagnetically-driven metabolism or brainwaves? Certainly we don't hear radio stations in our brain—unless of course we have a tooth filling as an antenna. This is because our body's electromagnetic fields fall within a different part of the spectrum. In the same way, a television broadcast will not interfere with a radio broadcast because they are on different frequencies.

So far much of the EMF dialog has polarized (ironically) into whether or not electromagnetic radiation causes different forms of cancers. While this is surely an important question, it is not the *only* question. The larger question is whether synthetic radiation has *any* negative effects upon the physical body. And if so, how critical are those effects, and is there anything we do to prevent them?

These of course are the essential questions we will answer. First let's discuss how the body circulates electromagnetic radiation through the body, and then we'll start digging into the EMF research. With this fundamental information, we should be able to understand both the research and the potential solutions.

☯Three
Body Currents

Ancient texts tell us that Ayurvedic and Chinese physicians were manipulating the body's channels of electromagnetic currents thousands of years ago. The Ayurvedic physicians described these currents as *prana* or "the life airs," while the ancient Chinese physicians called them *chi* (or *qi*) or "vital energy."

Archeologists confirm this with findings from the ancient Indus Valley of India—many dating well over 5,000 years ago. Its texts documented a science that had been previously been handed down from master to student for thousands of years prior. Today we know this knowledge as the science of Ayurvedic medicine. Its language was Sanskrit—understood to be the world's oldest complete written and spoken language.

The Ayurvedic healthcare system has been clinically applied throughout these five thousand years among billions of people throughout the world. The primary writings regarding the practice of *Ayurveda* were presented within the texts of the *RgVeda* and the *ArthaVeda*. Additional texts followed over the centuries, authored by various Ayurvedic physicians, focusing on various specialties within *Ayurveda*. Among other topics, these various texts explored the human and universal anatomy together, providing a process for achieving harmonic balance between the two.

Ancient texts from other cultures indicate that the Ayurvedic science attracted early physicians and philosophers from ancient Egypt, Arabia, Greece and Rome. As these other medical sciences evolved, we find many *Ayurveda* principles ingrained in their treatments and philosophies.

Today *Ayurveda* is the world's oldest existing clinical medical science. Thousands of years before the Europeans began leeching, bloodletting and other grotesque surgical techniques in the Dark ages, Ayurvedic doctors of the Indus Valley civilization performed diseased organ removal and even brain surgery as early as 2500 B.C.E. Long before the European pharmacopeias came into being, Ayurvedic medicine had already developed centuries of clinical herbal and biochemical experience. Early *materia medica* of herbal extract treatments and various techniques such as *pancha karma* and *tridosha therapies* set early standards for health care and detoxification.

115

Ayurveda is currently practiced by billions of Indians, Indonesians, Asians, Europeans, Americans, Australians, New Zealanders, South Americans and Africans. The reason *Ayurveda* has outlived most other medicines of the world is its foundation upon the harmony between the human physiology and the universe around us. The power of nature is fundamental to Ayurvedic practice.

Closely related to the Vedic medical system is another great medical science from Asia: *Traditional Chinese medicine* (TCM). Silk scrolls dating from the fifth century B.C. document the application of TCM herbal medicines and the manipulation of various energy channels through which currents called *qi* moved. Early texts included the Emperor Huang's internal medicine classic *Huang Di Nei Jing* and *Yin Yang Shi Yi Mai Jiu Jing* from over 2100 years ago. Two earlier texts excavated in 1973 focused on stimulation with hot herbal swaths, or moxibustion: *Moxibustion Classic with Eleven Food-Hand Channels* and *Moxibustion Classic with Eleven Yin-Yang Channels.* These early texts described the location, use and treatment of various disorders and diseases by manipulation of particular energy channels, now referred to as *meridians.* The treatment of numerous diseases through the stimulation of these channels has been extensively recorded over the centuries.

Today, TCM has become widely used throughout the world in numerous clinical settings, including many hospitals and emergency rooms. Traditional Chinese medicine and acupuncture has a long history of effectiveness and safety. TCM has been the subject of many controlled clinical studies. TCM also has been used as a treatment for billions of people with a myriad of disorders. Little or no side effects have been the norm for TCM acupuncture treatments.

As mentioned, the wisdom of these traditional medicines played an important role in the Greek, Roman and Egyptian views of the body and health. Hippocrates' concept of disease closely mirrored the Ayurvedic and TCM views. Hippocrates believed that health required a balance of *humors,* of which he professed there being four. When these *humors* were out of balance, he thought, disease resulted. As Hippocrates' influence on medicine is well known, this concept pervaded much of the perspective of health and medicine for centuries in the region. Though the humor count might have been slightly different, the concept of disease resulting from an imbalance between the *humors* of the body had been promulgated over thousands of years in *Ayurveda* and TCM.

It is with this strong foundation of science and tradition between these ancient medical systems that we present a unified basis for describing the flow of electromagnetic information throughout the human anatomy. We describe this waveform channeling system as laid out in both the ancient Ayurvedic and TCM versions, utilizing references to western scientific research and the western anatomical perspective. Because much of our electromagnetic anatomy is beyond the reach of the physical eyes and most of our instruments, we will attempt to bridge this gap with the recent research on electromagnetic conductance as described in the last chapter.

Electromagnetic Channels

From the *RgVeda* texts, we find elaborate descriptions of a system of waveform conducting nodes and channels, referred to as *chakras* and *nadis*. From the TCM texts, we find elaborate descriptions of what appears to be a subset of the *nadi* system flowing through the organs and nerve plexus—commonly termed the *meridian* system. *Meridians* and *nadis* may also be technically referred to as pathways or channels, and *chakras* as conduits or energy conversion centers—to better elucidate their operational functions.

The existence of *chakras, nadis* and *meridians* has been disputed by modern allopathic medicine. This is because this network of conduits and conversion centers cannot be observed through anatomical dissection. For this reason, a certain level of disbelief of this technology exists within modern western medicine circles. In defense of this western view, the presentation of these channels and centers has yet to satisfy peer-review. We find several post-era texts written on these subjects, many of which appear too deeply entrenched in the ancient descriptions to deliver the information within the context of modern science. We hope to offer some new perspectives to this debate.

As we discussed in detail in the last chapter, researchers have discovered a variety of pathways through which the body relays information biowaves between cells, tissue systems, nervous system and the outside world. Western science has documented and confirmed the existence of these informational pathways through highly technical *in-vitro* research, *in-vivo* research and clinical human research.

Scientists over the past few decades have found that the body conducts electromagnetic information through brainwaves, ion channels, sensory nerve conductance, microtubules, hormones, neurotransmitters, peristalsis, and DNA-RNA. All of these fall within the spectrum of electromagnetic conductance and signaling mechanisms perceived by the ancient physicians of TCM and Ayurveda.

Just as modern researchers utilize language such as *cascades* and *signaling mechanisms,* the ancient physicians utilized a language of *prana, qi, meridians, nadis* and *chakras.* The basic difference between the two descriptions of the anatomy is that modern research has uncovered the biochemical and electromagnetic detail regarding these channels, while the ancient physicians utilized an intuitive approach to reveal a broader scope of the network: what types of consciousness are being transmitted within each channeling system, and the general location of the conduits. While the lens and magnification of modern research has been sharper, it has also been more myopic.

Controlled and double blind research using acupuncture and various electrotherapy techniques have confirmed the body's ability to conduct particular EMF pulses by stimulating key points along a network of *meridian* channels. Over the past three decades, electrotherapy acupuncture has been successfully applied in clinical environments throughout western medicine. Thousands of randomized, double-blind studies have illustrated acupuncture's ability to reduce pain, increase healing times, and provide acute therapy for many disorders.

These studies have been performed around the world, successfully proving predictable and repeatable responses in patients being treated with channel therapy. Controlled research showing acupuncture's effectiveness typically entails forming two groups of subjects with the same condition. One group is treated with acupuncture while the other is treated with needle insertion at non-channel points (called *sham treatment*) or simply not treated. The comparison of the groups, considering the placebo effect, requires a large threshold of success. Using these strict controls, acupuncture research from around the world has confirmed TCM's legitimacy as an effective medical treatment.

The therapeutic modulation of our electromagnetic channels is also confirmed by the growing body of research and clinical use of electrostimulation technologies such as the *transcutaneous electrical nerve stimulator* (or TENS) units. These have shown positive results in patients with various nervous system and/or muscular disorders. *Spinal cord stimulators* (or STIM) have also shown effectiveness for damaged spinal columns and nerve systems in many studies and clinical applications. A STIM is implanted into the body with wires inserted into the epidural spaces of the spinal column. Some STIM units are coupled with radiofrequency receivers. The use of the *cranial-electro stimulator* (also called cranial electrotherapy stimulation or CES) is also increasing. Among other effects, CES has been shown to stimulate the flow of serotonin.

All of these therapies stimulate the body's conduits and modulate the energies being channeled through the nerves and tissues, and key signaling mechanisms within the body. Each of these methods infuses particular biowaves into specific locations of the anatomy—locations found to have the most effective response. Interestingly, most of these positions are also points described in both Ayurvedic and TCM texts.

Acupuncturists stimulate or reduce waveform flow through the *meridian* channels. When the correct waveform is utilized, the channel circuits are properly stimulated. This in turn provokes healing responses and the modulation of pain gateways.

For example, microwave (30-300 gigahertz) stimulation therapy was applied along acupuncture *meridians* among 1500 treatment centers in Russia and the Ukraine in the 1980s. More than 500,000 patients with over 60 pathologies participated in the study. The results showed that electrostimulation significantly improved disease conditions in most cases (Jovanovic-Ignajatic *et al.* 1999).

Research by Kandel *et al.* (1991) showed an increased electrical conductivity at the skin along *meridian* and *nadi* points when compared with surrounding tissue. This skin conductivity confirms an increased waveform potential within *meridian* and *nadi* pathways. Increased ion resorption along these points has also been observed.

Newer research into the nerve synapse regions also called *gap junctions* has illustrated significant ion concentration levels inside acupuncture points and *meridians*. The research shows these gap junctions are each made up of two cylinders, called *connexons*. These connexons meet in the gap junctions between pre-synaptic and post-synaptic nerve cells.

Connexons provide passage for biowaves through the modulation of calcium ions and pH. Connexons also provide a gateway shuttering system, which can block certain biowaves. This waveform channel gateway has a range of 3.5 to 20 nanometers of separation. This separation allows connexons to manage communications between nerves.

Testing with electrostimulation equipment has confirmed that gated channels resonate with both 50-80 gigahertz and 2-4 hertz ranges. This means these channels conduct frequencies from the ultra-low (seismic) range to the microwave range (Jovanovic-Ignjatic 1999).

These findings were confirmed by Schlebusch *et al.* (2005): After light stimulation of the body in the 3-5 micron range, *"light channels"* appeared on the body precisely in the locations of the *meridians*.

Further research by Yang *et al.* (2007) found clear evidence of *meridian* channels—consistent with TCM *meridian* charts—among thirty healthy volunteers using infrared thermal imaging. Hu *et al.* (1993) had conducted forty-nine passes over another thirty healthy volunteers, revealing 594 channels of *"radiant track"* using infrared beams. Thirty percent of these tracks were consistent with the fourteen traditional *meridians* of TCM, confirming the existence of the TCM *meridians* as well as numerous others. The others are most certainly a part of the larger network of *nadis*.

Biochemical conductors such as hormones and neurotransmitters are connected to the flow of informational biowaves through these subtle channels. Electrostimulation of acupuncture points with two-hertz electrodes was found to stimulate endorphin release, while serotonin and norepinephrine release were stimulated at 100 hertz (Ulett, 1998). Other acupuncture studies have stimulated endorphins at four hertz, and serotonin and norepinephrine at 200 hertz.

Further research substantiating the scientific basis for the existence of *meridian* channels was led by Dr. Hiroshi Motoyama—author of over fifty books and numerous scientific papers. In the 1970s, Dr. Motoyama began experimenting with electrocardiograms to detect the electrical potential and/or energetic change along *meridian* channels. In order to gain enough sensitivity, (the EEG was not sensitive enough for this type of energy exchange).

Dr. Motoyama invented a machine called the *AMI machine*—or *Apparatus for measuring the functioning of the Meridians and the corresponding Internal organs.* Dr. Motoyama applied this machine on thousands of subjects. In a study published in *Science and Medicine* (1999), Motoyama applied a painless rectangular waveform pulse to the skin of subjects. Following the pulse, sympathetic nerve responses rendered a significant change in potential within milliseconds at the traditional *meridian* points. There was no potential change at the non-meridian locations. Furthermore, he found that while *yang meridians* recorded positive potential changes, *yin meridians* recorded negative potential changes to the waveform pulse from the AMI.

A few years later, Dr. Motoyama designed a second machine, which he named the *chakra machine*. This more sensitive machine took readings of the changes in static field potentials between the environment and the skin. The level of the energy disturbances rendered an "energy shadow" over the *chakra* region. Dr. Motoyama's research included both control subjects and subjects advanced in controlling physiological states. The higher electromagnetic disruptions occurred around the *chakra* regions in all cases, but varied in intensity from person to person. The results also indicated a greater energy displacement at the *chakra* centers among subjects who were proficient in *kundalini* (the ability to raise the life air through the *chakras*) (Jackson, 2007).

University of California at Los Angeles researcher Dr. Varie Hunt evaluated the existence of *chakra* regions with *electromyography* (or EMG) electrodes in 1978. Her research found sinusoidal waveforms extending from the *chakra* regions ranging from 100 to 1600 cycles per second (Hunt 2000).

Schwann cells and other *glial* nerve cell systems have been shown to conduct electrical impulses through current potential shifting. Through a variance of voltage, waveform information is conducted through exchanges between ions within and around the neurotransmitter fluid. As nerve impulses move through these nerve cell connection systems, the characteristic waveforms of each voltage shift forms a unique waveform pulse of information. When these voltage-shifted biowaves are received through receptors, their circuit is completed through a biocommunication synchronizing mechanism. This biocommunication system serves to connect the conscious source of the instruction (the self) with the physical activity intended.

Physical movement is seismic in nature with cycles of 1-4 per second. Brainwaves range from 10 to 100 cycles per second, with a predominance of 30-hertz speeds. Muscular activity stimulation from the central nervous system will range up to 225 cycles per second. Here we see a boosting of frequency as information moves from brainwave to nervous system conductance. Following this boost, the muscles translate and reduce the waveform frequencies to the seismic level. This can be compared to a computer system. Information is translated from keyboard input to machine language through a software conversion. Once in machine language, the computer can execute the hardware operations, screen imaging and execution.

We might remember from our discussion on waveform mechanics that frequency is not the only characteristic of a waveform. Other characteristics include amplitude, wavelength, and the waveform characteristics of wave shape, slope, angular momentum, and spin. When we break down the electromagnetic spectrum as it translates through the medium of our physiology, interfering waveforms may take on spiral or helix character. This is reflected in many molecular structures within the body, inclusive of proteins, enzymes and DNA.

As we investigate the anatomical holography of the physical body, we can also correlate different types of organ activity with these distinctive biowaves. Each primary *chakra* region resonates with a particular range of biowaves, and each resonates with particular organs and physiological functions. As would be expected, the primary *chakra* regions are positioned within innervation ganglia that serve these organ systems.

For example, we find *chakra* regions located within nerve ganglia that serve the gonads/ovaries, the adrenals, the spleen, the digestive system, the liver, the heart, the thyroid and larynx, the pineal gland/hypothalamus and the limbic system, respectively. Because each of these organs has characteristic physiological functions, we can undoubtedly make the case—regardless whether the term *chakra* is used—that each organ system is supported by specific nerve regions that are located up and down the spine and central nervous system.

The Elements

According to the ancient texts of *Ayurveda*, both the universe and the body are comprised of eight basic elements. The origins of these layers come from the Almighty through three basic modes: goodness, passion and ignorance. From these spring the three basic physical elements or *doshas: vata* (from goodness), *pitta* (from passion) *and kapha* (from ignorance). From these basic elements arise the five gross physical layers or planes: Solids, liquids, gases, thermals, and electromagnetics. These five relate to each other in the *tridosha* system: *Vata* conducts solids and liquids. *Pitta* conducts liquids and thermals. *Vata* conducts gases and electromagnetics.

Just as the earth is layered with chemical elements stratified by density and waveform function, our physical body is also layered by these elements that conduct waveforms of particular frequencies and amplitudes. The gross physical world is made up of the five elemental states; the solid elemental state, the liquid elemental state, the gas elemental state, the thermal elemental state, and the electromagnetic elemental state. Each elemental state contains a medium of different density, and as the density decreases, the types of waveforms radiating within that elemental state change.

Solids, liquids and gases are the standard elemental states taught in any college chemistry course. Yet physicists told us decades ago that molecules are electromagnetic in essence, and consequently, "solids" per se are actually non-existent. While quantum physics has defined matter within the context of its electromagnetic content, we know that there is a density issue here: The greater density of atoms relates to a medium or state. The solid elemental state produces an architecture where molecules are rigidly connected within a static architecture of standing bonding orbitals or energy states. In the liquids state, molecules are further apart and moving around each other with polar forces that keep the molecules connected. In the gas state, the molecules are further apart (less density) and attracted through ionization forces.

In the thermal state, molecules are being radiated with infrared waveforms. While we might not see this as being a physical "state," one look at a fire tells us that this elemental state is as real as any other elemental state. The molecular activity within a fire is substantially different than the molecular activity with a gas. Yet we know that molecules do move within this state, as we see wood converted to ash and smoke rising from the flames.

Finally, the electromagnetic state has been sought out for definition by a venerable group of western scientists over the centuries. Most of these presented it as a definite state of matter. Remember that Dr. Oliver Lodge, the inventor of the coherer—considered that radiowaves transmitted through a medium called the aether. The aether state was also assumed by many of the Greek philosophers, and many Renaissance scientists. Dr. Albert Einstein also weighed in on this topic, as he defined the medium of 'space' that electromagnetic radiation traveled through. Dr. Einstein proposed that the electromagnetic medium or state was a vacuum. Recently, some physicists have challenged this proposal, as the speed of light has been observed changing. Some researchers have more recently coined this state as the *plasma* elemental state.

Each of the five gross elemental states also provide a medium for a particular type and range of biowaves. Solids provide the medium for seismic waves. Liquids provide the medium for fluid waves. Gases provide the medium for pressure waves. Thermals provide a medium for the spectrum of infrared and microwave radiation. The plasma or electromagnetic state provides the platform for the movement of waves in the visible spectrum, the ultraviolet spectrum, radiowaves, x-rays, cosmic rays, gamma waves, ultra-weak waves (biophotons) and others—some of which have yet to be quantified by our equipment. To this, most physicists and cosmologists agree that we have only discovered a small percentage of the total electromagnetic spectrum to date.

With each successive elemental layer, we find a decrease in density and an increase in wave frequencies. Thus we find a layering of energy and information potential. This makes sense because higher frequency waveforms are capable of transmitting more information in the same amount of time.

To illustrate this, Morse code can transmit thoughts and feelings, but very slowly and crudely. A radiowave can communicate voices and images—a greater amount of information—almost instantly. The wave has higher frequency, and transmits through an elemental state of less density.

Our bodies utilize all these waveform mediums. Each is designed to support transmission of particular types of information. Together these elemental waveform states provide a type of layering system, covering the inner self with layers of interacting biowaves. This hierarchical layering of biowaves essentially provides both a vehicle and a barrier between the external physical world and the self within. Just as a building or automobile is built with a layering of different elements to give its structure strength to protect the driver from the outside world, the human body is also built with a mix of layers. In a building we find concrete and wood framing as the foundation materials. Then narrower beams of wood, paneling and sheetrock will make up the walls. Glass will be put into window spaces. Electrical wiring will be installed. Plumbing systems will be installed, and roofing material will be installed. Each of these installations is made up of different compounds with varying degrees of strength and durability. A light fixture cannot provide a foundation. The more subtle parts of a building, such as its sprinkler system, satellite TV installation and so on might be compared to the more subtle parts of our body that include the mind, intelligence and physical ego. We might compare physical ego to the building design.

We can also associate different parts of our body's physiology with the different elements, according to *Ayurveda*:

- ❖ *Solids:* Bones nails, and supporting tissues
- ❖ *Liquids:* Blood, bone marrow, lymph and cellular fluids
- ❖ *Gases:* Lungs, oxygen transport and flatulence
- ❖ *Thermals:* Digestive, lower endocrine and liver systems

- ❖ *Electromagnetics (Plasma):* Senses, nerves, neurotransmitters, and hormones
- ❖ *Mind:* Brain, pineal, pituitary, thalamus, and hypothalamus
- ❖ *Intelligence:* Immune system and genetic system
- ❖ *Physical ego:* Reproductive system and epigenetic system

Though each layer may have its solid physical organs and attributes among the other elements (liquid, gas and so on), each system is connected to a prevailing element. Each elemental state interacts with the various structures, architecture and specific biowaves moving within those parts of the body. These are best described with the understanding of the body's biomolecular structures as waveform converters and conductors. Each of the body's different anatomical systems transmits and conducts waveform information. This conduction is verified by empirical evidence as we have discussed. All of the body's ions, cells, nerves, hormones and neurotransmitters are all part of a signaling and execution system that ties together different types of biowaves traveling through different mediums (or elements).

This might be compared to differentiating the wire cable from the electricity network and energy generator. Without the wire cable that connects the utility company to the houses, electricity would not have anything through which to transmit. Therefore, the wire cable is included when we describe an electrical system, although we understand that the current itself is not the physical wire. We can simply unplug the wire to understand this. Within our body, the various biochemical molecular components are part of the conducting system for the body's energy systems. The different biowaves of life energy—well, we can see them switch off as the body dies.

Just as the solid layer corresponds with the earthly elements of rock, mountains and soils, the solid layer relates to the bony structures of the body. The solid layer also connects the molecular elements within the muscles, ligaments, organ systems and outer skin tissues. These parts of the body are primarily mineral and carbon-based, and provide the harder 'shell' architecture of the body. They also allow the body a grounding vehicle for the magnetic fields of the earth. Without this grounding, the body could not plant its feet solidly onto the ground. Nor could it lie down restfully and sleep. The earth's seismic waveforms thus harmonically 'flow' through the bone and tissue cells of our body. Because the solid layer vibrates at lower frequencies, its movement is slower and more perceptible. Our solid body layers resonate with these seismic frequencies.

The solid layering of our molecular biochemistry is in motion at all times, however. Our bones may not look like they are circulating, but they are. They are absorbing elements like calcium, silica and boron while excreting these in a constant flow of molecular recycling. This circulation of the bones compares favorably to the circulation of soil or elements of rock through oceans, lakes and streams. Soils and rocks circulate their contents slowly through adjoining waters, which form channels of rivers and streams through them. Soil and rock runoff in turn helps nourish aquatic organisms. Bones circulate nutrients and water through small channels that flow between osteocytes, ridding toxins to the lymph and blood stream. We might question the ability of solids to transmit information. A simple knock on the door or tap on the floor will answer that question. Rhythmic waveforms transmitted through the solid elemental state can be quite clearly informational.

At the macroscopic level, the liquid element relates to the movements of the various fluids around the planet. This includes the rivers, streams, oceans, lakes and aquifers of various substances, including water, lava, oil, and other natural fluids of the planet. The liquid layer of the body also deals with the rivers and streams of the blood and lymphatic systems, as well as the fluid-filled cavities of cells, interstitial regions, organs and basal cell membranes. Fluids also provide a means for transferring various signaling biochemicals such as hormones around the body via blood circulation. The blood also provides structure via dissolved ions as they circulate amongst cells and organs. The physical body's fluid nature also provides the body with its ability to detoxify and nourish. Fluids give the body the ability to respond with flexibility. This means that water is a means for the body to adapt and alter course. Solidity tends to be stable and stubborn, while liquidity tends to be adaptive and compromising. Emotions are often expressed with liquid movement. The formation of tears expresses certain emotions. A person might spit to express another emotion. Some people react with shock when seeing their own blood, as we identify emotionally with this fluid. The fluid layer also provides a turnover of nutrients and toxins, which drive metabolism and detoxification. Proper liquid movement through the body is critical for the body's balance.

The gaseous layer moving through the living organism is less dense and even more motion-oriented than the liquid layer. On the macro basis, this element covers our planet and provides several layers of protection—including blocking some of the dangerous radiation like cosmic rays pulsing into our atmosphere. The gases inside the atmosphere also provide the elements of oxygen and nitrogen for mammals, and carbon dioxide for plants and algae. Our ability to see into this medium as we do with the solid and liquid elements is hampered by the density of the medium. Our eyes cannot perceive spectra from other mediums outside the primary sensory receptor abilities of the rods and cones. At the same time, the gas state provides a good medium for the transmission of sound.

The gaseous elemental state exists throughout the body. Gases travel through the bloodstream in the form of oxygen, nitrogen, carbon dioxide (in the form of carbolic acid) and others. Gas states of various molecular structures are present throughout every tissue system, cell, organ and of course the lungs and digestive tract. While cadaver dissection does not reveal much in the way of the gas element, we can see the gas state interacting through respiration and digestion. A simple belch or 'passing of gas' will quickly illustrate the role gases play within the digestive system. Gases circulate within our body through channel systems just as the other elements do. The gas elemental state also provides balancing mechanisms within the body just as do the other states. The gas state also forms a means for expression. Breathing patterns and digestive efficiency reflect emotions quite well. Heavy breathing tends to reflect anxious moments, and we tend to belch when we feeling comfortable after a fine meal.

Thermal currents conduct through our environment within the water, the atmosphere and even through the earth. Weather systems provide an expression of the movement of thermals through the atmosphere—reflected by pressure and temperature change. The thermal element within our body is easily identified with thermal-sensing equipment. This can be done by the casual observer with a thermometer or more precisely with thermal sensing units available to medical facilities. These units allow us to see that the body is not necessarily the temperature of the environment, and not one temperature throughout. Rather, temperature gradients tend to flow through the body just as water or gas circulates. The body thus will have different temperatures in different locations, and these gradients will interact with a variety of metabolic and physiologic functions.

Certain instruments can "see" these thermal waveforms. Heat detectors such as thermographic cameras image temperature radiating from a hot surface in distinct gradients. Occasionally we will also see thermal waves rising up from a heated asphalt road. The thermal state may present some confusion because infrared waves and microwaves are also usually considered part of the electromagnetic spectrum. Actually, thermal radiation is a byproduct of the interaction between these electromagnetic waveforms and the bonding orbitals (or energy states) of atoms. It is this interaction that creates the heat considered in this elemental state.

Research has indicated that thermal radiation is the primary energy moving through the *meridian* system. Thermal radiation will transmit through the nervous system and the bloodstream as well. Thermal radiation also circulate through the spaces around the cells—the intercellular spaces or basal membrane. Thermal radiation transmits information that produces a suitable environment for muscle exertion, organ activity, and cellular response. In addition to these support mechanisms, heat-producing molecules like glucose, cortical and thyroid neurochemicals transmit thermal potentials as they produce reactions that convert glucose, oxygen and minerals to kinetic energy. The citric acid ATP-transfer (or Krebs) cycle is an example of a thermal waveform-producing energy reaction working within a catalytic (conversion) environment.

The *meridians* provide heat conduction channels within our bodies, which in turn drive the various enzymatic and metabolism activities. We identify greatly with the thermal element, as we connect thermal radiation with our body's energy levels. Most of us will comment that when a person is productive, they are "on fire." We may also call someone "dynamic" or "hot," when they appear attractive to us.

This indirectly reflects on his or her level of thermal radiation. Thermal radiation directly influences metabolism. Faster metabolism typically produces a more attractive physical appearance due to better energy utilization and increased activity. When we describe someone as a dynamic person, we are usually referring to someone who is active and radiates in a way they resonate with. These characteristics relate to their thermal conductivity, because thermal radiation also transmits passionate feelings and emotions along with the inner self's drive for achievement.

Incidentally, many incorrectly relate the layer of thermal radiation directly to the self. It is true that without the host of the inner self within the body, no heat can be generated. Therefore, many interpret the result of thermal contact with photographic paper—rendering the famous *Kirlian corona*—as a vision of the soul or inner self. Again, while we can easily connect the inner self with the body's ability to transmit thermal radiation, the visual observation of Kirlian photography would not be any more "spiritual" than seeing the color of ones skin or hearing a person's voice. Rather, the corona image of Kirlian photography simply reflects the body's thermal radiation generated from the channeling of these biowaves throughout the body.

As we reach the lower density, higher frequency state of the plasma or electromagnetic medium, we find increased information disbursement. The higher frequency electromagnetic transmissions that occur around the body reflects the flow of conscious information requiring immediate and precise transmission and reception. Just as we would pick up the phone to reach someone as opposed to physically traveling to meet them, this broadcast medium allows for immediate communication around the body. The nerves provide the primary pathway for electromagnetic waveform biocommunication, but as we discussed in the last chapter, there are a variety of different conductors of electromagnetic frequencies within the body. As mentioned, electromagnetic information is transferred via brainwaves, ion channels, neurotransmitters, hormones (ligands and receptors) and paracrine communications.

Electromagnetic radiation will also travel through the higher density states, just as each of the waveforms of higher states will travel through the lower states. However, the lower states will often modify the information. Solids can delay, distort or muffle electro-magnetic waveforms. Crystals may stratify and disburse them. These alterations are present in the design of the body. The interaction between pure electromagnetic waveforms and the covalent bonds between the atoms and molecules of a substance produces a wave-form interference pattern—a platform for communication. Liquids tend to refract electromagnetic radiation, altering their waveform transmission. Gases tend to diffuse electromagnetic radiation, but this also depends upon the content of the gas. Electromagnetic radiation may refract through gas as well. Both are seen among the sun's different electromagnetic rays as they enter our atmosphere. The thermal energy state will often magnify or intensify particular electromagnetic radiation. Electromagnetic waves can also produce thermal waveforms, as seen in microwaves and infrared waveforms.

The inner self or consciousness of the body interacts with all these interference patterns. Using the facility of the mind, the self utilizes and responds to the information provided through the re-flection of these interference patterns upon the pre-frontal cortex. This might be compared to a person utilizing a flashlight and hand to create a particular hand puppet on the wall. The light would have no meaning without the conscious interaction by the person ma-nipulating his hand in front of the light. Without the interaction between the two, there would be no image.

This manipulation of waveform interference patterns is pre-cisely what the inner self learns to do to achieve goals and objec-tives. The various biowaves transmitted through our body relate to information. The utilization of information from our physiology requires a sorting and conversion process. This is what the mind does. The mind assembles the various biowaves from the five ele-ments into interference patterns that most closely match the goals and intentions of the self. These interference patterns are then im-aged by the self, followed by emotional responses sent back through the mind and converted into physical instructions.

When we speak, for example, we are broadcasting something that was translated by the mind. How do our thoughts and inten-tions find their way to the voice box? There is an electromagnetic conduction that connects the self, mind, brain and voice box. Wave-form signaling provides the mechanism.

Intelligence is channeled through the mind from a more subtle state. The inner self views the input from the body and senses upon the screen of the mind. The self uses intelligence as a sorting and filtering tool during the viewing and response process.

The five elements of solids, liquids, gases, thermals and electromagnetics are quite easy to understand. The more subtle layers of the mind, intelligence and physical ego require another perspective of reality. These subtle facilities exist on a platform that lies beyond the senses. We know the mind exists because of its sorting, translation and conversion effects. We know intelligence exists because we have all drawn upon a deeper sense of morality or logic, often beyond what the senses present. As for physical ego, it presents as a shield covering the spiritual being within. The shield presents a perspective that our physical bodies will supply the inner self with fulfillment. The shortcoming of this ego (identification) is characterized by *Ayurveda* as temporary. The physical body is temporary, while the spiritual self within is permanent (etermal).

The layered waveform elements of the physical body are classified appropriately within the unique *Ayurveda tridosha* system. The grosser elements of solids, liquids and gasses reflect a more grounded consciousness, called *kapha*. This is more closely identified with the characteristic of consistency and predictability. *Ayurveda* generally classifies thermal activities as characteristic of *pitta* consciousness. *Pitta* reflects the characteristics of activity, passion, anger, and responsiveness. Meanwhile, the higher frequency electromagnetic biowaves pulsing through the body and mind are considered *vata*, reflecting a higher consciousness of sensitivity and intensity.

The Chakras

The Sanskrit word *chakra* means 'wheel.' This literal translation relates to the *chakra*'s ability to radiate its translation of intention through a particular pathway or network of the body. Another translation of the word *chakra* is *vortex*. This word relates to the multi-dimensional aspect of *chakras*, and their ability to convert consciousness into physical expression.

There are seven primary *chakra* centers located vertically within the central nervous system according to *Ayurveda*. Each translates consciousness a little differently and through a slightly different elemental medium, just as each knob and lever in a car translates the driver's purpose differently. As such, each of these *chakra* centers also stimulates particular organs and tissue systems within the body.

In the western world, *chakras* are often discussed as though they are some type of strange organ system within the body. Some have offered sayings such as *"balancing the chakras"* or *"subduing"* or *"correcting"* a *chakra* in order to bring about a better physical result or emotional outlook. These descriptions may have validity on a certain analogous level. Still, they misconstrue the *chakras'* true structure and function. Such concepts might be equivalent to the car driver blaming the car's speed and direction on the gas pedal and steering wheel. *"That damn pedal needs to be fixed,"* the driver might complain upon receiving a speeding ticket. He actually just made some bad decisions regarding his speed. Or perhaps he simply did not watch the speedometer.

Of the seven major *chakra* regions within the human body, the lower four are aligned vertically within the spinal region, and the upper three align with key loci in the brainstem and cortex systems. There are five general body regions overlaying these *chakra* centers. They are in the pelvic region at the base of the spine, the navel region, the solar plexus region, the throat and cervical region, and the brain region. Each of these centers provides a control or lever of influence into a particular elemental state, a particular organ system, and particular sense organs. The brain region contains three different *chakra* regions, however. The last two rise above the plasma element of the electromagnetic, into the biowaves of the mind, intelligence and subtle false identity field.

Here we clarify that these *chakra* centers are made up principally of neurons, ganglia and their supporting cell networks. These together form a region that provides a conversion or translation mechanism for biowaves. Collectively, these effectively translate the intentional purpose and consciousness of the inner self into biophysical instructions and activities. Each of the centers is designed to convert particular types of conscious intention into specific biowaves. These translation centers simply provide a bridge between consciousness and the physical body.

The *chakra* waveform interference patterns are crystallized within neuron biochemical structures and DNA sequencing. The network of nerve cells that innerve particular organs and tissues in that region of the body thus resonate with particular waveform frequencies. Programming instructions from the mind set up informational interference patterns with certain biowaves, which are collectively held or crystallized by these arrayed neurons. These crystallized (standing) interference patterns form gateway states together create response patterns to incoming waveforms (from sensory inputs). A series of these gateway states would be analogous to a combination of on-off (1-0) states of computer machine language (bits) forming *if-then* statements in bytes. These gateway-triggered responses include stimulating particular endocrine glands to release neurotransmitters and hormones, or initiating immediate motor responses in key muscle fibers, for example.

In this way, the neural network cells and supporting tissue cells within and surrounding that *chakra* region are all programmed to respond in particular ways to sensory perception. Seeing a tiger would initiate a response within key *chakra* programming for the various endocrine glands to produce adrenaline, vasopressin, cortisol, insulin and a number of other conductors to initiate and support immediate motor response, along with immediate skeletal muscle responses like running.

The seven *chakras* are positioned along the spine and central nervous system. Here is an explanation of each *chakra* region and its specific characteristics according to ancient Vedic texts:

The first chakra: This is considered the first and *root* energy *chakra*. It is also referred to as *muladhara*, which means 'foundation.' This *chakra* is located in the region at the base of the spine near the pelvis, in a lateral position between the anus and the genitals. This *chakra* transmits biowaves within the solid elements of minerals and lattice structures. It is thus considered connected to the earth, and survival.

This *chakra* region is often referred to as the *seat of the vital energy,* because it is the most grounded center of the body. This region controls the activation of survival instincts, and this is translated through the activities of the lower adrenal system or the adrenal medulla gland, which releases adrenal hormones like epinephrine and cortisol. These hormones stimulate physical activation of the survival and fear responses.

This *chakra* region also activates the muscles that control ejaculation and orgasm, and thus form the basis for our attraction to the physical forms of the opposite sex. This *chakra* region is often referred to as the *coil* for procreation and physical perpetuity.

The foundation *chakra* region connects with the olfactory senses. This also relates to survival, as we often use the sense of smell to find food and avoid danger. The primary work organ this *chakra* region is the anus according to the ancient Vedas. The anus is of course located between our sit bones—so it is also appropriately positioned for grounding when we sit. The skeletal system is the primary structural tie to this *chakra* region, as its biowaves are related to the minerals and seismic waveforms of earth.

This *chakra* region is dominant between the body's first and seventh years. As a result, survival and security are critical issues during these ages. Fear is also more relevant during these years.

This *chakra* stimulates adrenal hormones such as cortisol and related glucocorticoids. These neurochemicals mobilize physical response during stressful times by stimulating an increase in blood glucose and fatty acid levels. The adrenal cortex also releases mineralocorticoids like aldosterone and androgen steroids. These increase muscle size, stamina and power, especially during critical times when extra response is required. The adrenal medulla produces epinephrine and norepinephrine. These stimulate blood flow into skeletal muscle regions of the body. This in turn helps stimulate greater heart rates in a survival-threatened response.

The second chakra: The second *chakra* region in the human body is called *svadhisthana* in *Ayurveda,* meaning 'dwelling place.' This *chakra* stimulates tendencies surrounding reproduction and family. The location of this *chakra* region is at the sacral region of the spine, in the region of the groin. Waveforms that stimulate the testes and the ovaries are conducted through this *chakra*.

The element of this *chakra* region is liquid. The biowaves conducted through this *chakra* are predominantly transmitted through the liquid elements within the body. This means we find its functional interactivity within the bloodstream, bone marrow, lymph, cytoplasm, and interstitial (between cells) fluids. The waveform effect of the fluid layer is expressive, which is why emotions are often expressed through tears, stomach acids, sweating and spitting. Because neurochemicals often circulate through the body's fluids, this *chakra* region stimulates emotional responses through the bloodstream and into the endocrine system.

The human organism resonates more predominantly through the second *chakra* region between years eight and fourteen according to *Ayurveda*. New emotional drivers bring varying states of awareness during this period. During this period, the inner self also begins to translate friendships into sexual relationships, which also stimulates hormones and brings initial instability and mood swings.

The second *chakra* region resonates with the sense of taste, so it is tied to the activities of the tongue. The tongue and the genitals are considered connected with this *chakra*.

This *chakra* region is said to reflect light blue light. This *chakra* is also influenced greatly by the moon. Coincidentally, we find that the moon's lunar cycles influences physiological moods—just they affect the ebb and flow of the tides. A woman's menstruation is therefore also connected to the moon's cycles and this *chakra* region. For this reason, we often see a woman's emotional cycles pacing with menstruation and the moon's cycles as well. Many medical researchers have connected these mood swings to imbalances of estrogen, progesterone and testosterone. These hormones conduct the biowaves that resonate with this *chakra*.

The third chakra: The third *chakra* region is called *manipura*, meaning 'the city of gems.' This term is used because this energy center is tied with ten key nerve endings that distribute the biowaves that resonate with the activities and organs within the region between the solar plexus and navel region. Its waveforms are transmitted through the medium of thermal radiation. It is also thus coherent with the radiating heat of the sun and the thermal nature of the digestive process.

This *chakra* region directly stimulates the liver, gallbladder, pancreas and the ongoing processes of the digestive system. This *chakra* is also involved in the metabolic processes of the body involved in thermoregulation. These work hand in hand with the liver's multifarious tasking. Various glucosteroids work in tandem with pancre-

atic hormones such as insulin. Together they regulate energy conversion and glucose utilization to and within cells.

The sense organ connected to this *chakra* region is the eyes, and
thus its sensory accommodation is sight. The air of this *chakra* region is the upper abdominal air. The rhythmic shape of this *chakra*
region is said to be triangular—and said to reflect waveforms that
resonate with the red part of the color spectrum.

The thermal orientation of this *chakra* stimulates the pace of
energy conversion and metabolism. When a person dominates
through this *chakra* region, they may exhibit a fiery or hostile personality—one imbued with arrogance and anger. Exercise, bursts of
physical energy, determination to accomplish a particularly difficult
task, and a tendency to rush things are notable aspects of those
who express themselves through this *chakra* region.

This *chakra* tends to dominate during years fourteen through
twenty-one. This is one reason why we see more competitive and
volatile behavior during these years.

The fourth chakra: The fourth *chakra* region is located along
the spine in the region of the cardiac plexus, known within the
medical community as the heart. This *chakra* region is referred to as
anahata, which means 'unstricken.' This *chakra* thus resonates with
emotions connected to friendship, compassion and intimacy. This is
likely the reason the heart has been connected to loving relationships over so many generations and cultures.

This fourth *chakra* region innervates the organs of the heart and
lungs. Its activity is therefore pressure-oriented (as in blood pressure and air pressure). Its biowaves are primarily transmitted
through the gaseous elemental state. As air is taken into the lungs,
oxygen is bound to hemoglobin within the boundaries of the alveoli—small sacs that line the lungs. The alveoli draw the hemoglobin
from the bloodstream. Oxygen's attachment to hemoglobin is
stimulated with pressure—a waveform. The binding between oxygen and hemoglobin increases as the pressure approaches the most
efficient 104mm Hg level. Meanwhile, the normal atmospheric
pressure of oxygen is 159mm Hg.

As oxygen-attached hemoglobin is drawn back into the blood,
oxygen is transmitted through the body's cell network through
thousands of blood vessels and capillaries. This process of pressur-

ized attachment of oxygen is reversed as oxygen is released from hemoglobin into cells around the body. Cellular tissues maintain pressures typically around 40mm Hg—far less than atmospheric pressure. At this lower pressure, oxygen disassociates from the hemoglobin bonds, releasing the oxygen into the cell. Here oxygen is used in the oxidative phosphorylation portion of the ATP-electron transport chain, which is the key to the cell's production of energy.

This phosphorylation process upgrades adenosine-diphosphate (ADP) to adenosine-triphosphate (ATP), releasing kinetic energy and heat. This energy is translated into muscle contraction and other cellular functions.

Here we can see how the gas element imposes its waveform effects upon movement. As the oxygen gas is used for energy production, carbon dioxide is released as a byproduct. Carbon dioxide is carried via hydrogen ions in the bloodstream, forming H_2CO_3. These molecules are brought to the lungs, whereupon the carbon dioxide is released into the lungs, again through a pressure exchange through the alveoli. This also illustrates how the standing gaseous waveforms resonate through the liquid layers as they move to their operational directive of exhalation.

This fourth *chakra* region also resonates with the immune system. It stimulates immune cells throughout the body. When the thymus gland is stimulated by this *chakra*, it activates T-cells.

This fourth *chakra* region coordinates with the sense of touch. This of course relates to the waveform motion of the atmosphere or local environment.

This center also reflects the frequencies of the green part of the color spectrum. The skin is this *chakra's* organ of action. This *chakra* also connects with the hands.

We tend to resonate through the fourth *chakra* region between the our twenty-first and twenty-eighth years. During this time, conjugal relationships and friendships tend to peak.

The fifth chakra: The fifth *chakra* region is referred to by ancient Vedic texts as *vishuddha*, meaning *"pure."* This *chakra* region is located in the region of the throat. The fifth *chakra* region is associated with the plasma medium of higher-frequency electromagnetic biowaves. The connected sense organ is the ear, and the mouth is the primary work organ activated through this *chakra* region. This *chakra* region tends to dominate during the body's twenty-eighth through thirty-fifth years.

The fifth *chakra* region also innervates the thyroid gland. This connects it with the production and release of hormones that regulate the cells' metabolic activities. Thyroid hormones T3 and T4 are stimulated through the mediation of *thyroid stimulating hormone* (TSH), produced by the anterior pituitary gland. The waveform energies that regulate the process of converting TSH to T3 and T4 connect through the fifth *chakra* region.

The sixth chakra: The sixth *chakra* region is located near the medulla plexus and pineal plexus, posterior to the axis between the eyebrows. This *chakra* region is referred to in the Sanskrit texts as *ajna,* meaning 'unlimited command.' It is not the point on the forehead as one might imagine from some illustrations. Rather, its region lies beneath, reaching back towards the brainstem. It also encompasses the limbic system—the translating system between the various neural networks, emotions, the master endocrine system and executive control.

This *chakra* also conducts biowaves through the electromagnetic plane, but instead through the more subtle (ultraweak) biowaves of light and consciousness.

The sixth *chakra* amalgamates the frontal cortex and neocortex within its network. The frontal cortex is seen by brain researchers as the dispatching center for the broadcasting of the decisions and directions that stimulate the limbic system. The frontal cortex amplifies brainwaves and neuron transmissions that are converted to executable physical instructions. The deeper stimulus of the frontal cortex is of course the prefrontal cortex and the inner self.

A significant part of this *chakra* is the harmonic synchronization between the body and the waveforms of the larger universe. This synchronization takes place among this *chakra* region, more specifically around the pineal gland and its innervations. Within the pineal gland is a network of SCN cells. Here the body's master clock and the pacing of time are orchestrated with the infusion of light. As these SCN cells respond to light, they also broadcast in biowaves to synchronize the other body clock systems around the body. Some of this process takes place with a hormone pathway between the pineal gland, the pituitary gland and the hypothalamus.

This center also uses subtle waveform broadcasting mechanisms to stimulate the network of clockwork genes around the body. Our research has yet to catch up with this technology, just as our research has yet to fully understand and characterize the biowaves of the mind.

This sixth *chakra* region is positioned above the first five *chakra* regions. These five 'gross physical' *chakra* centers directly convert and translate particular types of intentions to physical action. The first five *chakras* can also be programmed for response, and synchronized with each other to respond congruently. This ability of the self to organize and program the first five *chakras* all lies within the facility of the sixth *chakra* region.

Thus through this *chakra* region the subtle intentions of the inner self translate into the waveform web we refer to as the mind. As intentions are converted to the more significant brainwaves, they are further translated through the limbic system.

The limbic system is composed of a number of devices that each translates these biowaves from the mind into physical activity. These include the thalamus, the hippocampus, the amygdale, the gyrus of cingulated and fornicate, the hypothalamus, the nucleus accumbens, the mammillary body, the orbitofrontal cortex, and the parahippocampal gyrus. These centers negotiate the signals firing between the mind and the sensory nerves. They are crystallized into impulses that drive neurotransmitter and hormone release. They are also sorted into static standing biowaves and shuffled into groups of storage neurons. This constant sorting of waveform interference patterns of billions of signals forms the basis of our physical memory.

The bridge chakra: In between the sixth *chakra* and the seventh *chakra* is a gateway that provides the bridge between the inner self and the mind. It is called the *soma chakra,* and located in a position referred to as the prefrontal cortex. *Soma* is usually referred to as 'nectar' or 'moon.' The moon signifies illumination, and nectar signifies desire. This gateway is often referred to as a 'minor *chakra'* because it does not provide the full conversion of consciousness to physical action. Rather, the *soma chakra* is a viewing station and steering module for the self. Biowaves organized within the frontal cortex and neocortex are viewed by the self almost as if being projected onto a screen. This viewing platform allows the self to access an array of sense information together with incoming feedback from the body. Through this 'module,' the self can steer the functions of the sixth *chakra*, which set up the programs that orchestrate the five elemental *chakras* of physical action.

The seventh chakra: The seventh *chakra* is complex because it is said to contain several different sub-features. Depending upon the evolution of the inner self, this *chakra* may or may not be developed. At the crown of the cranium, we typically find a slight indent at a spot called the *fontanel*. In babies, this spot is more pronounced, and it is typically soft, until the bones of the skull grow together. This takes place as the inner self becomes increasingly entrained into the physical body.

Sahasrara is the name of this *chakra* region. *Sahasrara* means *"thousand petalled."* Some also refer to this *chakra* as the *crown chakra*.

The seventh *chakra* region resonates with the activities of the higher intellect. Its biowaves conduct issues of logic, justice, and decision-making. Through this center, the inner self can resonate with the higher Authority.

The seventh *chakra* region also channels our sense of direction from a deeper realm. This direction becomes evident should we mature in our spiritual evolution.

The ancient practice of *kundalini* is described as the development of the ability to raise the life air through the chain of *chakras* and out of the body through this seventh *chakra* region. This skill is considered quite rare during the modern era, although Ayurvedic and TCM texts contain descriptions of yogis who have accomplished this feat.

The Nadi Channels

A close translation of the word *nadi* is *'motion.'* This is because the *nadis* provide channels for the movement of the body's biowaves. The *nadis* are a network of pathways for the various biowaves (originating from consciousness) that move through the body after being translated through the *chakra* regions. The *nadi* channel system is thus the network for biocommunications between the *chakras* and the physical body.

The *nadi* channel networks each circulate unique biowaves that resonate within the mediums of the solid, liquid, gas, thermal and plasma-aether states. According to ancient Vedic texts, there are hundreds of thousands of these channels circulating the airs of the body, each originating from a particular *chakra*. Some sources have specifically named over 72,000 *nadis*. The basic types of channels connect the various organs, glands and tissue systems, linking them with a particular *chakra* region. Each type of *nadi* network will resonate with the biowaves related to its particular element. Thus, the *nadis* include the distribution of nerves, blood vessels, lymphatic system, alveoli, bones, endocrine system, digestive tract, urinary tract, organs, cells and the more subtle energy channels (including the *meridians*).

From the major thoroughfares, branch more minute pathways, which circulate through all the information conductors. These *nadi* channels are conducting pathways recognized in modern physiology as ion channels, brainwaves, peristalsis, blood pressure, respiration, heat transfer, microtubules, hormones, neurotransmitters, and all the other means for electromagnetic biowaves. The major and most obvious gateways of the *nadis* include each nostril, each eye, each ear, the mouth, the genitals, the throat, the tongue, the fontanel, and the anus.

The *nadi* channels thus connect every tissue and organ system to the *chakra*s. They also link together the *chakra*s. They provide the various energy production systems within the body. In the language of computers, *nadis* contain inherent semiconductors, resistors, and integrated circuitry, giving them the combined capability to shunt, amplify or block information and energy as they flow through the body.

Here are a few of the primary *nadi* networks as explained by *Ayurveda*:

The **sushumna network** has several *nadi* channels, including the famed *brahma* and *sarasvati nadis*. *Sushumna* also provides the main channeling for the gross and subtle waveform channels of the seventh *chakra* region. The *sushumna* originates at the first *chakra* region at the pelvic plexus, and runs up the spinal column. From the base of the skull, the *sushumna* branches into two directions, one anterior (front) and one posterior (back) within the skull. The anterior branch pierces the palate and moves upward and around the skull where it meets the posterior branch—which branches through the posterior skull—and terminates at the cerebrospinal axis in the gap between the two brain hemispheres. This is located at the fontanel, known for its softness. The fontanel region is also the location of the seventh energy *chakra* as we have discussed. This channel thus provides a constant gateway for the inner self to exit while in the womb. The fontanel typically stays soft through the sixth month after birth, when it begins to harden.

Through this *nadi* network flows the waveform currents between the grounded earth elements and the intellectual and creative elements related to artistic development and intuition. This *nadi* is well utilized in artists and other creative people, as well as those involved in philosophy and devotional practices.

The *ida network* flows through the gate of the left nostril, and through the left side of the body to the groin area. It is often referred to as the *left air* channel because it flows on the left side. It also is sometimes referred to as the *inner left eye* channel. This network supports the expression of maternal and feminine emotion and is thus nourishing, potentially purifying, and spontaneous. Closing the right nostril and breathing through the left nostril can stimulate and increase relaxation, balance and alertness. This is because *ida* stimulates the endocrine glands and the emotional, intuitive energies of the conscious body. *Ida* has also been connected to the flow of lunar energy, and thus can affect the functions of the more subtle mental biowaves.

The *pingala network* flows through the gate of the right nostril and through the right side of the body, terminating at the right groin region. It is considered the *inner right eye* and the *right air* network. This network supports masculine energies, along with verbal and rational natures. Efficiency and power are traits of this network. As it is energized with masculine consciousness, it increases vitality, stamina and vigor. This network also conducts the logical activities of the neural network and physical responsiveness. To stimulate the *pingala* network, one can inhale through the right nostril while closing off the left nostril. This method can also be helpful to increase strength and endurance when challenged by physical or logical stress.

The *gandhari network* flows from the lower left eye corner and terminates at the left big toe. The rhythmic energy of this *chakra* region supports *ida's* feminine, intuitive biowaves. This assists in the raising of consciousness. Grasping the left big toe with the right hand while abdominal breathing can increase the circulation of the airs flowing within this network. Abdominal breathing is vital for the overall immune health of the body and its digestive functions.

The *hastajihva network* also supports the flow of the *ida* biowaves, but crosses the body from the lower corner of the right eye, and terminates at the big toe of the right foot. This crossing allows a more balanced movement of the *ida* flows. Grasping the right big toe with the left hand while abdominal breathing can increase the circulation of this network.

The *yashasvini network* supports and balances the flow of the masculine vitality of the *pingala* biowaves. It originates in the left ear and terminates at the big toe at the right foot. Again, grasping and holding this toe, but also holding the ear with the other will increase waveform circulation within this network. Acupressure or acupuncture can also be used to stimulate the biowaves flowing within this network.

The *pusha network* also supports the flow of the *pingala* biowaves, and runs from the right ear to the big toe of the left foot. Again, these locations can be stimulated to increase its circulation.

The *alambusha network* flows between the anus and the oral cavity. Its biowaves stimulate the assimilation of food and the evacuation of digested food. This network incorporates the vagus nerve and the action of digestive peristalsis. Within this network also flow creative biowaves for new thoughts and ideas.

The *kuhu network* flows between the throat and the genitals. Its biowaves stimulate or channel the release of seminal and vaginal fluids. Its flow can also channel conscious expressions of love. For this reason, the *kuhu* is extremely important to raising consciousness. Expressing love through this network can override the expression of sexual lust. The expression of love also increases the expression of neural talents such as memory and concentration.

The *shankhini network* begins at the throat and terminates at the anus, but it is positioned between the *sarasvati* and *gardhari* networks. Through this network flow detoxification biowaves stimulated through the colon and anus. Enemas and colon hydrotherapy (otherwise known as the *colonic)* are powerful tools to stimulate this network. Other ways to stimulate this network include exercise and fasting.

The **sarasvati network** flows through between the gates of the tongue and throat. Its path begins at the tongue and ends at the throat. Its waveform flow extends into speech and taste. The biowaves created by our vocal cords can have various effects upon ourselves and others. With kind words, we can add harmony to the environment. With words of insult and criticism, we can add discord to our environment. Therefore, this network can be used to express both harmony and conflict.

CHAKRAS, NADIS AND MERIDIANS
(channels not to scale, exact position or number)

The *payasvini network* conducts biowaves between the right earlobe and the cranial nerves. Through this network flow the bio-waves translating pleasure-seeking behavior. Acupuncture also utilizes this location for needle insertion to assist in the curing of addictions. This network also provides a gateway for ionic travel. The traditional use of earrings on the right ear had its original basis in the stimulation of this network with particular minerals from metals like silver, gold and copper. These metals were chosen originally because of their various effects upon health and detoxification.

The *varuni network* flows in the opposite direction, parallel with the *alambusha* network. Together the two networks create a polar waveform current, which stimulates the release of waste within the body. This network originates on the left side between the throat and ear, and terminates at the anus. This network also synchronizes with the flows of the rhythmic airs of the lower intestine. It is thus a critical network for colon function and defecation.

The *vishvodara network* flows between the *kuhus* and *hastajihva* networks, and localizes around the navel area. This network is the center of the flow of the emotional biowaves reflecting the consciousness of the self. The waveform flows through this network stimulate the activities of the various organs, including the adrenal glands, the liver and the kidneys. This network also creates heat in these various parts of the body. We can stimulate the circulation of this networked network by exercising the *core muscles,* of which the primary is the *rectus abdominis.* The flows of this network can be stimulated through properly executed breathing exercises and abdominal strengthening.

The Meridians

A clinically manipulative sub-network channel system within the *nadi* network was expanded upon in China approximately 3,000 years ago. Here we will summarize the twelve basic channels, which are now referred to in TCM as *meridians.* As described in these texts and promulgated over thousands of years of clinical experience, these *meridian* channels connect and flow thermal *qi* biowaves through twelve organ and tissue systems. *Qi* and its Sanskrit version *prana* are considered synonyms for the biowaves emanating from the self. The *meridian* channels have been described as a branched subset of the *vishvodara* network. In this view, they would be considered channels that conduct thermal biowaves between critical organs and tissue systems.

Recent research has confirmed that within the *meridians* flow biowaves in the microwave and infrared part of the spectrum (Litscher 2006). A practitioner will directly influence the health of the body through the facilitation or modulation of these biowaves by stimulating the gateways along these *meridian* channels. These gateways are typically referred to as *acupuncture points*.

Though examination, an acupuncturist will diagnose a set of symptoms, and determine the connection between the flow of biowaves and the possible cause of the issue. In some situations, the waveform flow will be blocked or otherwise modulated. In other situations, the flows could be imbalanced between different *meridian* channels. For example, an acupuncturist might see a liver problem being caused by the liver not having enough heat. The acupuncturist will then penetrate or manipulate particular gateways along the liver channel to stimulate heat within the organ.

Over the past few decades, thousands of studies have been performed on the clinical effectiveness of acupuncture *meridian* therapy. Many of these have been controlled and double-blinded, and many have compared electronic manipulation as well as needle therapy. In studies too numerous to document here, acupuncture has proven to be effective for the treatment of hundreds of disorders related to the nervous system, the skeletal system, the digestive system, the cardio-pulmonary system, the brain, the liver, the kidneys and various endocrine systems. A recent review of the literature reveals over 12,000 research papers and studies have been published on the therapeutic effects of acupuncture over the past few decades. Some of the more recent research illustrates efficacious acupuncture treatment for herpes (Yu *et al.* 2007), autism (Yan *et al.* 2007), paralysis (Fu, 2007), hyperlipidemia (Chu, *et al.* 2007), diabetes and pancreatic disorders (Chu *et al.* 2007; Tian *et al.* 2007; Liao *et al.* 2007), kidney diseases and chronic pain (Grasmuller and Imich 2007), insomnia (Chen *et al.* 2007), myofascial pain (Shen and Goddard 2007), arthritis (Wang *et al.* 2007), chronic fatigue (Guo 2007), hormone balance (Bai *et al.* 2007), gastrointestinal discomfort (Wang *et al.* 2007), osteoarthritis (Brinkhaus *et al.* 2007), lipid metabolism (Kang *et al.* 2007), Sjogren's syndrome (Bai *et al.* 2007), cancer pain (Cassileth *et al.* 2007), and many others.

In the early 1980s, the Shanghai Institute performed exhaustive research on the various physiological effects of acupuncture therapy. Their research concluded immune system stimulation, cardiovascular improvement, digestive function improvement and many other positive effects from acupuncture treatments. They also confirmed that acupuncture significantly increases or modulates the secretion of various hormones. These include oxytocin, vasopressin, follicle stimulating hormone, corticosteroids, ACTH, and norepinephrine (O'Connor and Bensky 1981).

Today many western hospitals are using acupuncture for chronic pain, surgery, childbirth, and speeding the healing response. The quality of training and its long safety record give acupuncture therapy one of the best health records of any clinical and acute therapy. For this reason, a growing number of disorders are now being referred to acupuncturists.

The *meridians* are invisible to the naked eye and gross instruments. This is simply because they conduct biowaves with lower power and amplitude than medical science typically measures. Here are the main twelve *meridians* utilized in acupuncture therapy. Each channel is connected to a particular organ system. Each also has either a *yin* or *yang* feature. Most *meridians* consist of two channels, one on the right side of the body and another on the left side:

Liver (Liv) is a paired set of channels also called the *lower yin meridian*. They run from inside the big toes up the inner (medial) legs and out to the hips, where they travel up through the rib cage on the side under the arm and towards the midline where they end under the breasts. The liver *meridian* resonates greatest between one a.m. and three a.m.

Lung (L) is another paired arm set also called the *upper yin meridian*. They travel from the nail-side of the thumbs up the medial (inside) arms to the front of the shoulder and then down the chest, ending above the breasts at the pectoral muscles. This *meridian* pair is most active between three a.m. and five a.m.

Large intestine (Li) is a paired arm set also called the *upper yang meridian.* They start at the index fingernails and run directly up the top of the arms, over the shoulders and up the neck and jaw to the upper lip, where they split to end just outside the nostrils. They are most active between five and seven a.m.

Stomach (S) is a paired leg set also called the *lower yang meridian.* They start under the eyes on each side, circle down through the cheek and back, heading over the forehead and down to the inside of the eyes near the nose bridge, and down the front side of the neck, down each breast, abdomen and legs, ending at the second toe. This *meridian* pair peaks in activity between seven and nine a.m.

Spleen-pancreas (S) is a paired leg set also called the *lower yin meridian.* They travel from the big toes up the inside of the legs, up the abdominal region to underneath the armpits and back down toward the outside of the ribcage. This *meridian* pair is typically most active between nine and eleven a.m.

Heart (H) is a paired arm set also called the *upper yin meridian.* They start at the inside of the pinkies and head up the inside of the arm to the arm-side of the armpits. They are most active between eleven a.m. and one p.m.

Small intestine (Si) is a paired arm set also called the *upper yang meridian.* They start at the outside of the pinkies and flow straight over the shoulder, down over the scapulae (shoulder blades) and then up the neck to the cheekbones, where they run back towards the ears. They are most active between one p.m. and three p.m.

Bladder (B) is a paired lower leg set also called the *lower yang meridian.* They start between the eyebrows and head up over the top of the head and then down the back of the head, neck and back, over the buttocks—ending at the little toes on each side. They are most active between three p.m. and five p.m. everyday.

Kidney (K) is a paired lower leg set also called the *lower yin meridian.* They start at the bottom of the feet and head up the inside of the legs, up the midline of the abdomen and chest, ending at the sternum area. They are most active between five p.m. and seven p.m. each day.

Pericardium (P) set is also called the *heart constrictor meridian.* Some also call this the *circulation-sex meridian.* They travel up the outside of the breasts on each side up the armpits and up the arms ending at the middle fingers. They are most active between seven and nine p.m.

Triplewarmer (T) is a paired arm set also called the *upper yang meridian*. They start at the ring fingers and head up the outside of the arms, shoulders and neck and up around the ears—ending at the temples. They are most active between nine p.m. and eleven p.m.

Gallbladder (G) is a paired lower leg set also called the *lower yang meridian*. They start at the second toes, head up the outside of the legs, up the obliques, over the back shoulders up the neck over the crown and then back around the ears—ending at the temples. They are most active between eleven p.m. and one a.m.

Conception vessel (Cv) and **Governor vessel (Gv)** are both unpaired mid-body line *meridians*. They serve to balance the body from the front and back. The Cv starts at the pubic bone and travels up the midline of the abdomen into the chest, neck and chin to just below the lower lip. The Gv starts at the tailbone and heads up the spine, neck and over the top of the head—ending at just above the upper lip.

The **auricular channels** are located around the ear. According to TCM, within the ear pinna anatomy exists a holographic image of the *meridian* mapping of the entire body. Therefore, the auricular points may be stimulated simultaneous to the stimulation of the main *meridian* points, or even alone to stimulate particular organs or channels.

The piercing of the meridian points with acupuncture needles modulates these waveform conduits. This is meant to open up the channel, allowing a free flow of biowaves through the channel.

Contrary to popular belief, the needles in themselves do not open the *meridians*. The needles provide a conducting mechanism between the acupuncturist and the patient. This allows the acupuncturist's waveform energy to be transferred via the needle into the *meridian* channel. Just as a match will ignite paper with fire, the waveform energy of the practitioner is innervated through the channel of the patient.

This will typically increase the waveform flow through the channel and open the gateways, although some treatments may also require a slowing or blocking of the flow. The *meridians* are 'charged' by the practitioner's own biowaves. The acupuncturist simply utilizes the needle as a transducer or conductor for the waveform flow.

This might be compared to splicing a wire into an electrical circuit. A dangling wire without any connection to anything else will not affect the flow of electricity within a circuit. However, as soon as that wire is connected to another circuit or electrical source, there is an immediate change to the circuit.

In the same way, a needle in itself inserted into an acupuncture channel will have no effect. The focused intentional conductivity of the practitioner is being inserted into the channel. The needle is simply a carrier, just as the spliced wire is a carrier of this electromagnetic current. Therefore, we must consider our acupuncturist's qualifications and patient reviews carefully before a treatment.

There are many other established means to stimulate or modulate *meridian* conduction, including *trigger-point, acupressure* (finger and thumb pressure) and *moxibustion* (the burning of the mugwort herb and putting the smolder onto the points).

Some acupuncturists also use electro-acupuncture. Here the 'charging' waveform energy is being generated by the electrical device instead of the acupuncturist's own body.

Lasers are also being increasingly used to stimulate the *meridians*. As Sutherland pointed out in 2000, the term *"meridian therapy"* is a better description than acupuncture, because there are many efficacious alternatives to piercing the skin.

The TCM acupuncture system has located and mapped about 500 specific gateway points on twelve *meridians*. Almost any deficiency of a particular organ or area intersected by a *meridian* channel can be energized by treating or even massaging the channel. Benefit may also be obtained by lightly massaging a channel over the entire *meridian* length; or even by *tracing* over it (Eden, 1998) without physically touching the skin.

As we will discuss, the *chakra* and *meridian* conducting channels relate directly to our body's ability to tolerate synthetic EMFs. If the body's energy channels are properly balanced and open, they can provide a protective shield against synthetic EMFs.

How does this take place? Let's use the radio station transmission analogy again. When a radio's antenna and crystal reception are tuned to the particular frequency of radiowaves broadcast from a particular station, the sound can be very clear. A building or other object will do little to disturb or interfere with the strong resonation between the radio receiver and the radio station's broadcast. This isn't the case for a poorly tuned radio station, however. Practically any little local disturbance or object in the way can interfere in the reception of a weakly tuned station—creating a flurry of irritating static.

The body's various channels and conduits that broadcast the body's biowaves all utilize conductors and receivers that must be tuned together. When the body is under stress—be it from toxins, infection or inflammation—the conductors and receivers of the body become maligned. This malignment causes distortion and a shunting of biowave broadcasting around the body.

When this happens, the body's *biowave shield*—consisting of an open-channel flow of all the *chakras, nadis* and *meridians*—becomes weakened, and the body becomes vulnerable to synthetic EMFs, along with many other environmental invaders.

In the *Star Trek* series of movies and television shows, the space ships maintained a defense mechanism called the *shield*. When the *shields* were down, the ship was vulnerable to the various rays and beams that its enemies could throw at it. But when the *shields* were "up," the ship was practically impervious to these types of attacks.

While the Enterprise's shields may be science fiction, the body's *shields* are actually not much different. Each of the circulating electromagnetic pulses within the body do not just circulate inside the body. They also circulate just outside the body, as evidenced by Kirlian photography. Because of their layered densities, we might visualize the different biowaves as layers surrounding the body—in addition to their broadcasted circulation within the body. Just as our clothing wraps our skin, these biowaves wrap our tissues in different frequencies of electromagnetic fields.

☼Four
Light and Color

Synthetic Light

A typical incandescent light bulb will emit visible light by heating a filament inside a bulb of ionized gas. The filament is usually made of tungsten in an atmosphere of halogens such as nitrogen, krypton, or argon. The incandescent bulb will typically produce three or four color spectrum visible light, together with near-infrared waves, which create the mild heat typical of a light bulb.

Though the bulb will produce visible light, there are various wavelengths missing when comparing to the visible light from the sun. An incandescent bulb typically discharges visible light in the red, green, blue, and violet waveforms. The sun, on the other hand, will emit these along with various others, including yellow, purple, turquoise, and so on. For this reason, visible light from the sun allows us to see more colors with better crispness. As these additional waveforms are reflected or absorbed by the objects around us, our eyes see a brighter array of color.

In addition to these other bands of color waveforms within the visible spectrum, sunlight also emits a full (UVA/UVB/UVC) ultraviolet and (near and far) infrared spectrum, along with microwaves, radiowaves and other waveforms—many of which are partially filtered as they pass through the atmosphere.

We have had limited success trying to duplicate the sun's waveform complex. Despite its name, "full spectrum lighting" is still very different from sunlight. Currently there is no real standard for what is called "full-spectrum lighting," so its reference is often misused. There is a quantifying standardization called the *General Color Rendering Index* (or CIE). This gauges the intensity of the color temperature. While red and infrared waveforms are "hot," blue and violet waveforms are considered "cool." A CIE rating that approaches 100 is considered cooler, in that it covers not only some of the ultraviolet waveforms, but also emits at least a range of the main colors such as red, blue, green, and violet.

Tanning bed lighting typically provides primarily ultraviolet radiation. Many tanning lights emit about 95% ultraviolet-A and 5% ultraviolet-B in order to produce the tanning (and burning) equivalent of the sun. Indoor "full spectrum" lights will usually provide some ultraviolet waveforms as well, usually near-ultraviolet, which covers part of ultraviolet-A as well as a decent part of the visual spectrum. Many of the newer "full-spectrum" lamps provide cooler CIE numbers, reflecting a good dose of the blue and green spectrum as well.

The effects of "full-spectrum" light are still being debated. In one review by McColl and Veitch in 2001, research from 1941 through 1999 concluded that "full-spectrum lighting" research has for the most part, not shown any positive effects on either behavior or health—inclusive of hormonal and neural effects. Most researchers have also concluded that there is only marginal vitamin D production from "full-spectrum" lighting. Vitamin D deficiency is one of the more prevalent issues in light-deficiency disorders.

Crystal Fields

The electromagnetic nature of light became difficult to argue with after the development of the *crystal field theory* of the 1930s. When light travels through a substance, a portion will be absorbed by the atoms and a portion will be reflected back—depending upon the substance. A ruby looks red because the chromium in the ruby absorbs some of the blue-green wavelengths (around 490 nanometers) while reflecting back a greater amount of red wavelengths (around 650 nanometers). As these 650 nm wavelengths strike the retina, we perceive the color red. This technology is basically the same process of spectroscopy used today by chemists to determine the atomic makeup of a particular molecule or substance. Because atomic particles making up molecules interact distinctively with light, the molecular configuration of a substance can simply be identified by the wavelengths absorbed, reflected, and/or diffracted.

X-ray crystallography and absorption spectroscopy are now two of the most used processes for atomic and molecular identification. Crystallography utilizes the interaction between radiation and substance-matter. X-rays are shot into a crystallized version of a particular substance glued onto the glass of a diffractometer tube. The x-rays react with atoms within the molecular substance and the waveforms of these diffracted rays are recorded onto film or otherwise charted. These diffraction recordings are measured for frequency, amplitude and wavelength to yield the theoretical atomic structure. Because x-rays are short-wavelength electromagnetic waves, they interact with the electromagnetic waves within a material's electron clouds. As these interactions occur, the microwaves are absorbed or diffracted. The angles of diffraction can be plotted out onto photographic film or computer imagery to display the shape and probable location of the electron clouds.

The resulting crystallographs can indicate any number of angles of wave diffraction. Using diffraction measurements and a formula created by William Bragg and his son in 1913, these plotted angles measure the level of constructive or destructive interference between the x-rays and the subatomic particles of the substance. Constructive interference creates a resulting larger wave while destructive interference creates a smaller wave. The type of interference is often a factor of the extent the waves are in-phase or out-of-phase with each other. This in turn relates to polarity, which indicates the possible orientation of the electron cloud.

The interesting thing about spectroscopy is that it is virtually no different from the process our eyes undertake every moment as we look around us. The eyes do not actually see matter. What they see are light rays interacting with molecular electromagnetic bonds. It might be compared to looking into a mirror. When we look into a mirror, we are not seeing our actual face. Rather, we are seeing a reflection of our face onto the surface of the mirror.

The Necessity of Natural Light

Over the past half century, researchers have been observing the effects of natural sunlight (or a lack thereof) upon plants, animals and humans. In the 1950s, while producing a Walt Disney time-lapse photography film, Dr. John Ott discovered that when flowering pumpkins are grown indoors under fluorescent light, the male flowers would blossom but the female flowers would not. Meanwhile, outdoor pumpkins typically produce both male and female flowers.

Dr. Ott filmed and photographed flowers and plants indoors and outdoors. His time-lapse photography sessions revealed that plants without a full spectrum of infrared and ultraviolet light become, in one respect or another, disturbed. Dr. Ott's research on light and color continued into the 1980s and 1990s. He published numerous articles documenting his research—spanning over forty years—on how light affects the human, plant and animal organisms. These studies showed various negative effects resulting from a lack of natural sunlight upon the human body. They included mood disorders, learning disabilities, increased stress, abnormal growth, and poor eyesight among others. Without regular sunlight, humans—like plants—will begin to degenerate in a number of ways. As many of us have observed, should a plant be shut into a room with nothing but artificial incandescent light, its flowers and/or fruits will soon begin to whither.

The effect of sunlight on animal and plant fertility has been known by farmers and ranchers for many years. The poultry and hog industries have known for years that full-spectrum light increases egg production and larger hog litters respectively. It has also been observed that human fertility also improves with sunbathing. We also know the increase in the warmth and duration of the sun stimulates the production of pollen and flowers among plants.

Dr. Ott's experiments with sunlight and rabbits revealed that rabbits raised under artificial light—especially among males—became more aggressive even to the point of becoming cannibalistic. Meanwhile, rabbits raised in sunlight showed none of these tendencies. Male rabbits raised in natural sunlight were not only less aggressive: They were also observed graciously tending to the litter in the absence of mama rabbit.

Humans are no exception. Significant research has established that not only do humans require light for health: They specifically require natural light. Several studies have found a link between fluorescent lights and hyperactivity among children (O'Leary 1978). Research performed by Küller and Laike (1998) in Sweden has illustrated that fluorescent lighting powered with conventional ballasts increases stress and lowers accuracy. This study, done on adults working in laboratory offices, found that conventional ballast fluorescent lighting increased stress and alpha wave activity among subjects.

A lack of natural sunlight will also disrupt the body's endocrine systems. German ophthalmology Professor Dr. Fritz Hollwich published a study in 1979 showing that subjects working under white fluorescent tube lighting for a period of time produced significantly higher levels of stress hormones such as adrenocorticortropic hormone and cortisol. He also found that full-spectrum or natural light lowered levels of these hormones, and lowered stress among the subjects. Dr. Hollwich's research was pivotal in the decision to ban white fluorescent bulbs from most German hospitals.

For some time it was assumed that *seasonal affective disorder* (SAD) relates only to the amount of light. However, this does not explain the lower levels of SAD among many northern climate cultures such as Eskimos as compared to lower latitude dwellers. SAD, as many of us know, is a serious disorder causing depression, anxiety, fatigue, and lethargy.

For example, a study from Iceland's National University Hospital (Maqnusson and Stefansson 1993) found that Icelanders experience lower SAD prevalence than do people on the east coast of the United States. In another study from Turku University's Central Hospital (Saarijarvi *et al.* 1999), the prevalence of SAD was higher among women and younger ages, but was more prevalent among those with a higher body mass index. Higher BMI is more common among people who spend less time outdoors. Furthermore, there are a number of studies that show lower rates of SAD among those who exercise more—and likely go outdoors more.

Indoor light ranges from 60 lux at low lamp level to 200 lux in average indoor lighting. The brightest indoor lighting might produce about 1,000 lux. Levels of over 1,000 lux typically require some sort of daylight.

Light Intensity

Source of Light	Illumination Intensity (Lux)
Direct Sunlight	25,000-125,000 lux
Overcast day	100-20,000 lux
Daylight (out of sun)	7,000-13,000 lux
Sunrise and sunset	300-500 lux
Typical office lighting	200-400 lux
Typical home lighting (60-100W bulbs)	50-200 lux
Outdoor night (full moon/clear)	.25-1 lux
Outdoor night (1/4 moon)	.001 lux
Outdoor night (moonless/clear)	.002 lux
Sirius (brightest star)	.000001 lux

The typical American gets a few hundred lux per day on average, experiencing only quick bursts of a higher lux—likely barely over 1,000 lux. 1,000 lux is about as much light as is available in the twilight period—just after sunset or just before sunrise. Light above this level for three hours will re-establish sleep cycles and positive moods within 48 hours. Light greater than 4,000 lux is needed for most endocrine-stimulating functions. Going outside into the sunlight is required for these levels.

Daily sunlight with dark nights is best. In a study of 1,606 women 20-74 years old (Davis *et al.* 2001), those who had either bright bedroom lights at night or worked graveyard shifts had higher breast cancer rates.

The research shows that those with consistent exposure to nature's visible light, ultraviolet light, infrared radiation and geomagnetism will be less likely to experience the depression, fatigue and other symptoms often experienced by those who spend their days inside amongst the artificial suns of our indoor world.

Healthy Sunlight

The sun has been used therapeutically for many centuries. It has been a central healing agent in the world's oldest medicine, *Ayurveda*. The sun was described as a prescriptive agent in the ancient Egyptian medical text, the *Ebers Papyrus*. It has been a central component for North and South American and Polynesian native tribes. It has been a key element used in Traditional Chinese Medicine. The Greeks and Romans both used sun cures for many infectious diseases such as tuberculosis. Hippocrates was a big proponent for the use of sunbathing treatments for a number of illnesses. In later centuries, large healing centers have been erected for the purpose of healing with the sun. The Nords, Scots, Irish, Aborigines, Iranians, Assyrians, Japanese and Indonesians all treated disease with sunbathing.

For centuries, a devastating disease became prevalent in Europe, where bones would twist and spindle. This seemed to arbitrarily attack children, sometimes fatally. This disease was termed *richettes*—a derivative of the word 'wretcheds.' It devastated Europe, especially in the winter. In the early 1800s, French physician Cauvain recommended sunlight for rickets. Controversial at first, this hypothesis was also published by the Polish physician Andrew Snia-decki in 1822. The theory was virtually ignored until the late nine-teenth century. An English missionary physician named Theodor Palm, while traveling in the east, realized the connection between rickets and sunlight and advocated sunlight for the prevention of rickets. This treatment was eventually adopted by Swiss physician August Rollier.

A century later, it was discovered that a combination of vitamin D from the sun, calcium, boron and phosphate work together to form bone tissue cells, or osteocytes. Without enough sunlight, not enough vitamin D will be produced, leaving the bones unformed or maligned. Today this same disease has become relevant in the form of osteoporosis and osteomyalgia.

As modern-day adults age, they are spending less and less time outside. With less vitamin D production, bones become weaker. Hip fractures and other bone breakages become common. This is well documented. Over ten million people in the U.S. now have osteoporosis. More have osteopenia, which puts them at risk of osteoporosis and bone fractures. Research has shown that about 50% of women and 25% of men over the age of fifty will suffer an osteoporosis-related fracture.

Swiss physician Dr. Arnold Rikli was considered one of the earliest modern proponents of sunbathing as medicine during the nineteenth century. Dr. Rikli propounded what he called *atmospheric healing*, which included open-air sunbathing, nighttime open-air huts, water treatments, barefoot walking and constant fresh air. Dr. Rikli established a famous health clinic in Bled, Slovenia. People traveled from around Europe to his center, and many found success with his treatments for many years. Rikli himself, a vegetarian, naturalist, and early naturopath, lived to the ripe age of 97. His open-air sun treatments are still referred to as the *Rikli Cure*.

In the 1860s, Dr. Hermann Brehmer was successful in treating tuberculosis and other infections with open-air sunlight in a German sanatorium. Dr. Brehmer himself was diagnosed with tuberculosis, and was cured using his treatments. His healing center is said to have contained over 300 beds, and his tuberculosis sun cure was considered the most successful tuberculosis treatment to date.

Dr. Dio Lewis was also a leading sunlight expert. He documented treating rheumatic diseases, dyspepsia, neuralgia, and other diseases with great success using sunbathing in a book entitled *Weak Lungs and How to Make Them Strong* (1863).

Dr. James Jackson, in his book, *How to Treat the Sick Without Drugs* (1868) documented treating up to 125 patients with sunbathing. He commented that even those who had failed various other conventional treatments were significantly *"strengthened and innervated."* He commented that patients who had trouble sleeping were not only able to fall asleep after sunbathing: They were also able to nap outside. His conclusion was that sunlight was one of the most therapeutic agents known to him and his peers of the day.

Dr. Niels Finsen was awarded the 1903 Nobel Prize in medicine for revealing that sunshine was extremely therapeutic for a number of infectious diseases, including lupus vulgaris, small pox, and Pick's disease. Dr. Finsen's famous sunbaths and separated light colors became known as *Finsen Light Therapy.*

In the early 1900s, two Swiss physicians Dr. Oskar Bernhard and Dr. Rollier found that the sun in thin atmospheres such as the Swiss Alps provided an effective therapeutic protocol for surgical tuberculosis and lung tuberculosis. Sunlight has since been shown effective as a part of treatment for various other conditions.

Dr. Benedict Lust, considered the father of American naturopathic medicine, prescribed sunbathing treatment for various degenerative diseases. Dr. Lust's nude sunbathing treatments got him in trouble more than once with the authorities.

Dr. Jethro Kloss and Dr. John Harvey Kellogg were also physicians held in high esteem and national recognition for their various naturopathic therapies. Both had popular treatment centers, also called sanitariums, in which they utilized sunbathing for a variety of disorders. Dr. Kellogg also used artificial sunlight treatments, which he called, together with sunlight treatment, *phototherapy.*

Dr. Herbert Shelton, in his book *The Hygienic System: Fasting and Sun Bathing* (1939) was also a physician with a significant amount of research and experience with sunbathing. Dr. Shelton prescribed sunshine for heart disease, tuberculosis, asthma and nervous diseases.

In a study by Dr. Fritz Hollwich (Hollwich and Dieckhues 1989), 110 cataract patients underwent metabolic testing before and after cataract opacity surgery. Prior to surgery, the opacity of their cataracts significantly reduced the amount of light they could see to about 10% of normal. Testing prior to surgery showed reduced metabolism, adrenal insufficiency and hormone imbalances among the subjects. After surgery—the removal of the lens opacities—metabolism and hormone levels returned to normal.

These results were confirmed with another study (Hollwich and Hartmann 1990) performed shortly thereafter on fifty cataract patients with the same results. This later study also looked at water balance, blood sugar and blood cell count—all of which improved following surgery and more light. Dr. Hollwich described the link between the retino-hypothalamic pathway and human health.

Research has indicated that the visible light spectrum (400-700 nm) received from the sun through both the eyes and the skin increases the body's immune response. As light is received through the retina, its energy is delivered to the LGM and visual cortex through transduction, while being delivered to the suprachiasmatic nucleus in the hypothalamus. This stimulates the release of hypothalamic-pituitary hormones. Light also stimulates the pineal gland directly, stimulating a cascade of hormones and neurotransmitters through the pituitary gland. Melatonin, norepinephrine, and acetylcholine secretions decrease, while cortisol, serotonin, GABA and dopamine secretions increase with increased sunlight. These latter three are noted for relaxation and calmness, while cortisol is related to inflammation reduction. All are related directly or indirectly to immune response.

Visible light also penetrates the epidermal and dermal skin layers, interacting directly with circulating lymphocytes. Sunlight thus increases immune cell responsiveness, which allows the body to defend itself against practically every pathogen and toxin currently known (Roberts 2000).

Ultraviolet-A in particular has been shown to directly assist the immune system by aiding the repair of DNA damage. This effect was illustrated in a series of studies on tiny unicellular paramecia led by Dr. Joan Smith-Sonneborn, a University of Wyoming professor. While bursts of unscreened ultraviolet-C caused DNA damage, ultraviolet-A exposure reversed the damage. Going beyond the reversal of genetic damage, additional exposure to ultraviolet-A radiation extended the paramecia's life span as much as fifty percent (Smith-Sonneborn 1979; Rodermel and Smith-Sonneborn 1977).

The sun is also an effective antiseptic. Various studies have shown the sun to be antimicrobial in many respects. Many pathogenic bacteria and fungi are intolerant to the rays of the sun. Some are overheated by the sun's thermal rays. Many others are destroyed by the sun's infrared radiation (Piluso and Moffat-Smith 2006). These include certain molds and bacteria, which can significantly multiply in a dark, wet environment.

In a review of various cardiovascular system studies from the Department of Medicine of the University of Alabama (Rostand 1997), a correlation between ultraviolet radiation and blood pressure was reported. In multiple studies, blood pressure increased with increased distance from the equator. In other words, increased sun exposure decreases blood pressure. This report also correlated the increased hypertension rates with northern populations of darker skin and higher melanin content. Because melanin levels block ultraviolet rays, darker skin types require more sun exposure to reach the same level of benefit from the sun.

Hypertension is not the only heart disease-related issue that has been connected to decreased sun exposure. The Cardiovascular Thrombosis Research Center from the University of Massachusetts Medical Center (Spencer *et al.* 1998) studied 259,891 cases of myocardial infarction. After adjusting for controls and standardized seasons, it was found there were 53% more heart attacks reported in the winter than in the summer. Fatalities also followed a similar seasonal pattern. Another study done at Australia's Monash University in 2008 (Loughnan *et al.*) reviewed 33,165 myocardial infarctions over 2,186 consecutive days. The data showed a definite peak in the colder months, with a 33.7% increase in heart attacks during winter months for men.

Multiple studies have shown vitamin D deficiencies among congestive heart failure episodes (Zittermann 2006). This research also indicated other associations between sunshine and cardiovascular health.

In fact, a significant amount of research over the past few decades has linked a lack of sunshine to many other diseases. In addition to the those mentioned above, these include multiple sclerosis, rheumatoid arthritis, Crohn's disease, irritable bowel syndrome, acne, psoriasis, jaundice, depression, eczema, high blood pressure, heart disease, diabetes, hypothyroidism, angina, prostate cancer, lung cancer, colon cancer, ovary cancer, kidney disease, hyperparathyroidism, uterine cancer, stomach cancer, kidney cancer, lymphoma, pancreatic cancer, ovarian cancer, tooth loss, bone loss, obesity, joint inflammation, insomnia, Parkinson's disease, fibromyalgia and a variety of immune- and autoimmune-related diseases (Cuppari and Garcia-Lopes 2009, Egan *et al.* 2005, Giovannucci 2005, Holick 2004, McCarty 2003).

The sun is the best source for vitamin D. The vitamin D_3 molecule is produced when ultraviolet-B in wavelengths of 270-290 nanometers enters skin cells. Here a derivative of cholesterol called *7-dehydrocholesterol* undergoes a *conrotatory electrocyclic reaction* to produce a pre-vitamin D. The pre-vitamin D molecule undergoes hydroxylation in the liver and kidneys to convert to the final D_3 structure—1,25 dihydroxyvitamin D (some refer to this as 25-OHD). The conrotary reaction illustrates a synchronous circular waveform reaction, as atoms and their bonds rotate around the ring.

This conversion process is oddly similar to the photosynthesis conversion process in plants. The molecular structure of the chlorophyll molecule is also conrotary or daisy-shaped—called a *porphyrin ring*. The ring-shaped structure allows the sun's radiation to freely migrate, stimulating an electron transport process called *fluorescence resonance*. This energy transfer process converts the radiation into excited orbitals (or energy states) within the molecule. The excited state forms a constructive interference between the radiation from the sun and the bonding orbitals of the electrons, creating standing waves within the chlorophyll molecule. This coherent interference creates an electron-transport chain. As the electrons are transferred, NADP+ is reduced to NADPH, which enables the conversion of carbon dioxide to carbohydrates—the fuel of choice for other organisms.

In addition to this process, when the sun's rays hit the skin, the 7-dehydrocholesterol environment of the epidermis stimulates the production of melanin within special cells called melanocytes. Once produced from the melanocytes, melanin is transferred to the keratinocytes, which lie on the external skin barrier. Melanin is the biochemical pigment that makes the skin turn brown. Melanin also provides a natural sunscreen for the skin: The greater the melanin content, the fewer ultraviolet-B rays reach the 7-dehydrocholesterol molecules, and the less vitamin D_3 is produced. Vitamin D is used in thousands of metabolic processes around the body. What is not used is stored within fat cells for later use.

Natural vitamin D from the sun is extremely important to all of the body's tissues—and an essential part of the immune system. Vitamin D is most known to regulate calcium levels and absorption. As mentioned earlier, without proper vitamin D_3 production, calcium will not be absorbed into our bones and teeth. For this reason, osteoporosis and other joint problems are becoming more commonplace in modern society. Vitamin D is also critically important for immune function, nervous function, cardiovascular health, mood regulation, pain regulation, insulin/blood sugar balance, as well as numerous endocrine and digestive functions. Vitamin D is a necessary component for good health, and its most natural form (D_3) comes from natural sun exposure (Lehmann 2005).

Because vitamin D_2 will also convert to 1,25 dihydroxyvitamin D, it was assumed until recently that D_2 and D_3 were functionally identical within the body. This assumption has since been proven incorrect. In a study done at Creighton University and the Medical University of South Carolina (Armas *et al.* 2004), twenty healthy males were measured following supplementation of either D_2 or D_3. While both converted to 1,25 dihydroxyvitamin D, D_2 converted at far lower levels and even those levels fell off more quickly. The research shows that D_2 has only about one-third the potency of D_3.

In a Boston University study published in 2008, forty-five nursing home patients took a multivitamin containing 400 IU of vitamin D_2. During the study period, their 25-OHD levels registered deficient from a range of 49% to 78% in measurements over an eight-month period.

A 1998 study (Thomas *et al.*) of 290 medical ward patients at the Massachusetts General Hospital in Boston showed that 57% were vitamin D deficient (164) and 65 of those (22%) were severely deficient. Surprisingly, 46% were deficient despite taking the recommended dosage of vitamin D. The elderly and those in pain are most often vitamin D deficient. One study (Al Faraj and Al Mutairi 2003) found that 83% of 360 low-back pain patients had vitamin D deficiency. Another study (Plotnikoff and Quigley 2003) showed that 93% of 150 nonspecific pain patients had vitamin D deficiency. In this latter study, nearly all of those patients declared pain relief after three months of vitamin D supplementation, and in the former study—of the 360 low-back pain patients—95% showed clinical improvement after treatment with supplemental vitamin D_3.

Chronic kidney disease is also more prevalent among those deficient in vitamin D (Khan 2007). Vitamin D deficiency was linked to tuberculosis by Sita-Lumsden *et al.* in 2007. Vitamin D has also been shown to protect against macular degeneration by Parekh in 2007. Cognition, mania, depression and other mood related disorders are also linked with vitamin D deficiency (Berk *et al.* 2007). Vitamin D deficiency was linked to a higher incidence of osteoporosis by Barone (*et al.* 2007). Fetal diabetes, pre-eclampsia and fetal neurological disorders were connected to vitamin D deficiency by Perez-Lopez in 2007. Serum vitamin D was also connected with higher insulin sensitivity by Kamycheva *et al.* in 2007.

Vitamin D, when taken together with calcium, was linked to better glucose metabolism by Pittas *et al.* in 2007. In a Creighton University study (Lappe *et al.* 2007) of 1179 postmenopausal women, cancer rates among those supplementing with calcium and vitamin D_3 had an almost 60% lower cancer rate than the control subjects. A number of cancers are apparently prevented or ameliorated by vitamin D.

These are but a few of the hundreds of clinical studies confirming at last count, that over 70 disorders are linked with vitamin D deficiency!

The Indoor Life

About ninety percent of us now work indoors. In contrast, our ancestors worked mostly outdoors. For this reason and many more, the National Institutes of Mental Health in Bethesda, Maryland included the following statement in a 1988 report (Skwerer *et al.*) on seasonal affective disorder: *"Along with food, air and water, sunlight is the most important survival factor in human life."*

A significant amount of research has confirmed our need for being outside among nature. The necessity of natural light and an outdoor environment was rejuvenating in research by Azar and Conroy (1992). Camping had a therapeutic effect upon subjects attempting addiction recovery in Bennet *et al.* (1998). Bishop and Rohrmann (2003) illustrated how natural environments produced more positive subjective responses than simulated environments. Davis-Berman and Berman (1989) illustrated how adolescents were positively affected by wilderness settings. Gesler (1992) illustrated how natural geography affects medical disorders therapeutically. Hammit (2000) illustrated that even an urban forest environment resulted in the reduction of stress and anxiety. As for the placement of windows and entrances, Heerwagen (1990) established that the size, design and placement of windows in a house had significant psychological effects upon those living in the house. Honeyman (1992) established that increased vegetation in the surrounding area significantly lowered stress levels. Kaplan (1983; 1992; 1992) also established that being surrounded by nature had positive psychological effects, increased well-being and significant positive behavioral responses. Pacione (2003) established that natural landscapes—even in an urban environment—positively affect well-being. Dr. Robert Ulrich showed in over two decades of research that nature's landscapes, natural scenes, natural environments, and being surrounded by plants have a significant therapeutic effect (1979; 1981; 1983; 1984; 1992; 2002).

While millions of people have been diagnosed with seasonal affective disorder (or SAD) over the past few years, some estimate a good 25 million Americans are afflicted with some form of the disorder—at least the milder yet more pervasive winter blues version of SAD. According to Norman Rosenthal, M.D.—a leading expert on seasonal affective disorder—about 6% of Americans have SAD, and 14% have winter blues. For some, a move from the southern latitudes to the northern latitudes precipitates the disorder. Depression seems to be associated in many cases. In nearly all cases, a lack of sunlight is present.

As the fall and winter descend upon those in northern or southern latitudes, sunlight hours decrease and melatonin levels should increase along with levels of dopamine and GABA. These three biochemicals work together to sedate and relax our bodies. They also improve moods at the same time. Dopamine and GABA are both mood-boosters that balance the increase in melatonin to relax us during the winter months. However, poor diets, a lack of exercise, increased stress and a lack of natural light all counteract these mood biochemicals. Stress alone can boost cortisol and adrenaline, which make us more irritable and less relaxed. Stress and a poor diet, together with a reduction of light and exercise, toss our body cycles out the window. We are now subject to a wicked combination of stress chemicals and imbalanced hormones. The result is the millions of SAD cases throughout our modern society.

SAD becomes a vicious cycle. As our stressload increases and our sunlight decreases, our hormones and other biochemicals go out of whack. Most people will try to resolve the issue with more activity indoors, most of which increases our stressload. As stressload increases, SAD symptoms increase.

A number of other diseases often comingle with SAD and winter blues: Hypertension, atherosclerosis, early dementia, Alzheimer's, multiple sclerosis, allergies, psoriasis, fibromyalgia, depression, arthritis, and low back pain are only a few of the ailments linked to a lack of sun exposure. A lack of natural sunlight during the winter depresses the immune system, weakens eyesight, and lowers endocrine activity—disrupting hormone secretion. This lowers concentration, increases stress and contributes to depression. Studies have also shown that winter sunlight reduction increases hyperactivity in children.

Illustrating this, one of the fastest growing illnesses in modern society is autoimmune disease. Research from Australian National University (Staples *et al.* 2003) found a strong relationship between various autoimmune diseases and ultraviolet radiation exposure. One of the most prominent results of the study was evident among multiple sclerosis, rheumatoid arthritis and insulin-dependent diabetes mellitus. The research also analyzed photo-immunology trials that showed that UV-B radiation seems to reduce the Th1 cell-mediation process, which stimulates inflammatory responses. This new perspective was considered a factor additional to the metabolic effects of vitamin D production in the body (Ponsonby *et al.* 2002). Another report from Pennsylvania State University two years later confirmed this correlation.

In the converse, an increasing amount of research is indicating that a lack of sunshine during the day combined with the lack of complete darkness during the night—as our environment has become increasingly lit up at night—reduces melatonin availability. This reduction in melatonin has been linked with various types of cancers, including breast cancer, prostate cancer, colorectal cancer and endometrial cancer (Reiter *et al.* 2007).

In a study done by the Heschong Mahone Group (1999), students learning within environments with the most natural sunlight tested better and exhibited faster rates of learning. Another study supporting this was conducted earlier by Anderson *et al.* (1991).

University of Alabama researchers studied 16,800 adults over the age of 45. Higher levels of sunlight exposure increased cognitive function. The benefit was even greater among depressed or near-depressed adults (Kent *et al.* 2009).

Nature's Color Spectrum

Sir Isaac Newton first projected the sun's rays onto a wall after passing them through a prism and a narrow slit in the seventeenth century. As he contemplated the amazing rainbow of colors on the wall, he considered the cause. Did these come from the light or the prism? Rene Descartes had tried to explain it as refracted light—the colors were created by the refraction angle. Newton provided the answer to this debate as he then passed the light coming from one prism through another prism, which changed the color rays back to the original single white ray. Upon passing through yet a third prism, the light again resumed the color spectrum. This clarified to Newton that the refraction explanation could not provide the solution. If so, the second prism would yield yet more colors rather than reverting back to white light. Light, Newton proposed, must actually contain these colors. The concept of the *electromagnetic spectrum* was born.

Current instrumentation indicates that the visible spectrum is composed of red, orange, yellow, green, blue, violet, and ultraviolet waveforms. Each of these waveforms has a distinctive wavelength and frequency, which gives it a unique perception of color. The rate of oscillation is different between each color. In essence, each color beats to its own drum. The smallest wavelengths of light have been observed to have the highest energy potentials. Violet for example, has a wavelength of about 375-450 nanometers. Red has one of the longer wavelengths, at 625-750 nanometers.

When color radiation strength is measured, violet has the potential to create more energetic change than the red part of the spectrum. Thus, we can say that its wavelength is inversely relative to its energy potential. This relationship indicates the ability of certain wavelengths to distinctly affect the electromagnetic energy orbitals within atoms. It also indicates a relationship between color and the elements of the periodic table.

Sir Newton proposed that the spectrum of color could be arranged within a circle, with each color relating to a particular musical note and planet within the solar system. Although he missed several planets we now recognize—and his red range failed to reveal purple as it ranges to black—the color-harmonic concept certainly made sense to Sir Newton and his colleagues.

As we broaden our view of the color spectrum with our understanding of polarity within the electromagnetic spectrum, we can relate to this circular view of Newton's. We can also see this illustrated within the modern artist's *color wheel.*

Dr. Alexander Beddoe illustrated in 2002 that the electron cloud frequencies of the elements within the periodic table correlate with sound octaves. Each row of the table corresponds to a particular octave. The fourth row (potassium, calcium and so on) corresponds with the seventh octave, the third row (sodium, magnesium and so on) coincides with the sixth octave. The second row correlates with the fifth octave and the first row corresponds with the fourth octave. The rows under the fourth row correlate with seventh through ninth octaves.

This is consistent with the relationship between the elements and color frequencies, as Newton and his colleagues proposed.

While visible light's electromagnetic properties are preserved from the effects of the sun's geomagnetism, color is perceived when light interacts with the elements in our atmosphere. Rainbows are a good example of this. As light refracts through water vapor, it displays an array of majestically brilliant colors.

The *aurora borealis* also illustrates this interactive effect between the sun's electromagnetic activity and our atmospheric layers. As solar storm waveforms (protons) are trapped within the magneto-sphere of the earth, the atomic energy orbitals of our atmospheric particles become excited. This results in the fantastic shapes and colors are seen in the northern skies.

The confluence of spectra in the electromagnetic has been codified as light. Light can be encapsulated within the auspices of the notion of an all-encompassing *white light*. The white light has never been visually proven to exist, although Georg Cantor, a German mathematician at the turn of the nineteenth century and inventor of the *set theory*, spent many years attempting to prove the *continuum hypothesis*. This proposed that finite sets related to infinite sets. Extending his logic into the plane of spectra, this continuum would connect visible light to an all-encompassing white light.

The white light, first documented in the ancient *Vedas* of India, has been discussed for thousands of years. Here the white light is referred to as the *Brahman effulgence*—an manifestation of the Almighty. This effulgence is considered by the *Vedas* to be the source of the physical universe. The white light has since been documented in many other texts as a vehicle for transcendence.

The concept of the white light containing many other sub-spectra that make up the waveforms of matter is analogous to the notion that visible light rays contain the various spectra of color. Remember that colors is only visible as the visible spectrum waveforms diffract, refract and reflect through our environment.

Color, or *chromatics,* is the translation of particular energy waveforms by the photoreceptor neurons (primarily the cones) of the eyes. This means that colors have a number of characteristics besides what our minds perceive as color. William Snow, M.D. documented that blind people can perceive color without the use of eyesight. He explained that the *"radiant light, heat and color are capable of setting up responsive vibrations in animal tissue, inducing responses relative to their intensity…. their wavelengths and frequencies."*

We have discovered through research that other rays of the electromagnetic spectrum are capable of unique physical effects.

Consider cosmic rays and gamma rays, which can penetrate tissue, causing various organ and cell damage. Consider x-rays, with their potential for radiation damage with too much exposure. Consider ultraviolet rays with their potential to damage or mutate skin cells. Consider radio and television waves with the ability to carry information through buildings and other physical obstructions. The visible part of the spectrum maintains similar waveform character, with frequency and wavelength differences. The colors of the visible spectrum certainly can influence atomic orbitals just as do these other waveforms. However, their effects are generally more subtle and less damaging. Furthermore, each color has distinct effects.

Color and light is required for long-term health and disease prevention. Research has illustrated that when a person is entrained to an indoor darkened habitat, the risk of depression grows substantially. Along with depression comes the risk of various other diseases such as fibromyalgia, back pain, digestive difficulties, decreased circulation and so on. While deficiencies in vitamin D, melatonin, serotonin and dopamine are relevant to sunlight, clinical evidence has pointed to associations between health and color.

Color has been used therapeutically for thousands of years with overwhelming success. It has been an important element of Ayurvedic, Chinese and Egyptian medicinal therapies. Goethe's 1810 book, *Theory of Colours* related color with Hippocratic medicine. He described the four basic colors intertwining with the four basic humours of the physical body within a circular wheel, which he coined the *"Temperamental Rose."* Goethe tested subjects and moods, describing character associations with colors, stating that, *"Every colour produces a corresponding influence on the mind."* Light and color therapy has been used amongst psychologists thereafter. Colors were used therapeutically in European asylums. Painted walls with violet or blue brought about a calming effect for anxious patients; while red, yellow and orange brought about mood elevation among depressed patients.

Color therapy in *Ayurveda* has utilized therapeutic gems for thousands of years. Utilizing some of these principles, during the first part of the century, an Indian Colonel and self-described metaphysician and psychologist named Dinshah Ghadili wrote and lectured famously on color therapy. In 1920, he invented a machine called the *Spectro-Chrome*. Equipped with a 1,000-watt light bulb, the device had five sliding glass color plates that could be mixed and matched to create up to twelve colors. Ghadili's instruction manual for the device—*The Spectro-Chrome Metry Encyclopaedia*—documented a number of therapeutic case histories using the machine. While Ghadili was subsequently dubbed a quack and his machine described as a fraud by the FDA and others, some 10,000 of his devices were sold and used by a wide range of healthcare providers for many decades. There were also several other similar *chromotherapy* devices commercialized during that era. Ghadili's was simply one of the best known.

Ghadili was also influenced by Edwin Babbitt's *The Principles of Light and Color* (1878). Babbitt's book proposed that everyone has a particular energy color. Babbit suggested that illness is at least partially caused by disturbing our unique color balance. Healing, he proposed, could be hastened by re-establishing ones color balance. A schoolteacher, Mr. Babbit also invented a popular device for this purpose, called the *Chromolume*.

In 1946, Ghadiali was tried and eventually convicted of fraud. The FDA put the theory of color therapy on trial along with Ghadiali himself, and color therapy was functionally discredited in western medicine. Ironically, in that same year, a Swiss psychologist named Dr. Max Luscher designed a well-received study using colors to assess personality characteristics along with a risk assessment of potential disorder trends. Developed for psychiatrists and physicians, Luscher's color test indicated patients with higher risk factors for ailments of cardiac, cerebral, or gastro-intestinal origin, depending upon the types of colors the subject selected. His test became a standard among therapists, as it proved clinically useful.

Indeed, marketers and advertisers—who have been successfully using color in their marketing campaigns and packaging—have drawn upon a wealth of practical and measured experience relating colors with purchase decisions. It is for this reason we see fast food restaurants advertising in yellows and oranges—hunger colors. Banks, on the other hand, will pick blues and grays with some reds showing stability. Healthy food brands will choose greens and browns to appeal to the ideals of certain consumers. Some marketing research has indicated that green is by far the most appealing color to food consumers. Not surprisingly, we see lots of greens among labels on our supermarket shelves.

The use of color in the practice of psychotherapy has remained somewhat consistent over the past century despite the FDA's case against Ghadiali. Over the last two decades, controlled research has increasingly confirmed color's therapeutic effects. Today color therapy systems like *Colorpuncture* (Peter Mandel) and *Chromo-pressure* (Charles McWilliams) are emerging, combining color therapy with other established therapeutic methods (Cocilovo 1999).

There is a volume of research now confirming the usefulness of color therapies. In a study done by Lund Institute of Technology researchers (Kuuler *et al.* 2006) on 988 subjects in indoor work environments, it was concluded that brighter colors and lighting created higher moods among workers in four different countries.

In 1992, poor reading children were studied by researchers in the psychology department of the University of New Orleans (Williams *et al.*). Color overlay intervention increased reading comprehension in about 80% of the children.

Hypertension has been successfully treated with color therapy (Kniazeva *et al.* 2006). Preterm jaundiced infants have been successfully treated with blue and turquoise lighting. Significant reductions in plasma bilirubin have been achieved with color therapy (Ebbesen *et al.* 2003). The application of ultraviolet B light resulted in a lowering of blood pressure in Krause *et al.* (1998).

The visible part of the electromagnetic spectrum ranges in wavelength from 380 nanometers to 740 nanometers. Within this range, the color red has the longest wavelength, ranging from 625 to 740 nanometers. Meanwhile, orange ranges from around 590 to 625 nanometers; yellow ranges from around 565 to 590 nm; green from 500 to 565 nanometers; blue from 450 to 485; and purple from about 310 to 380 nanometers. Of course, as the wavelength increases, the speed or frequency of each waveform cycle decreases. Red ranges from a frequency of 405 to 480 terahertz (10^{12} hertz) while on the other side of the visual spectrum, purple ranges from 790 to 840 terahertz.

The color spectrum is called *continuous* because there is no cessation or absolute break between colors. Rather, the true color of a range is apparent in the middle of the spectrum while the edges transition into the next color. This means there are a lot more colors in between the main frequencies.

The mind perceives thousands if not millions of colors. Some researchers have documented up to 10 million colors as potentially distinguishable by humans.

The eyes are equipped with two visual receptors: rods and cones. The cones of the eyes are the primary receptors of bright light and the color spectrum. Humans typically have three kinds of cone cells, each with a different pigment: one is sensitive to the short violet color waves; one is sensitive to the medium green waves; and one is sensitive to the longer yellow waveforms. Cones are not very sensitive to light, yet they pick up colors better in brighter light than in darker light. The rods are primarily light-sensitive cells, and thus they are useful for night vision. In fact, rods will usually only begin functioning during weaker light, distinguishing primarily black and white images.

The perception of distinct colors takes place through a contrasting process between the three types of cone cells and a *bleaching* out of others. Each different cone type has specific photoreceptors oriented to receive particular wavelengths of light. Each particular wavelength will stimulate a specific type of cone over another. A blending of multiple images from each type of cone is transmitted through the optic nerve and brain cells, providing a pallet view of various colors on the mind's screen.

The conversion of light into the neural pulses takes place through a transduction process. Like many other sensory receptors in the body, cone photoreceptor pigments become polarized by particular waveforms. When light of a particular waveform strikes a receptor, a depolarization takes place. The depolarized photoreceptor acts as a gateway, opening micro-channels through which sodium ions travel. The sodium ion movement stimulates the release of glutamate. Glutamate in turn adjusts the polarity of the neuron membranes, blocking or accessing further ion movement between receptors. This causes the bleaching effect between color determinants. The cone pigment itself is a protein called *iodopsin,* which resonates with a molecule called *retinal*—a molecule derived from vitamin A. When light hits the pigment, retinal's molecular bonding structure changes from a *cis* configuration to a *trans* configuration.

If we translate this oscillation to a static image, we might imagine it being similar to the wing of an airplane being bent downwards towards the ground. This *trans* configuration closes the ion channel through a protein messenger called *transducin*. When the ion channel is blocked, the neural signaling impulses are sent through the optic nerve with a negative feedback of calcium ions.

Rather than initiating the flow of current, the stimulation of light onto the cones *shuts off* the regular flow of ions through the membrane. The concept of the *dark flow*—where a steady stream of ions flow between these cells and the nerves is shut down when stimulated by light—was reported in 1970 by Hagins *et al.*, from rod pigments removed from the eyes of rats. This dark flow halting process was evidenced through the measurement of tiny voltages and currents among the photoreceptors.

What we are discussing then is a steady electromagnetic current moving between the optic neurons, only to be intruded upon with the reception of light through retinal cells. When our eyes are closed or we are walking in pitch darkness, the current flows. When light hits the cones, a preponderance of retinal pigments stimulate particular waveforms. These intercept and shut down the ion channels. This interception process of shutting off the ion channels is called *hyperpolarization* (Nakatani and Yau 1988).

The photocurrents running between the retinal cells and the brain have specific waveform frequencies. These are classified as alpha waves, beta waves and so on (Breton and Montzka 1992). This classification of waveforms is defined by the orientation of the brainwave oscillation frequencies that pulse through the central nervous system. The interaction between these *visual reception waves* and the other oscillating rhythms circulating around the brain's neurons integrates visual perception into the mind's web, enabling a reflective picture to be observed by the self.

Note that this image reflected onto the mindscreen is not the actual image. It is a composite of waveform patterns, expectations, and a process of filling in the blanks. This filling-in process creates a unique visual experience for each person. Though we may compare and confirm that we are all seeing some of the basic transmissions, each of us brings together a slightly different impression. This differential allows each of us an interpretive element, infusing our individual goals and objectives into our perception of a scene. This is why many people can watch the same event and come away with a different interpretation. Perception is not an automated process. It is an act of consciousness.

As further evidence of this, in 1999 the *Proceedings of the National Academy of Sciences* published a study out of Stanford University firmly establishing that speaking the names of colors invokes the same brainwave response in subjects as the seeing of those colors (Suppes *et al.* 1999). Upon hearing a word describing a color, the brain triggers a translation into a mental image. The perception by the observer or conscious self makes no distinction between the sources of the input.

Color Energy

Research has continued to connect the visual perception of color and brainwave response to our moods and behavior. Brain imaging has indicated that color stimulates corresponding brainwave patterns, which have been linked to metabolism and cognition. The ancient science of *Ayurveda* correlates colors with particular energy states and subsequently, different *chakras* and energy centers around the body. The mechanism for this subtle electromagnetic bridge is explained using wave resonance and interference. If we were to hit a piano key in a room full of pianos, the other pianos would begin to vibrate in the same chord. With color resonance, we can associate particular waveforms with other oscillations occurring within the body. After all, colors are part of the electromagnetic wave spectrum. As these waveforms connect within our body, they stimulate waveform responses—just as touching a hot burner stimulates the response of pulling our hand away.

Here is a review of the major colors. Some of this information comes from research, and some comes from traditional and/or anecdotal sources.

Red's longer wavelengths tend to stimulate higher frequency beta waves in the brain, vibrating at more than thirteen cycles per second with wavelengths of 630-700 nanometers. Its longer wavelength is responsible for the redness of the sunset. The longer wavelengths scatter less than the blues and violet waves as they interact with the atmosphere particles. Red tends to stimulate the body's autonomic systems, increasing heart rate and blood pressure.

Shorter (brighter) wavelengths of red will suppress melatonin release (Hanifin *et al.* 2006). However, longer-wave (darker) red colors have been shown to aid sleep and even induce melatonin. This latter effect has prompted some small studies showing that sleeping quality may be increased with periodic low-intensity red light. Other studies have shown that red light therapy restores glutathione balance, stimulates the immune system and improves wound healing (Yeager *et al.* 2006).

Traditional therapy indicates that red stimulates physical stamina, circulation, hostility, violence, competition, and jealousy. It also is considered stimulating to sexual activity. For this reason, a bright red dress or red roses often stimulates passion between the opposite sexes. It also seems to make sense that we find passionate people or very active people wearing reds and driving red cars. Red cars also tend to receive more speeding tickets. Whether this is because red car drivers drive faster or red cars are more noticeable is debatable. Red has been attributed to the planet mars, known for its connection to war, passion, and the struggle for survival. While red can be stimulating and aggressive, it is known to help relieve chronic pain. It also can stimulate the circulatory system and the liver. Because it stimulates greater stamina, red is considered helpful for completing projects requiring great amounts of physical energy and focus.

Orange tends to stimulate high alpha brainwaves, which oscillate between ten cycles per second and thirteen cycles per second at wavelengths of 590 to 630 nanometers. Orange has many of the stimulatory effects of red, but without some of the intensity and passion. Orange is therefore warming and anti-congestive. It is known to stimulate the lungs. It promotes enthusiasm, creativity, and inquisitiveness. Orange is often accompanied by sincerity, thoughtfulness, and health. Orange resonates with the sacral area—the back and lower spine—and the lower abdominal area according to *Ayurveda*. Orange stimulates reproductive activity—as opposed to the sexual passion of red. It also stimulates appetite and the movement of the colon. Orange resonates with aspects of family and parenting. Orange is also associated with wisdom and enlightenment. Activities that resonate the most with orange include family relationships, friendships and group organizations.

Yellow stimulates lower alpha brainwaves, eight or nine cycles per second with wavelengths of 560 to 590 nanometers. Yellow is known to stimulate the digestive tract. It is associated with the capacities of the stomach and upper intestines. Yellow also stimulates the adrenal glands. Thus, yellow is considered a trigger for stress. Activities associated with yellow include hyperactivity, memorization, study, and focus. For these reasons, yellow is also considered draining. Because yellow stimulates the adrenals, it can also stress the body and mind through the corticosteroids that it produces. Yellow resonates with spontaneity, compassion, memory, learning, and appetite. Yellow also reflects light with a greater intensity, so it can be exhausting on the eyes and mind after some time. This intensity can also stimulate digestion and nutrient assimilation, however. Yellow can be cheerful, but too much of it can be fatiguing. In behavioral research, yellow rooms seem to cause more anxiety. Babies cry more and couples argue more in yellow rooms.

Green stimulates brainwaves in the higher theta region, about six to seven cycles per second with a wavelength of 490 to 560 nanometers. Green is calming and balancing. It stimulates growth, love and a sense of security. Green resonates with the pituitary gland and is thus good for strengthening the endocrine system and regulating hormones. It tends to reduce blood pressure and congestion. It is also connected to devotion and giving. Green is soothing, yet it stimulates the immune system. It stimulates the activities of the thymus gland. Thus, green is considered a healing color. This is consistent with the fact that most green foods are immunostimulating and detoxifying. The green frequencies of light tend to suppress the body's endogenous melatonin levels. In a study from the U.K.'s Loughborough University (Horne *et al.* 1991), six sleep-deprived human subjects were given 10 minutes of green light per hour in the evening, resulting in more alertness, less sleepiness and lower melatonin levels. This, combined with green's calming nature tends to help increase focus and alertness. The greens of nature's forests and gardens are testimony of green's ability to bring about calm focus. This effect is why green packaging is a favorite among consumers. Green radiation is also associated with problem-solving, negotiation, resolution, gardening and cooking.

Green may also help relieve depression. In a study at the University of California-San Diego (Loving *et al.* 2005), 33 elderly human subjects with depression were given bright green light for one hour per day or dim red light as a placebo. Mood improved for 23% of all the green-light subjects. Another study showed that green light slowed high frequency heart rate variability (Schäfer and Kratky 2006).

Blue stimulates lower theta waves in the five to six hertz area at wavelengths of 450 to 490 nanometers. Blue is cooling and calming. It slows metabolism. The rhythm of blue is gentle and holistic. Blue is associated with creativity and communication on both a spiritual and physical level. Like green, blue wavelengths help lower melatonin as the body increases adrenal hormones in the early part of the day. Blue activity is associated with relaxation, playing music and cleanliness. For this reason blue is associated with purification. Blue is also considered a color of stability and conservatism. Corporate executives and government administrators often choose blue for this reason. Blue is also a very good color to use around children, as it is calming and increases focus. In a study of 104 office workers, blue-enriched white light improved alertness, work performance and increased sleep quality (Viola *et al.* 2008). Schäfer and Kratky (2006) also showed that blue light significantly reduced heart rate variability. According to *Ayurveda,* blue resonates with breathing, speaking and the thyroid gland. The thyroid is the endocrine gland known to regulate body temperature and cellular metabolism. Light blue appears to increase mental performance. This relates to not only the calming effects of blue. The softness of the color stimulates intellectual cognition.

Indigo stimulates low delta waves around one cycle per second and wavelengths of 400 to 450 nanometers. Therefore, indigo resonates with deep thinking, clarity, intuition and intelligence. It is associated with decision-making and meditative thinking. The sinuses, vision, and the immune system are therefore stimulated by indigo. Activities traditionally associated with indigo include highly intellectual activity, humanitarian behavior, medical research, and philosophical contemplation. It is a color is often associated with exploring the reason for existence.

Violet stimulates higher delta waves from two to four hertz. These waves vibrate at a higher frequency than indigo, primarily because they are more stimulating. Violet has been traditionally associated with raising consciousness and stimulating spiritual quests. Violet is also associated with nerve conduction, brain circulation, spinal fluid movement, and synovial fluid condition. Violet promotes activities associated with deep meditation and inspiration, prayer, and spiritual insight.

Purple, a color blending the effects of indigo and violet, is associated with luxury, royalty and nobility. It is considered a favorite of the wealthy and political-powerful, as it expresses feelings of superiority and dignity.

Pink is a blended color. Nevertheless, pink has been associated with sedative and muscle-relaxing effects. Behavioral therapists like Alexander Schauss, Ph.D. have reported that pink colors create a tranquilizing effect, preventing or slowing anger and anxiety. Surprisingly, Dr. Schauss also reported this same effect among color-blind patients.

Black is a shade and not a color. Even so, black appears to influence seriousness and even depression. Former prisoners of the former Soviet Union have reported that the KGB utilized black prison cells to induce depression in their interrogations. Black is of course the color most associated with death, as it is worn at funerals. Other black clothing events (such as "black tie affairs") are associated with seriousness and the need to establish dominance and order. On a brighter note, black is also considered elegant and straightforward. Black clothing or black automobiles may also reflect an intent to be conservative and uncomplicated. At the same time, black can also express boldness. Black is associated with both because it absorbs light. This absorption is what gives black its blackness. At the same time, black will reflect a gloss, which is transparent.

White, on the other hand, reflects light more completely, with little or no diffraction. This gives white its simplicity. White tends to be a cooler shade because it reflects much of the waveforms, leaving its material less disturbed by radiation. This is why white houses, white cars and white clothes can be cooler to wear or be inside of. White also represents honesty and service, as it communicates clarity of purpose. White clothes are thus associated with humility.

In general, colors with lower frequency and longer waveforms such as red, orange, and yellow tend to stimulate physical activity and resonate with physiological activities such as reproduction, survival, digestion, and thermal energy production. The higher frequency, shorter wavelength color waveforms of blue, violet, and indigo tend to stimulate brainwaves associated with thoughtfulness, problem solving, and intuition. Green is considered the crossover waveform, as it tends to bring balance among these activities.

When choosing colors to wear or otherwise surround our physical environment with, we might consider the goals we intend to achieve. The colors with the longest wavelengths such as red, yellow, and orange can be used when we need speed, energy, stamina, and immediate responses. When we need to be 'upbeat' about an activity or event, brighter colors will lift our mood and behavior. These brighter colors are also useful to fight depression and sluggishness. If we need to boost our enthusiasm, these brighter colors are significantly useful.

The cooler colors of violet, indigo, blue, and green will taper down and balance our energy levels. These colors will provide a relaxing meditative environment. We can better let stressors and traumas slide right over us as we surround ourselves with these colors. Certainly, it is quite easy to be surrounded by the greens and the blues of nature. All we have to do is take a walk in a natural environment with lots of green trees under a blue sky. This environment will stimulate greater intuition, problem solving, intelligence, and even possibly spiritual insight.

The bottom line is that the light and colors that nature produces are the healthiest versions. Research has confirmed that while we can see nicely using indoor synthetic light, it cannot duplicate the light rays produced by nature. When natural light reflects and refracts off of the structures produced by nature, it produces nature's colors. Each of nature's colors is due to the combination of absorption, refraction, diffraction and reflection of natural light as it interacts with the biomolecules produced by nature.

So when we interpret a natural scene as beautiful, we are actually perceiving a resonation between our inner biowaves and the interference patterns produced by nature's diffracted and reflected electromagnetic waveforms.

☻Five
Radiation Research

Most of us living in the modern world have replaced the sun with a synthetic version: electromagnetically driven lights and appliances. Modern humankind has harnessed electromagnetic radiation in the form of alternating current. For thousands of years, humans used the light of the sun as the primary means for observation and lifestyle. Fire, of course, augmented the sun at night. As any candlelight dinner will attest, the light given off by flame is a significantly different experience than today's fluorescent or incandescent lights.

Together, these two energy sources—sun and fire—provided the primary means of light and heat. Today these have been replaced by an electronic light show with innumerable blinking lights and pulsing electronics. Today's environment is drowning in supercharged alternating currents.

The question is, are there any negative health consequences from this replacement of energy? Does the synthetic surging of alternating current create negative effects upon our bodies and/or minds as compared to those currents driven by sun and fire?

We have addressed some of the issues of using artificial lights and sun tanning beds elsewhere. In our discussion of the sun's rhythmicity, we illustrated the research showing that artificial lights of even 100 lux can throw off the body's natural entrainment to the sun. The intrusion of artificial light has been shown to disrupt sleep cycles, increase stress and change hormone balance. Each of these effects, in turn, has negative consequences. Sleep, for example, is vital to practically every metabolic process and cognitive process in the body. Without a consistent pattern of enough sleep, our bodies can fall prey to mental stress and physical illness. Stress is known to be a causative or contributing factor in almost every illness. Hormone disruption can cause a variety of other metabolic problems, ranging from inflammation to pain.

In the sections on natural light and color, we discussed how sunlight produces, reflects and refracts a balance of waveforms that stimulate particular hormones and mood cycles. The research has shown that without natural light we will experience greater levels of stress, anxiety and even anger. The replacement of artificial light with sunlight has, in a number of studies, been shown to increase cognition, learning, and development among children. Among adults, natural sunlight increases memory and positive moods. Full-spectrum lighting has been shown to provide some of these effects. However, we should point out that it will be unlikely that human-kind will ever be able to reproduce the entire electromagnetic spectrum of the sun. As discussed, the sun produces a host of different waveforms with a precisely coherent balance.

In our sun medicine section, we will also discuss briefly how synthetic sun tanning bed lights can provide a mix of UV-A and UV-B that stimulates vitamin D production in the body. The downside is that these lights have also been shown to produce higher levels of cancers such as melanoma. The reason made obvious, once again, is that we have yet to reproduce all of the sun's balance of waveforms in the right proportion. In other words, our bodies are *tuned* to the total spectrum of electromagnetic radiation produced by the sun.

Today we have enclosed our bodies inside an environment of synthetic alternating electromagnetic radiation (EMR), effectively shielding or dampening the sun's natural radiation. Is this development a healthy one?

It has been assumed that, outside of electrocution, alternating current had little or no negative effects upon the body. Then about two decades ago, a sounding alarm was made. A plethora of research and documentation offered the possibility of negative effects from EMR. A controversial and embattled thesis arose: Perhaps electromagnetic radiation from alternating current creates unhealthy effects upon the body.

The primary question—taking up our focus—posed whether and to what degree electromagnetic radiation from alternating current sources causes cancer. Yes, this is an important question, but not the only important question. Equally important is to what extent electromagnetic radiation from alternating currents may affect our vitality and general wellness. Does it burden our immune system? Does it deplete our energy? Does it slow cognition? These questions have been curiously missed in much of the debate and research on EMR.

Today's environment is embedded with a plethora of electromagnetic pulses our bodies have never faced. We are surrounded by electronic appliances that emit varying degrees of electronic and magnetic field strength. Our buildings are wired with EMR-emitting circuits and breaker systems. Most of us spend multiple hours in front of computers and televisions, absorbing magnetic fields. The battery and transmission systems built into our phones, music players and laptops bring our skin in direct contact with EMR-emitting appliances.

With billions of us partaking in at least some of these activities daily without obvious negative effects, some wonder what all the fuss is about, and why some health proponents are still arguing the case against synthetic EMRs.

There are two basic forms of radiation to consider: *Ionizing radiation* and *non-ionizing radiation*. According to a 2005 report by the National Academy of Sciences on low levels of ionizing radiation, about 82% of America's ionizing radiation comes from natural sources: the earth, sun, space, food and the air. The rest—18%—comes from human origin. The bulk of this fabricated radiation comes from x-rays and nuclear medicine. This accounts for close to 80% of the 18%. Other elements like consumer goods, toxic water, occupational exposure, and nuclear power account for the rest of the ionizing radiation exposure according to this report.

Ionizing or Non-ionizing?

Ionizing radiation is typically defined as electromagnetic radiation capable of disrupting atomic, molecular or biochemical bonds. This disruption takes place through an interference of waveforms between the ionizing radiation and the waveforms of atomic or molecular orbital bonds. As this interference is likely to cause the atom or molecule to lose electrons, ions are likely to develop as a result. These ions can often turn to oxidative species or otherwise imbalanced molecular species. Should ionizing radiation with enough intensity impact the physical body, it can result in cell injury or mutagenic damage. Various natural and synthetic radiation forms are considered ionizing. Natural ionizing radiation includes portions of ultraviolet radiation, x-rays, cosmic rays and gamma rays. Fire can also cause ionizing radiation at high temperatures if the radiation comes close enough. Synthetic versions of ionizing radiation include electrically produced x-rays, CAT-scans, mass accelerator emissions and a host of other electromagnetic radiation produced through alternating current.

Non-ionizing radiation also can be split into natural and synthetic versions. Natural versions include sound, light and radiowaves. Most natural non-ionizing radiation can also be synthetically produced. For example, sound may be digitally produced through the manipulation of alternating current by stereo receivers and speakers. This effect utilizes electrical semiconduction. Some scientists also categorize radiation from electrical power lines, electricity generating or transfer stations, appliances, cell phones, cell towers and other shielded electricity currents as non-ionizing radiation. Microwaves are also considered non-ionizing. Most assume that non-ionizing radiation is not harmful. This assumption, however, has undergone debate over the past few decades.

The 2005 National Academy of Sciences report, after a review of most of the available research regarding non-ionizing radiation, concluded that even low doses below 100 milliseiverts were potentially harmful to humans and could cause a number of disorders from solid cancer or leukemia. This jolted the scientific community, because for many years researchers thought that small doses of non-ionizing radiation were not that harmful.

A rem is one unit of radiation dose in roentgens. The mrem is one thousandth of a rem. One hundred rem equals one sievert. One sievert equals one thousand milliseiverts. Ten sieverts (10,000 mSv) will cause immediate illness and death within a few weeks. One to ten sieverts will cause severe radiation sickness, and the possibility of death. Above 100 mSv there is a probability of cancer, and 50 mSv is the lowest dose that has been established as cancer causing. Twenty mSv per year has been established as the limit for radiological workers. About one to three mSv per year is the typical background radiation received from natural sources, depending upon our location and surroundings. About .2 to .7 mSv per year comes from air. Soil sources are responsible for about .8 mSv. Cosmic rays give off about .22 mSv per year. Japanese holocaust victims received .1 Sv to 5 Sv from the bomb.

Our total radiation dose is a thus a combination of natural sources and those emitted by our artificial electromagnetic empire. A report from the Hiroshima International Council for Health Care of the Radiation-Exposed noted that the world's average radiation dose from natural radiation sources is 2.4 mSv. However, they also noted that Japan's natural radiation average is comparably low at 1.2 mSv. Japan's average radiation dose from medical radiation is higher than average, at 2.4 mSv. This gives Japan a significantly higher radiation average of 3.6 mSv.

UK's National Radiological Protection Board estimates that the national radiation exposure in Britain for the average person is 2.6 mSv, with an estimated 50% coming from radon gas, 11.5% coming from foods and drinks, 14% coming from gamma rays, 10% coming from cosmic rays and 14% originating from appliances—primarily medical equipment.

Recent research indicates that radiation from medical equipment is increasing. This is primarily driven by the growing use of CT scans, which generate a larger dose of radiation than the more traditional x-rays. About sixty-two million CT scans are now given a year in the U.S., as opposed to about three million per year in 1980. Brenner and Hall (2007) reported in the *New England Journal of Medicine* that a third of CT scans given today are unnecessary. The article also estimated that between one and two percent of all cancers are caused by CT scan radiation exposure.

In contrast, the maximum radiation a nuclear electricity generating plant will emit at the perimeter fence is about .05 mSv per year. A set of dental x-rays will render a dose of about .05-.1 mSv. A CT scan can render a dose of about 10 mSv—*making a CT scan a hundred to a thousand times the dose of an x-ray.*

A grand electromagnetic human self-experiment is unfolding. Unsuspecting humans and animals are the subjects of this experiment. The findings will be available in a decade or two from now.

Most researchers are quick to say gamma rays—from radon and other natural sources—produce significantly more radiation than do appliances. This might be true for someone with a minimal amount of electrical appliances who rarely visits the hospital and dentist's office.

The question that persists is whether humankind's synthetic "non-ionizing radiation" is as innocuous as is currently assumed.

Power Lines

The American Physical Society, an association of 43,000 physicists, said in a 1995 National Policy (95.2) statement, *"....no consistent significant link between cancer and power line fields...."* This statement was reaffirmed by the APS council in April of 2005.

Power lines emit electromagnetic radiation at ELF or *extra low frequency* levels. Power lines typically release about 50 hertz of pulsed radiation. As an electric current moves through a wire or appliance, magnetic fields move perpendicular with electricity in a cross pattern. Thus, electricity fields form from the strength of the voltage while magnetic fields rise and break away from the electronic waveform's motion. While electricity voltage can shock us or burn the body, magnetic fields have more subtle yet lasting influences upon the body's natural biowave systems—such as brainwaves, neurotransmitter release, hormone production, and so on.

While magnetic influences are difficult to perceive directly, it is apparent they may substantially interrupt our immune systems. Between 1970 and 2000, about fourteen international studies analyzed the potential link between power lines and cancer among children. Eight of those studies showed a link between cancer rates and power line proximity, while four studies associated power lines with leukemia.

One of the U.S. studies to show a positive link in between cancer took place in 1979 in Denver, led by Dr. Nancy Wertheimer and Ed Leeper. This studied showed a more than double likelihood of cancer among children living within forty meters of a high-voltage line. Another Denver study published in 1988 (Savitz *et al.*) also found a 1.54x odds ratio (OR) positive link in all childhood cancers and high power lines. A Danish study (Olsen *et al.* 1993) also linked general cancer rates (1.5 OR) with power line proximity. A study done in Los Angeles (London *et al.* 1991) showed a 2.15 OR rate, a Swedish study (Feychting and Ahlbom 1992) showed a 3.8 OR risk and a Mexican (Fajardo-Gutierrez *et al.* 1993) study showed 2.63 OR increased rate of leukemia cancer rates among children with close proximity to high-voltage power lines. One Swedish study (Tomenius 1986) showed a 3.7 OR increased risk for central nervous system tumors among children living close to power lines. The

Danish study mentioned above also showed a 5.6 OR increased potential of all cancers among children. The other positive link studies showed rates above 1 to 1.5 OR, which are not considered by mainstream science to be statistically significant.

Following the release of these studies, a number of governments took steps to warn housing developers of the potential risks of building close to high frequency power line hubs. In some municipalities across Europe and the U.S., building departments have even taken steps to dissuade or ban developments close to larger power lines.

Adult power line studies have yet to illustrate as large a correlation between power line proximity and cancer rates. Still a few have been significant enough to confirm the need for concern. Werthheimer and Leeper's (1982) studies showed increased rates of all cancers. Still, this 1.28 OR rate was not considered that significant. However a U.K. study (McDowall 1986) showed a SMR 215 increased rate of lung cancer and a SMR 143 increased risk (SMR 100 or less = no risk) of leukemia. Another study in the U.K (Youngson 1991) showed a statistically insignificant 1.29 OR rate for leukemia and lymphoma and Feychting and Ahlbom's (1992) Swedish study showed a 1.7 OR risk for leukemia subtypes. Another significant study (Schreiber et al. 1993) showed a SMR=469 rate for Hodgkin's disease.

It must be noted that these studies are epidemiological. They are population studies where groups living in close-proximity to high frequency power lines are compared with groups living further away. The problems that can occur with these studies focusing on cancer are several. In cancer pathology, there can be a two to twenty year delay between exposure and cancer diagnosis. While some of the populations involved in these studies might have been living in a particular house for many years, most may have only lived there for a year or two at the most.

In addition, some of the studies limited the disease group population, restricting the usefulness of the information. Cancer is seen primarily in the elderly and middle-aged, where there may be a host of various different types of exposures. These would include smoking, alcohol consumption, job-related exposures, chemical toxins, and so on. For this reason, these studies can be difficult to weigh against the costs of preventing exposure. The economic issues involving power lines are quite substantial. Relocating schools and families away from high-voltage lines or even relocating power lines comes with a substantial economic cost.

Nonetheless, this is increasingly becoming a problem for both homeowners and utility companies. For example, in the mid-nineties, the New Jersey Assembly enacted legislation requiring disclosure from homebuilders of vicinity transmission lines in excess of 240 kilovolts (kV). Other states have followed with real estate disclosure laws for power lines. Lawsuits have followed on power line proximity issues between schools, buyers, builders and utility companies.

One of the problems existing with some of the power line studies is the comparable limits of the distances between households and power lines. For example, is the effect of a transformer 40 meters away significantly different from one 50 meters away? Another difficulty with these epidemiological power line studies is that some of the studies measured utility wire codes (wire thickness) and distance, while other studies used spot physical measurements to determine exposure levels. In addition, there has been a variance of controls related to whether the child was born in the house or moved there recently.

With regard to the significance of the leukemia studies, we should consider the incidence of leukemia cancer among the childhood population—close to 1 in 10,000. A 2 or 3 OR among a group, unless the size of the groups are in the millions (most of the studies were significantly smaller—in the thousands), would relate to only a small handful of disease cases over the entire study population. If the study group size was five or ten million, then these numbers might be considered more reliable. As the increased rates have been smaller (rather than the 4 or 5 OR rate that appears in many study groups) then the size of the disease group is not considered to be a significant factor with which to judge the quality of the study. To this point, D'Arcy Holman, a professor at the University of Western Australia, calculated that the UK studies' worst projections might mean one extra childhood leukemia death in Western Australia every fifty years (Chapman 2001).

Occupational studies regarding exposure to EMR have shown unclear results with regard to leukemia and cancer (Kheifets *et al.* 2008). However, studies have pointed to the increased risk of amyotrophic lateral sclerosis (ALS) due to EMR exposure (Johansen 2004). Studies on electricians, electric utility line workers and other electrical workers have consistently showed higher rates of leukemia and central nervous system-related cancers. In a 2006 meta-study of fourteen studies by Garcia *et al.* (2008), Alzheimer's disease was associated with chronic occupational EMR exposure.

One of the difficulties with assessing the data on EMR effects is the sheer volume of studies of different types that has been published over the past twenty years. The breadth of variances between the studies of plants, animals, and human response to various degrees of radiation is substantial. Because of this huge base of studies, most researchers have been forced to rely upon various reviews by publications and government agencies to assess the implications of this large base of varying research. These groups have assessed and compared studies to figure out whether there is a correlation between study results, and whether they are significant. Government-sponsored reviews have included the United Kingdom's National Radiological Protection Board, the Associated Universities of Oak Ridge, the French National Institute of Health and Medical Research; councils in Denmark, Sweden, Australia and Canada together with U.S. agencies such as the Environmental Protection Agency and the Department of Transportation. In addition, the U.S. National Council on Radiation Protection and Measurements and the US National Academy of Sciences have also put together major reports on EMR research.

A number of respected journals have published reviews of EMR research as well. While some of these studies have found some epidemiological evidence notable, few found conclusive results, and some have presented skeptical views of any significant positive pathological correlation with non-ionizing EMR exposure. Multiple reviews were also presented (Savitz 1993) in *Environmental Health Perspectives*. No interaction mechanism between power line EMRs and biological organisms was determined.

An electrical field is substantially different from a magnetic field. An electrical field is generated when there is a charge differential between two terminating points, regardless of whether current runs between them. An electric light bulb will still generate an electric field even when it is turned off. This electrical field allows alternating current to run between the two points when the switch is eventually turned on.

A magnetic field is created by a current flowing with electricity. The magnetic field will be emitted outward with perpendicular orientation to the electrical field. However, because magnetic fields have a particular polarity or direction, a current flowing in the opposite direction placed next to the current wire will cancel the magnetic field. Most power cords with double wires (hot and ground for a circuit loop) effectively cancel the magnetic field of the incoming current directly related to the distance between the wires. An increase in this separation increases the strength of the magnetic field. This occurs in power lines, where conductors are typically separated by poles and shields for fire protection.

For these reasons, excessive magnetic fields are considered to have the greatest potential for harm. The level of potential harm are thought to be related directly to the distance from the generating source, the distance between other conductors, the size of the coils on the transformer (if any) and of course the amount of current flowing through the system. It is generally accepted that the relative magnetic field strength halves with the amount of distance from the line. In other words, a line 100-foot away will have one-quarter of the magnetic field strength of a line 50-feet away.

Li *et al.* (1997), after testing 407 residences in northern Taiwan ranging from 50 meters to 150 meters from high-voltage power lines, found that the magnetic fields at the houses ranged from .93 mG for 50 meters to between .51 and .55 milliGauss for residences under 149 meters, and .29 mG for residences beyond 149 meters.

This data is somewhat contradicted by a 1993 cohort study from the Netherlands that revealed magnetic field intensities, ranging from 1 to 11 milliGauss from two kilovolt power lines connecting to one transformer substation (Schreiber 1993).

Higher voltage wires are typically thought to be an issue because the voltage and speed is boosted to travel longer distances. With a high-speed voltage line comes an increase in magnetic field. Magnetic fields have been connected with decreased melatonin secretion

(Brainard *et al.* 1999). A number of studies have linked lower melatonin levels with higher incidence of a number of types of cancers. It would thus seem probable that since lower melatonin levels are associated with higher voltage, high-speed power lines could well be a mechanism for cancer (Ravindra 2006).

In comparison, a typical house or office will range from .8 to 1 mG in magnetic fields. The magnetic field strength from a kitchen appliance at close range for a person working in the kitchen is significantly greater than the strength coming from power lines 50-100 feet away. Stepping a few feet away from a microwave oven will dramatically reduce this field strength, while that same relative power line reduction will require a more significant change. A typical microwave oven might cause a field strength of 1,000 mG, which can be reduced to a minimal 1 mG by stepping a few feet away. Moving ones house further away from a power line obviously requires a significant commitment to the reduction of magnetic field strength, and a few feet will not make a significant difference.

Epidemiological studies involving electrical appliances have been limited. They are more difficult because of the control parameters. Nonetheless, a few appliances have undergone controlled studies over the years. Electric blankets have undergone several studies. Some of these illustrated significantly increased risk factors for postmenopausal cancer (Vena *et al.* 1991), testicular cancer (Verreault 1990), and congenital defects (Dlugosz 1992).

Radio Waves

Radiofrequency waves range from about 3 hertz to 300 gigahertz. This means their waves travel from speeds of 3 cycles per second up to 3,000,000 cycles per second. *Extremely low frequency* (ELF=3-30 Hz) and *super low frequency* (SLF=30-300 Hz) broadcasting has primarily been used for submarine communications, as these wavelengths transmit well through the water. This is also the frequency range that sound waves travel. *Ultra low frequency* (ULF=300-3000 Hz) has primarily been used in mines, where the waves can penetrate the depths. Above these levels, *very low frequency* and *low frequency* (VLF and LF = 3-300 kHz) have been used by beacons, heart rate monitors, navigation and time signaling. *Medium frequency* (300-3000 kHz) radiowaves are typically used for AM broadcasts, while *high frequency* (HF = 3-30 MHz) is used primarily for short-wave and amateur radio broadcasting. *Very high frequency* (VHF = 30-300 MHz) waves are used for FM radio, television and aircraft communications while *ultra high frequency* (UHF = 300-3000 MHz) waves are used for certain television ranges, but also cell phones, wireless LAN, GPS, Bluetooth and many two-way radios. While often considered outside the radio spectrum, *super high frequency* (SHF = 3-30 GHz) waves are used in microwave devices, some LAN wireless systems and radar. *Extremely high frequency* (EHF = 30-300 GHz) is used for long-range systems such as microwave radio and astronomy radio systems. The audio frequencies are primarily ELF through VLF brands, covering 20-20,000 Hz.

Note that EMR wavelengths inversely vary to their frequency. For naturally occurring EMR such as sunlight, the frequency will equal the speed of light divided by the wavelength. Thus, an ULF wave can range from 10,000 and 100,000 kilometers long. An UHF wave will range from one meter to ten millimeters in length, while an ELF wavelength will range from one millimeter and ten millimeters long.

Adulterated radiofrequencies have been utilized by humans for only about the last seventy-five years. Early use was primarily for radio transmission, while during the past few decades, various communication and signaling systems have been developed that utilize radiofrequencies. Radiofrequencies are generated with alternating current fed through an antenna at particular speeds and wavelengths.

Studies on radiofrequency radiation proximity at work have also studied possible reproductive and cardiovascular effects. While many of the reports are inconclusive, there have been positive correlations between radiofrequency exposure and delayed conception (Larsen *et al.* 1991), spontaneous abortion (Quellet-Hellstrom and Steward 1993; Taskinen *et al.* 1990), stillbirth (Larsen *et al.* 1991), preterm birth after father exposure (Larsen *et al.* 1991), and birth defects (Larson 1991). However, many of these results have either not been replicated or remain uncorroborated. Three studies examined male military personnel exposure to microwaves and radar (Hjollund *et al.* 1997; Lancranjan *et al.* 1975; Weyandt *et al.* 1996). All three found reductions in sperm density.

A number of animal studies have illustrated adverse health effects from radiowaves but doubt has been raised regarding the dose comparison with humans. In one study, GSM phone frequency radiowaves caused the cell death of about 2% of rat brains. Researchers hypothesized that the blood-brain barrier was being penetrated by the radiation (Salford 2003). This was correlated by three earlier studies that reported blood-brain barrier penetration with radiowave exposure (Shivers et al. 1987; Prato et al. 1990; Schirmacher et al. 2000). For several years following the release of this last study, other studies could not replicate the findings, nor could they establish a confirmation of the permeation of the blood-brain-barrier from radiofrequencies (Kuribayashi 2005; others). However, Shivers and colleagues, and Prato and associates had previously determined the effect of magnetic resonance imaging upon the rat brain. They showed that the exposure to radiofrequencies combined with pulsed and static magnetic fields gave rise to a significant pinocytotic transport of albumin from the capillaries into the brain.

Rates of breast cancer, endometrial cancer, testicular cancer and lung cancer have been studied with close range radiofrequency radiation, primarily in occupational settings. Slightly positive correlations with endometrial cancer (Cantor et al. 1995) and male breast cancer (Demers et al. 1991) were found. A potential link between testicular cancer and radiofrequency radiation from traffic radar guns, particularly among a small group of police officers (Davis and Mostofi 1993) was also established. Slightly increased ocular melanoma was established among occupational radiofrequency exposure (Holly et al. 1996) in another small group. French and Canadian utility workers were found to have an increased likelihood of lung cancer (Armstrong et al. 1994).

Cell phone tower radiofrequencies are popular concerns. The first cell phones communicated with analog frequencies of 450 or 900 megahertz, for example. By the 1990s, cell phones were using 1800 megahertz, and various modulation systems. Now the Universal Mobile Telecommunication System is adhered to, which uses 1900 to 2200 megahertz.

In 2000, over 80,000 cell tower base stations were in use in the United States. By 2006, this number was estimated at 175,000. CTIA, the International Association for Wireless Telecommunications Industry, estimates that by 2010 there will be about 260,000 towers. These base stations transmit radiowaves using around 100 watts of power. The range of GSM towers is about 40 kilometers, while the CDMA and iDEN technologies offer ranges of 50 to 70 kilometers. This obviously is relative to terrain. In a hilly area, the range can be a few kilometers.

In populated areas, cell base towers are placed from one to two miles apart, while in urban areas they can be as close together as a quarter of a mile. Some cell phone bases are mounted on primary towers, and some are built onto elevated structures such as buildings and hillsides.

A base cell tower antenna is comprised of a transmitter(s), a receiver(s)—often called transceivers—an electrical power source, and various digital signal processors. The circuits will utilize copper, fiber, or microwave connections. They may be connected to the network via T1, E1, T3 and/or Ethernet connections. They are typically strung together through base station controllers and radio network controllers, typically connected to a switched telephone network system. The radio network controller will connect to the SGSN network.

There has been scant research on the risks of radiofrequency waves from radio stations or television stations. The primary reason for this appears to be that most of these have been located outside of densely populated areas, on high towers enabling greater ranges. Cell towers have created more concern because of their close proximity and relatively lower heights.

Research has suggested that exposure from cell towers is reduced by a factor of one to one hundred times inside of a building, depending upon the building materials and style of the building. However, exposure also increases with height. Upper floors can have substantially greater exposure levels than lower floors (Schuz and Mann 2000). Whether this is a factor of pure height or whether the earth provides a buffering factor is not known.

Exposure levels in regions surrounding cell towers will range from .01 to .1% of ISNIRP (International Commission on Non-Ionizing Radiation Protection) permitted levels for general public exposure directly around the station, to .1 to 1% of ISNIRP permitted levels between 100 meters and 200 meters from the tower.

Beyond the 200-meter level, the exposure returns to the .01 to .1% level and reduces as the range increases. It should be noted also that exposure levels from cell phone towers are not substantially greater than exposure levels of radiofrequencies (RF) emitted by radio broadcasting towers. In one Australian study, the greatest level found was .2% (Henderson 2006).

In a 2006 randomized double-blind study performed at the Institute of Pharmacology and Toxicology at the University of Zurich (Regel *et al.*) in Switzerland, UMTS signals approximating the strength of a cell phone tower emission were tested on 117 healthy human subjects, 33 of which reported themselves as sensitive to cell towers and 84 as non-sensitive. Physiological analyses included organ-specific tests, cognitive tests, and well-being questionnaires. Apparently, significant negative physiological or cognitive results were not found, although there appeared to be a marginal effect on one of the cognitive tests for each of the two groups. Because the difference was slight, and each group (sensitive versus control) had different results, this effect was considered insignificant.

In 2006, the British medical journal (Rubin *et al.*) reported a study done at the King's College in London, which tested 60 self-reported sensitive people and 60 control subjects with no reported sensitivities. Six different symptoms such as headaches were tracked, and subjects took questionnaires in an attempt to find whether the sensitive subjects could successfully judge whether a cell tower signal was on or off. While 60% of the sensitive subjects believed the tower signals were on when they were on, 63% believed the tower signals to be on when they were indeed off.

There have also been several international studies done on radiofrequency transmissions from masts. Tests in the United States, Britain, Australia and the Vatican City have shown no or low correlation between RF levels and health effects, rendering these studies for the most part, inconclusive. One study in the Netherlands using simulated mobile phone base station transmissions did conclude, however, that the UMTS-like spectrum of cell transmission might have an adverse affect upon the well-being of questionnaire respondents.

In July of 2007, an independent team of researchers (Eltiti *et al.*) from the University of Essex reported findings from a three-year double-blind study using a special laboratory to test potential cell phone tower effects. The study included 44 people who reported sensitivity to cell phone towers and 114 healthy people who had not. The study measured various physiological factors like skin conductance, blood pressure and heart rate while being exposed (or not) to 3G tower signals. During periods where the researcher and the subject knew the signals were on, sensitive people reported feeling worse, and their physiological factors were affected negatively. However when neither the subjects nor the researchers knew the cell tower signals were on during a series of tests, there was no difference between either the sensitive or non-sensitive subjects with regard to physiological factors. In fact, only two of the forty-four sensitive subjects were able to guess the cell tower signals being on correctly while five of the control subjects (non-sensitive) were able to guess correctly. Subjects who reported sensitivities to cell phone towers prior to the study reported negative symptoms more often, regardless of whether the cell tower transmitters were on or off.

Remote and Cell Phones

Typically, a digital cell phone operates at a power range of about .25 watts, while the newest digital phones might transmit as low as .09 watts. Analog phones were much higher power transmitters. The exposure level of a cell phone will depend greatly upon the way the phone is designed. The location of the antenna and the power supply/battery will typically govern the strength of the transmission to the dermal layers of the skin. The further away the antenna is from dermal contact (hand or ear), the less exposure.

The orientation of the power supply will also govern exposure. Some phones have shielding between the power supply and the antenna and earpiece. This is thought to reduce dermal exposure. In other words, the manner of carrying and holding the phone will vary the exposure.

There is another factor called *adaptive power*. When a cell phone is further away from a tower, or in a moving car, it will typically increase its internal transceiver power to send and receive signals. This increases the level of electromagnetic exposure as the phone is boosting power and transmissions. EMR cell phone exposure is thus typically less out of doors than indoors, because there is less interference from building materials out of doors. In addition, exposure to radiowaves is greatest on the side of the head the phone is most used and closest to where the antenna is located (Dimbylow and Mann 1994).

Radiofrequencies from handset use have been confirmed to heat the ear canal. In one controlled study of 30 individuals, 900 MHz and 1800 MHz phones against the ear for more than 35 minutes resulted in an increase of 1.2-1.3 degrees F (Tahvanainen et al. 2007). Other studies have confirmed this effect. For this reason there has been a great concern regarding the potential for tumor development either in the brain or in the areas surrounding the ears—referred to as an *acoustic neurinoma.*

Adverse effects of tissue temperature rise are not clear, but it is thought that the body's thermoregulation mechanisms may create an increased immune burden on the body. Lab studies have suggested a one-centigrade temperature rise at the tissue level will have immunosuppressive effects (Goldstein et al. 2003).

The International Agency for Research into Cancer has sponsored studies in thirteen countries to study the line between cell phone usage and cancer. So far, Australia, Canada, Denmark, Finland, France, Germany, Israel, Italy, Japan, New Zealand, Norway, Sweden and Britain have participated. Through 2005, the research tracked 6,000 glioma and menigioma cases (brain tumors), 1,000 acoustic neurinoma cases and 600 parotid gland cancers. Of these, the acoustic neurinoma results, primarily from Sweden, showed a significant link with handset use—from both cell phones and cordless phones. The German study also revealed a significant link between uveal melanoma and unspecified handset use. Other types of tumors had OR levels of around or just above 1 to 1.7 OR. The 2001 Swedish study on all brain tumors found a 2.4 OR link with ipsilateral cancer—more prevalent on the same side of primary handset use.

Again, we are faced with the fact that many of these associations are occurring at between 1 and 3 OR. A 2 or 3 level OR risk level creates questions in the minds of meta and review researchers. This should be combined with the fact that the rates of these tumors are so small among the general population (10-15 per 100,000 per year) for malignant brain tumors (Behin et al. 2003). Additionally, there is often a ten-year or more delay from exposure to diagnosis. This gives some researchers a myriad of reasons to question even the better correlations between cell phones and cancer.

Other researchers firmly disagree, stating that the weaker evidence is actually enhanced by the cancer diagnosis delay. Research from the Japanese nuclear victims of World War II has shown that many cancers arise ten to twenty years and more after the initial exposure. If we extrapolate this with cell phone use, we estimate that because cell phone use among the general population is still within this twenty-year period, especially for many younger adults (who were barely using cell phones five years ago). This means we should expect to see higher cancer rates among heavy cell phone users within the next five to ten years from now. Possibly this might be ameliorated somewhat by the improved cell phones being made now, with increased shielding (which begs the question; why did they increase the shielding if there was no danger?). Or not. We will see. The grand experiment with EMR rages on.

One of the more dramatic releases on cell phone use emerged in 2003 from a study conducted by Dr. Michael Klieeisen at Spain's Neuro Diagnostic Research Institute. This study revealed from a CATEEN scanner linked to a brainwave activity-imaging unit that radiowaves from cell phones could penetrate and interfere with the electrical activity of an eleven-year-old boy and a thirteen-year-old girl. Various hypotheses resulted from the release of this data. Among them, that radiowaves affect the moods, memory, and activities of children. Because brainwaves have been closely linked to moods, recollection, response time and other cognition skills, it is assumed that cell phone use has a disturbing effect upon cell phone users—particularly in children and adolescents.

In a 2004 study (Maier *et al.*), eleven volunteers' cognitive performance was tested with and without being exposed to electromagnetic fields similar to cell phones. Nine of the eleven (or 81.8%) showed reduced performance in cognitive tests following exposure.

It should be noted that there is a tremendous market resistance to the information that cell phones and remote phones could be dangerous when used consistently. The cell phone industry is now a multi-billion dollar international business. The damage undeniable evidence of a health risk would have upon this industry is nothing short of monumental. It goes without saying that this would also have a significant impact upon the human lifestyle.

This effect may be effectively illustrated by the events reported by Dr. George Carlo and Martin Schram in their 2001 book *Cell Phones: Invisible Hazards in the Wireless Age*. Dr. Carlo was a well-respected epidemiologist/research scientist and pathologist. He was retained by the cell phone industry's chief lobbyist to study and comment on research regarding potential dangers of cell phone use. However, it was not expected that Dr. Carlo would speak out against cell phone use after examining the research data. In his book, Dr. Carlo describes the extraordinary efforts of the cell phone industry to discredit him. As Dr. Carlo began to announce negative cancer-related findings, his clients began to apply both political and financial pressure upon him.

We should however note that although U.S. brain cancer rates have increased substantially over the past three decades, brain cancer incidence increased until 1987, and has been slowly decreasing from that point (Deorah *et al.* 2006). This statistic does not concur with a model of increasing brain cancer rates with increasing cell phone usage. Quite possibly, some of the environmental etiologies involved in brain cancer prior to 1987 have been somewhat mitigated. Perhaps some of the toxin exposure levels—such as the rampant use of DDT and toxic waste dumping in waterways—have been curtailed due to some of the EPA actions of the 1960s and 1970s—decreasing brain cancer rates in the years following. We also cite further controls on nuclear leaks and a massive reduction in tobacco use. Epidemiologically, these could well be masking a slow rise in brain cancer levels due to cell phone use.

Cancer is not the only issue to consider with regard to cell phones, however. Researchers have examined other disorders with respect to radiofrequency exposure. Heavy cell users commonly report a wide variety of negative symptoms. In a study of 300 individuals at Alexandria University in Egypt (Salama and Naga 2004), cell phone usage was positively correlated with complaints of headaches, earaches, sense of fatigue, sleep disturbance, concentration difficulty and burning-face sensation. The results showed that 68% of the study population used cell phones. All of the above health complaints were significantly higher among the cell phone users, and 72.5% of the cell phone users had health complaints. The frequency duration of cell phone usage was also extrapolated together with health complaints, and it was discovered that the higher the cell phone use, the greater the incidence of health complaints. While the burning-face sensation complaint correlated positively with call frequency per day, complaints of fatigue also significantly correlated (positively) with both call duration and call frequency.

The warming of the ear, face and the scalp around our ear from cell phone use is logically taking place as a result of frequency and waveform interference between our body's natural waveforms and these synthetic waveforms. Our body's natural waveforms include the shorter waves of the brain and nerves, and the weaker bio-photon waveforms of the cells, along with the molecular electro-magnetic bonding waveforms within DNA. Should electronically driven waveforms interfere with these natural biowaves, the molecular bonding structures of our genetic information could gradually become deranged.

The effects of this interference should appear on a number of fronts. We should see lower cognition levels and brain fog, as unnatural waveforms interfere with our brainwave mapping system. We should see body temperature interference within the basal cell network. We should see damage to the blood-brain barrier and damage to nerve and brain cells. These effects should release greater levels of radical species from the imbalanced molecular structures—damaging cells and tissues. All of these effects have been documented in the research.

This waveform interference mechanism is illustrated by a recent study (Thaker *et al.* 2008) showing that a certain popular brand of MP3 player will interfere with the mechanisms of a pacemaker if held close to the chest for about five seconds. Appliance interference has been directly correlated with waveform interference. This is one reason why the U.S. Federal Communications Commission closely monitors and licenses bandwidths. When we consider that the body maintains various natural biowave "bandwidths" as it cycles hormones, thermoregulation, cortisol, melatonin and the Krebs energy cycle to name a few, it is not difficult to connect the waveform interference of cell phones and other appliances with the disruption of these natural cycles.

Video Display Terminals

VDTs and televisions emit about 60 hertz of electromagnetic fields. Although a number of early studies suggested the potential of a health risk, many studies over the past few years have suggested that VDTs pose little if any health risks. The National Academy of Sciences reviewed a number of studies in 1999 and stated, *"....the current body of evidence does not show that exposure to these fields presents a human health hazard..."* In 1994, the American Medical Association stated, *"no scientifically documented health risk has been associated with the usually occurring levels of electromagnetic fields..."* Their review included both epidemiological studies and various other direct studies of EMR effects from terminals.

Another report, published in *Lancet,* the British Medical Association's journal, documented the largest childhood study comparing childhood leukemia and cancer rates and exposure to 50-hertz non-ionizing magnetic fields. No link was found.

The National Radiological Protection Board in 1994 confirmed that while existing conditions might be aggravated, their review of the research showed no link between skin diseases or cataract formation and VDT use. However, the board's Chairman Sir Richard Doll, did confirm that VDT use might aggravate conditions that have already formed.

In addition, a bevy of clinical research regarding pregnancy outcome for those working around or on computers has failed to show any links between miscarriage or birth defects and VDT use. The National Radiological Protection Board from Oxford, U.K. confirmed this in a review of the research.

In 1998, the International Commission on Non-Ionizing Radiation Protection submitted low emission field guidelines. They suggested an upper limit of magnetic field exposure of 833 milliGauss (mG). The electric field limit was set at 4,167 volts per meter (V/m).

Both VDTs and televisions are far below these exposure levels when measured individually.

Regardless of these reports, problems associated with vision, fatigue and headaches have been reported from VDT use. These problems have been attributed to such ergonomic issues as the potential for glare on the screen, lighting location with the position of the screen, the distance from the screen, and whether there are regular breaks from looking at the screen.

Other issues reported have been associated with static electricity generated through the keyboard and screen, posture problems, and repetitive injuries such as keyboarding without rest, which can create a risk of carpal tunnel and other motor difficulties.

As for television, there have been numerous efforts to study the effects of television on children and adults. Most of these have leaned towards its behavioral effects, but a few have reported significant effects on physical health. In 2007, Crönlein *et al.* found a significant link between television viewing and adolescent children insomnia. Thakkar *et al.* (2006) and Paavonen *et al.* (2006) found that watching violence on television increased insomnia and sleep disturbances among young children. Bickham and Rich (2006) showed that increased television viewing—especially violent TV—was associated negatively with friendships. Hammermeister *et al.* (2005) showed that viewers who watched two hours or less television per day had a more positive psychosocial health profile. Viner and Cole (2005) determined that early childhood television viewing was associated with people who had a higher body mass index later in life. Other studies have also correlated increased television viewing with childhood obesity (Robinson 2001).

Meanwhile Zimmerman and Christakis (2005) found that children who watched a significant amount of television before the age of three years (2.2 hours/day) scored lower on Peabody reading comprehension, memory and intelligence testing at ages six and seven. Hancox *et al.* (2005) found in New Zealand that increased television viewing was associated with higher dropout rates and lower rates of university attendance. Collins *et al.* (2004) found that watching sex on television increases sex activity at a younger age in children. Huesmann *et al.* (2003) found that watching violence on television increased violent behavior during adulthood. Vallani (2001) illustrated that research since 1990 progressively showed that increased television viewing increases violent behavior, aggression, and high-risk behavior such as smoking, drinking, and promiscuousness.

However, Anderson *et al.* (2001) indicated that television content might have more to do with these associations. 570 adolescents were studied from preschool, and their programming was monitored. Educational program watching was linked to higher grades, increased reading, greater creativity and fewer violent activities.

Microwaves

Microwave ovens produce two different forms of radiation: High frequency radiowaves produce electromagnetic radiation in the range of 2450 megahertz and magnetic fields at 60 hertz. The central question is whether this is enough bombardment to cause harm to the food. While some claims have been made that microwave ovens cause the food particles to spin and rotate, this statement has not been confirmed by scientific investigation. What we know is that the microwaves increase the waveform energy states of the molecules using thin microwave beams in much the same way fire increases energy states. Whether this is accompanied by a spinning or rotation of the molecule appears to be speculative, though it appears likely—understanding the physics involved.

Indeed, microwaves do create unnatural molecular structure results. A well-cooked microwave dinner reveals dry and rubbery textures not seen in other forms of cooking. Is microwaved food healthy?

Dr. Robert Becker (1985) reported that various disorders such as cardiovascular difficulties, stress, headaches, dizziness, anxiety, irritability, insomnia, reproductive disorders, and cancer occurred in the Soviet Union among microwave-exposed workers when the Soviets were developing radar during the 1950s. In fairness, though technically correct, these were people working amongst microwave transmissions, not eating microwaved dinners.

Dr. Becker also reported that research from Russia indicated nutritional reductions of sixty to ninety percent in microwave oven tests. Decreases in bioavailable vitamin Bs, vitamin C, vitamin E, minerals, and oil nutrients were observed. Alkaloids, glucosides, galactosides and nitrilosides—all phytonutrients—were found damaged by microwaving. Some proteins were found to be denatured.

Research (Knize *et al.* 1999) at the University of California Lawrence Livermore Laboratory concluded that microwaves produced heterocyclic aromatic amines and polycyclic aromatic hydrocarbons. Both are suspected carcinogens. Frying meats also produces polycyclic aromatic hydrocarbons (Felton *et al.* 1994).

Dr. Lita Lee wrote in her 1989 book, *Microwaves and Microwave Ovens* that the Atlantis Rising Educational Center in Oregon reported that a number of carcinogens form during the microwaving of nearly all types of foods. Microwaving meats caused formation of the carcinogen d-nitrosodiethanolamine. Microwaving milk and grains converted amino acids into carcinogenic compounds. Thawing frozen fruit by microwave converted glucosides and galactosides into carcinogenic chemicals. Short-term microwaving converted alkaloids from plant foods into carcinogenic compounds. Carcinogenic free radicals formed during the microwaving of root vegetables, according to this report.

In December of 1989, the British Medical Association's *Lancet* reported that microwaves converted trans-amino acids to cis-isomers in baby formulas. Another amino acid, L-proline, converted to a d-isomer version. These isomers have been classified as neurotoxins (toxic to the nerves) and nephrotoxins (toxic to the kidneys).

Swiss food scientist Dr. Hans Ulrich Hertel and Dr. Bernard Blanc of the Swiss Federal Institute of Technology reported in a 1991 paper that microwave food created cancerous effects within the bloodstream. The small study had eight volunteers consume either raw milk; conventionally cooked milk, pasteurized milk; microwave-cooked milk; organic raw vegetables; conventionally-cooked vegetables; the same vegetables frozen and warmed in a microwave; or the same vegetables cooked in the microwave oven. Blood tests were taken before and after eating. Subjects who ate microwaved milk or vegetables had decreased hemoglobin levels, increased cholesterol levels and decreased lymphocyte levels. The increase in leucocytes concerned Dr. Hertel the most. Increased leukocyte levels in the bloodstream are generally connected with infection or tissue damage.

The controls in some of these studies may be in question, however. For example, in Dr. Hertel's study he was a participant, the group knew whether the food was microwaved or not, and the group members were predominantly macrobiotic. The Russian studies and the *Atlantis Rising* report statistics all come unconfirmed from secondary sources.

Various forms of cooking will also destroy nutrients and generate carcinogens—especially frying and barbequing. Overcooking in general destroys nutrients and can create a variety of free radicals that can be tumor forming if eaten in excess.

There are other dangers reported from microwaves. The leakage of various toxins from packaging during microwaving has been documented. A 1990 *Nutrition Action Newsletter* reported that various toxins will leach onto microwaved foods from food containers. Suspected carcinogens including benzene, toluene and xylene were among chemicals released into food. Also found was polyethylene terphtalate (PET). Various plasticizers are almost certainly to be included in this list, as they will quite easily outgas when heated.

In addition, microwaving—unless done for extended periods—rarely completely sterilizes a food. This should be a warning for all those who pack leftovers into storage containers and assume a few minutes in the microwave will produce a sterile, cooked food. This fact has been become obvious from the *Salmonella* outbreaks among those who took food home in doggie bags to microwave later.

Approaching this logically, it is apparent that nature did not design food to be cooked in microwaves.

This is evidenced by a simple experiment conducted in 2006. Marshall Dudley's granddaughter completed a Knoxville science fair project that compared plant water feeding between stove-boiled filtered water and the same filtered water source microwaved. She started with sets of plants of identical species, age, and health. One of each set was fed filtered water boiled in a pan and cooled. She fed another the same filtered water, but microwaved until boiling and cooled. This 'watering study' went on for a period of nine days, and pictures of the plant sets (which sat together in identical potted condition) were taken each day.

The simple assessment of each plant's health was clear by looking at the photographs. Each day the plant watered with microwaved-water looked worse. It became increasingly withered and slumped over in obvious stress. By the ninth day, the microwave-watered plant had lost most of its leaves. Meanwhile, the boiled-watered plant stood tall with crisp green leaves, growing healthier by the day.

Radon

As research in the nineties focused on power lines, research has illuminated the fact that electromagnetic fields can interact with various elements in the atmosphere, creating radon gas. A further potential danger has been proposed for households not properly wired with copper and insulation. A lack of shielding can also increase the potential interaction of household electricity with radon.

Radon 222 comes primarily from the nuclear decay of uranium. This natural process takes place within the earth. As this decay proceeds, radon gas is released, together with decay byproducts, called *radon daughters* or *radon progeny*. These particles are known carcinogens. Should we breathe these particles, they can be caught in the lungs. Breathing radon gas delivers the potential of it continuing to decay inside our bodies. This will effectively deposit the radioactive daughters inside our bodies.

The National Council on Radiation Protection and Measurement has developed a maximum safe dosage of radon to be 200 mrem per year.

The relationship between radon and outdoor power lines has not been clearly established, because in order to measure the interaction, an aerosol component (a pollutant of some sort) must accompany the electromagnetic field. Nonetheless, significant *radon daughters* have been measured (Henshaw *et al.* 1998) among power line fields.

The subsequent dose and tolerance of radon particles in the human body is also in question. In some research, heavy electromagnetic fields have been shown to penetrate with no more than about .0001 of the original field strength of radon emissions. Still this penetration effect alerted researchers to the fact that there might be a radon penetration into the lungs and basal tissues of the body (Fews *et al.* 1999).

The link between radon and lung cancer has become more evident in recent research. Lung cancer has been the most prevalent form of cancer worldwide since 1985, and has been responsible for more than one million deaths worldwide. The highest rates of lung cancer occurred in 2002 in North America and Northern or Eastern Europe. Although smoking is widely considered to be the primary etiology of lung cancer, uranium miners—who are exposed to increased levels of radon along with dust—experience higher rates of lung cancer (Tomasek *et al.* 2008). Epidemiological studies on radon-exposure and miners have also revealed that thousands of miners die per year of radon exposure (Field *et al.* 2006).

Research has illustrated that while living outdoors does not increase ones risk of lung cancer, unnatural living or working quarters without enough ventilation can lead to a drawing in and encapsulation of radon radiation. A household with poor ventilation poses a higher risk of radon exposure than a well-ventilated house. This is exasperated by other electromagnetic radiation in the local environment. Research has illustrated that ventilation around electromagnetic current exposure is an absolute requirement because of a release of radon daughters into the immediate atmosphere (Karpin 2005).

Darby *et al.* (2005) reported in the *British Medical Journal* on a collaborative analysis of thirteen case studies of 7,148 lung cancer cases together with 14,208 control subjects. This found that increased radon exposure is responsible for about 2% of European cancer deaths. Further research has revealed that most buildings, especially work environments that are full of various power lines and equipment, retain higher levels of radon. Radon levels are additionally increased with unventilated soils, higher air temperatures and higher atmospheric levels. Higher household radon levels are particularly associated with leaking and unventilated soils in the house. This research has caused legislation in many states in the U.S. requiring property sellers to disclose known radon issues.

The majority of our everyday radiation input comes from radon. Natural concentrations of radon are found in some granites, limestones and sandstones. Higher radon levels come from disturbed ground. Disturbing the normal landscape allows more permeability, allowing the release of the normally contained daughters. Once a house is built upon disturbed ground, the radon can come in through cracked foundations and spaces around piping and wiring. Because radon gas is pulled in through pressure changes within the house created by temperature gradients, it is important that our houses be well ventilated. This is particularly significant during the nighttime and during cold weather, as the warmer temperatures inside with colder temperatures outside cause the most pressure differential—the *Bernoulli effect*. Ventilation will not only allow the escape of indoor radon gas, but it will release some of this pressure, resulting in a lower draw of radon gas into the house.

Household radon levels tend to increase dramatically during the winter, and decrease substantially during the summer for these reasons. Radon levels also go up dramatically during the nighttime hours, as the outdoor temperature cools. This is when ventilation is most important. Disturbed landscaping ground can also leak increased radon daughters.

The U.S. Environmental Protection Agency has recommended safe levels of radon to be 4 *picocuries of radon per liter* (pCi/L). Levels any higher than this should be remedied by cementing over the exposed ground or sealing cracks in current cement foundations. Ventilation systems have also been known to help. Radon detection kits are quite inexpensive and easy to use.

Magnetic Fields

Nature's magnetic fields surround us, and pose little threat. Many species utilize nature's magnetic fields to navigate migration and nesting. In other words, our cells are tuned to the geomagnetic fields of the sun and the earth.

Synthetic magnetic fields, on the other hand, are dispersed with the distribution of unnatural alternating current. The proliferation of electricity and electrical appliances created by power-generating plants that convert nature's kinetic energy into alternating current has deluged our atmosphere with unnatural magnetism.

Most early research on the health effects of electrical appliances and wires focused on the electrical fields and ignored the magnetic fields given off by appliances. While most electrical fields are shielded by insulators within most appliances, magnetic fields can be more disruptive and insidious to the health of the body. This is because they can directly interfere with the body's internal biowaves. Normally, synchronic and harmonic biowaves—including brainwaves, nerve firings, and so on—travel with synchronicity throughout the body.

A magnetic field surrounding the body can induce an abnormal electrical current flow within the body. In a Swedish study (Wilen *et al.* 2004) of RF operators exposed to high levels of magnetic fields, currents were induced within the body at mean levels of 101 mA and maximum levels of one Amp. During this study, exposure levels correlated positively with the prevalence of fatigue, headaches, warm sensations in the hands, slower heart rates and more bradycardia episodes among the subjects.

In a study done by the Fred Hutchinson Cancer Research Center and the Epidemiology Division of Public Health Services in Seattle, Washington (Davis *et al.* 2001), 203 women aging from 20-74 years with no breast cancer history were studied between 1994 and 1996. Magnetic field and ambient light in the bedroom were measured for a 72-hour period during two seasons of the year. Urine samples were taken on three consecutive nights for each subject. After adjusting for hours of daylight, older age, higher body mass, alcohol use and medication use, those women with higher bedroom levels of magnetic fields had lower concentrations of 6-sulfatoxy-melatonin. It was thus concluded that increased levels of synthetic magnetic fields depress nocturnal melatonin.

While this illustrates how unnatural magnetism can significantly affect the body's biochemical rhythms, reduced melatonin also causes negative effects throughout the body. Over several decades since melatonin was discovered in 1958 by Dr. Aaron Lerner and his Yale colleagues, decreased melatonin levels have been linked to a variety of pathologies and immune function deficiencies.

A three milliGauss magnetic field at 60 Hertz will induce about one-billionth amp per square centimeter of the body. A magnetic field at 120 Hz frequency will have double the current effect the same field will have at 60 Hz. A typical American office building or home—filled with various electrical appliances—will contain magnetic fields at levels between .8 and 1 milliGauss. In a study done at a Canadian school by Akbar-Khanzadeh in 2000, workers, schoolteachers and administrative staff environments had magnetic field exposure levels ranging from .2 to 7.1 mG.

MilliGauss levels will be substantially higher in instrument-heavy environments. Hood *et al.* (2000) recorded the pilot's cockpits of a Boeing 767 with magnetic field levels of 6.7 milliGauss, while the Boeing 737 recorded at 12.7 mG of magnetic field strength. Nicholas *et al.* (1998) documented a mean magnetic field strength of 17 mG among the cockpits of B737, B757, DC9 and L1011 planes. Meanwhile, cabin measurements ranged from a high of 8 mG in the forward serving areas to 6 mG in the first class seats and 3 mG in the economy seats.

Rail maintenance workers experience magnetic field levels from 3 to 18 mG (Wenzl 1997). In a study published in the *Journal of the Canadian Dental Association* (Bohay *et al.* 1994), dental operating rooms with various ultrasonic scalars, amalgamators, and x-ray equipment revealed magnetic fields ranging from 1.2 to 2225 mG, with equipment distances from zero to thirty centimeters.

Most of these magnetic field readings were accompanied by lower level radiation frequencies ranging from 25 hertz to 100 hertz (though the airline cockpits research recorded up to 800 hertz).

In a population study of 969 women in San Francisco, miscarriage levels positively correlated with higher magnetic field exposure. Li *et al.* (2002) concluded that fields in the region of 16 mG or higher produced the greatest risk of miscarriage. While higher levels of magnetic fields have been shown not to significantly affect nervous system biowaves such as cardiac pacemakers (Graham *et al.* 2000), 12 milliGauss magnetic fields operating from radiation frequencies of 60 hertz were shown to block the inhibition of human breast cancer cells by both melatonin and tamoxifen *in vitro*. While melatonin and tamoxifen have different mechanisms of retarding cancer growth, it was confirmed by Harland and Liburdy (1997) that synthetic magnetic fields prevented their immunity effects. When we consider that the magnetic fields blocked the immune activities of *both* biochemicals—which work within different mechanisms—the affect of synthetic magnetic fields on the human body illustrates an *immune system magnetic interference* model.

This magnetic field interference model of electromagnetic exposure is further supported by research published in 2002 by Saunders and Jefferys. Brain tissue testing showed that even very low frequency electric and weak magnetic field exposure will induce electric fields and currents inside the body. These fields excited various nerve cells and retinal cells, inducing abnormal metabolic activity.

The immune system magnetic interference model mechanism is further confirmed by a study of magnetic and electric fields on neural cells by Blackman (1993). While magnetic fields stimulated abnormal neurite outgrowth between 22 and 40 mG, increased electric fields did not stimulate the same morphological change.

In contrast, the natural magnetic field strength of the earth ranges from about .2 gauss to .6 gauss (200-600 mG)—often also measured as .05 Tesla (1 Tesla=10,000 gauss). To give some reference with nature's levels, an MRI magnet will range from one to three Tesla, or 10,000 to 30,000 gauss. This is equivalent to 10,000,000-30,000,000 mG.

Appliance Magnetic Fields

Appliance	At 4 Inches	At 1 Foot	At 3 Feet
Blenders	50-220	5.2-1.7	.3-1.1
Can openers	1300-4000	31-280	.5-7.0
Clothes dryers	4.8-110	1.5-29	.1-1
Coffee makers	6-29	.9-1.2	<.1
Crock pots	8-23	.8-1.3	<.1
Electric drills	350-500	22-31	.8-2.0
Electric shavers	14-1600	.8-90	<.1-3.3
Faust blowers	3-120	.25-37	<.1-3.1
Fluorescent desk lamps	100-200	6-20	.2-2.1
Fluorescent fixtures	40-123	2-32	<.1-2.8
Hair dryers	3-1400	<.1-70	<.1-2.8
Irons	12-45	1.2-3.1	.1-.2
Microwave ovens*	39-75	2.7-6	.18-.75
Mixers	58-1400	5-100	.15-2.0
Portable heaters	11-280	1.5-40	.1-2.5
Saber and circular saws	200-2100	8-210	.2-10.0
Televisions	4.8-100	.4-20	<.1-1.5
Toasters	10-60	.6-7.0	<.1-.11
Vacuum cleaners	230-1300	20-180	1.2-18.0

Source: Gauger, 1985 *Gauger 1997 (at 3.6, 10.8 and 25.2 in)

Conclusions

We can draw a number of conclusions from this research. The first conclusion is that at close distances, ionizing radiation can be harmful and we should avoid or remain far away from the source. Non-ionizing radiation is more complex. Close-range RFs should be avoided, and we should also keep some distance from non-ionizing sources of radiation. The immediate effects of non-ionizing radiation are certainly more subtle. This does not mean that non-ionizing sources of radiation are not harmful to our health in some way. We may not get cancer, but our normal metabolic processes—which involve the use of electromagnetic waves as discussed earlier—may be subtly affected by non-ionizing radiation of all types. For some, a very small increase in body core temperature will result. For others, there may be brain fog or a subtle slowing of cognitive response time.

The long-term effects of a chronic interference of the body's electromagnetic metabolism by non-ionizing radiation are still to be firmly established. Yet the research presents us with some plausible possibilities. These include reduced immunity, increases in inflammation, headaches, sleep disturbances, and cognitive disturbances. Some of these effects may be too subtle to isolate from the other toxins presented by our environment. Surely we can use the inference from some of the shorter-term studies showing effects on immunity, sleep and cognition to extend out the likelihood of further issues over decades of chronic use.

As revealed in some of the RF research, these effects can be induced to some degree by perceived sensitivities. These can have real effects, however. Just as a placebo can have a real affect on a significant part of a study population (often somewhere in the area of 33%), the perception of sensitivity to EMFs can lead to real effects. The lesson here is that we need to be realistic in our assessment of the danger. If non-ionizing EMFs were more dangerous, the evidence would probably be more obvious.

It makes better sense to wisely use our technologies, and embrace some strategies to increase our body's biowave strength.

🔔 Six
EMF Strategies

Proximity and Tolerance

As mentioned, the effects of synthetic electromagnetic radiation have everything to do with the proximity of the pulse, and our relative tolerance to it. Tolerance means the strength of our body's own biowaves. In this book, we have illustrated many of the body's waveform systems. These include brainwaves, microtubules, biophotons, hormones, neurotransmitters, ion channels and paracrines—inclusive of the ancient channels and conduits of the *chakras, nadis,* and *meridians.*

The relative strength of our body's biowave systems is unique to each of us. We each have varying degrees of tolerance, depending upon how deeply entrained our biowaves are. *Entrained* in this context means that our various body rhythms and biocommunication pathways are tuned to each other and tuned to nature's biowaves.

For example, consider a person who gets up every morning at sunrise and steps outside. The pineal gland receives the first light and begins to stimulate the hypothalamus' releasing hormone to the pituitary gland. This stimulates the pituitary gland to release master hormones, which in turn stimulate the endocrine system.

This relatively simple pattern over time deeply entrains the body's various rhythms. For example, if the person got to bed late one night, it would be difficult to sleep late, because the body is so adapted to waking at sunrise.

This hardening of the body's biowaves also produces more resistance to other interruptions. While these interruptions can include toxins and other stressors, here we are being more specific to synthetic radiation.

Waking with the sun is not the only pattern that will make our biowaves strong. Other biowave stimulators include eating natural, whole foods at the same times each day: drinking sufficient water approximately the same times each day; regularly spending considerable time outside sunbathing; and exercising about the same time each day can all strengthen our biowaves and body rhythms. Healthy patterns like these do more than give the body good fuel and metabolic stimuli: They also reinforce our body's natural waveforms. This reinforcement yields a stronger defense against intrusive frequencies. Reinforcement means that our various waveform rhythms are synchronous with each other. When our biowaves and rhythms are in sync, it is very difficult to interfere with them.

Let's use an analogy: Let's say that we are a drummer in a band and we are playing a song. If the band is all playing the song with the same key and rhythm loudly, a crowd of screaming fans in the audience will do little to interrupt the melodies and rhythms coming from our band's song. However, if our band is not well trained, and some of the musicians are out of sync or out of key, then the crowd's noise will easily interrupt the perceived hearing of the band. The entire combination of noise from the crowd and the disharmonic band will create a more chaotic orchestration: making it more difficult to hear the songs being produced by the band.

When our body's biowaves are reinforced and playing out with solidarity, our immune system will be stronger. Our breathing will be healthier. Our heartbeat will be steady and strong. Our liver will be stronger. Our brainwaves will be stronger. These will all resist any interference coming from most synthetic electromagnetism.

At the same time, we should still be careful about our proximity to synthetic radiation. The closer we stand to an electrical circuit or appliance, the larger the radiation dose will be.

For many appliances, the difference will be negligible. Standing close to a light will not have the same effect as standing next to a microwave, for example. This is obvious from the chart on page 213. Here we can see that the magnetic field strength at 4 inches is significantly greater than the field strength at one foot away.

Why is this? It is because magnetic fields disperse through the environment. We see the same effect in a pond. If we drop a rock, the wave amplitude of the circular waves coming off the rock are significantly less as they move further away from the rock's entry point. This is due to water's resistance, as we've discussed.

These phenomena were studied intensely during the 1940s, as the U.S. military measured the effects of nuclear explosions with respect to proximity. They determined that even a relatively short distance from a blast made a significant amount of difference in radiation levels.

The author's own meter testing has illustrated that there is a dramatic difference in magnetic field strength between touching the surface of a computer laptop and touching an external keyboard less than one foot away. There is also a dramatic difference between sitting directly in front of a television and sitting eight feet away from it.

These are quite simple methods to significantly reduce our exposure to magnetic fields from our appliances. The question of how far we should stand back from any electromagnetic appliance should be answered with: *How far can we stand back from it and remain functional?*

If we must use a microwave, for example, we can turn it on and immediately leave the kitchen as it *minimally* heats our food [not requiring sterilization]. The same strategy can be applied to any electromagnetic kitchen appliance. This includes toasters, electric ovens, refrigerators and more. We do not need to treat this as a medical emergency or panic about the EMFs in our environment. We simply need to minimize their use (also good for the environment as saving electricity will save our resources), and step back from them to the degree possible during their operation.

In many cases, we simply do not need an appliance. Cutting vegetables with a knife is not only better than using an electric cutting tool: It also exercises our wrists and fingers. Exercising our wrists and fingers reduces the risk of arthritis and other mobility issues. Can openers are another example. Electric can openers are completely unnecessary unless we are disabled. Manual can openers are quite effective, and are safer. They are also more effective in an emergency, should we face a blackout and still want to have some canned food. (By the way, canning vegetables preserves nutrients far better than freezing them over time.)

At three feet, EMR from most electric appliances falls off rapidly. For televisions, this extends to about ten feet. We can keep a distance of at least five feet away from a working microwave oven. Laptops can be taken off our laps whenever possible. Hands and wrists can be kept off the surface as much as possible. A peripheral keyboard can be considered.

Currently, there are several television projector screens available on the market that will project a large picture of the television image onto a wall. Sitting away from the projector and watching this projected image can reduce our magnetic field exposure.

Many other strategies to stand back and away from our appliances can be applied. The difference in exposure levels is so significant when standing back only a foot or two that we need not panic with regard to using appliances. We simply need to use them wisely and apply some common sense.

Ionization

We can determine whether the EMR source is emitting ionizing or non-ionizing radiation, as described in the previous chapter. Many appliance manuals give emission levels. Others can often be found on the internet. Ionizing radiation should be avoided or minimized to the greatest degree possible. Non-ionizing appliances can still produce significant magnetic fields as we have discussed. Here proximity is the issue.

Electricians and other technicians who work for many hours in close proximity to electronic appliances that emit large magnetic fields and/or radiofrequencies can consider other protective measures as discussed below. For these professionals, the risk of side effects from EMR is much greater, and a greater focus can be placed on this issue.

Power lines and RF Towers

Powerlines and cell towers can be approached with the same principles in mind. The further away the better. At some point, as we've discussed, they both have very little influence upon our metabolism. That safe level might be different for each of us, depending upon our age, general health and biowave strength.

We might consider selecting housing that is at least 100 feet away from any high-frequency power line, and double that for a large transformer or an RF tower. Certainly, this should be the case when having a baby or young children in the house.

Surge Protectors

Running power cords through surge protectors and switching them off after using the appliance has several benefits. This can significantly reduce the amount of idling power moving through the appliance and the wiring to the appliance. This can also lower electric bills and reduce house, power line and grid loads.

Medical Scans and X-rays

Lead aprons should always be worn whenever taking x-rays. The apron should cover as much of the body as possible, and can cover the neck region during dental x-rays. It is probably also not a bad idea to close the eyes during a series of mouth x-rays as well.

Often doctors or dentists will take extra x-rays even though a recent set is available. We may need to help this along by making sure a previous doctor's images are delivered to our current doctor. We might also tell the doctor that we would like to limit our radiation exposure to a reasonable extent.

CAT-scans (or CT scans) can be questioned and avoided if they are deemed to be unnecessary. If we ask our physician if the CAT-scan is absolutely necessary, we may find out that they can diagnose the same issues with x-rays or other, less invasive techniques. Often times, the CT is done in order to confirm a diagnosis, or worse, as insurance against a possible malpractice suit.

We should also know that magnetic fields in the equipment rooms in these facilities can often exceed 10 milligauss. This is considered an unhealthy level, so we might want to minimize our exposure to these facilities to what is absolutely necessary, and consider some of the below methods of biowave strengthening before and following such exposure.

Occupational EMF Hot Spots

Airplanes and other locations that maintain a large amount of electronic equipment can expose our bodies to significant levels of electromagnetic fields and RF waves. While the passenger area in an airline can present reasonably high magnetic fields for the duration of an occasional flight, the cockpit can presents a significantly higher level of magnetism—often more than 12 milligauss. This means that airline pilots—who spend many hours exposed in this way—should consider taking some precautions. Other occupations that present increased exposure to EMFs—magnetic fields in particular but also radiofrequencies as well—include nurses and doctors, electricians, control tower operators, radio technicians, electrical engineers, auto mechanics, and others who work around multiple electronics or in electrical facilities.

For these occupations, it makes sense to minimize exposure when possible, and keep our biowaves strong before, after and during periods of exposure, as described below. Any break times can be spent away from the exposure areas, and if possible, outside in the sun or in a garden or wooded area.

Tanning beds

The tanning bed industry is huge. Tanning salons in the U.S. take in some $5 billion a year now. This is especially true in northern areas, where tanning salons not only provide brown skin: They also supply UV light exposure and vitamin D production. The ultraviolet exposure from tanning beds may also help pain and fibromyalgia.

In one study, done at Wake Forest University School of Medicine (Taylor *et al.* 2009), nineteen fibromyalgia patients received either UV exposure or not over a period of eight weeks. The UV-treated patients experienced an increased general sense of well-being, more relaxation, and reduced pain levels compared to the non-UV patients.

Then there is the other side of the coin. In a study done by researchers at the University of Iowa (Ting *et al.* 2007), 1,518 clinic patients underwent analysis and survey for melanoma and tanning bed use. Those with a history of melanoma had more than three times the likelihood of having used a tanning bed in the past. Women under the age of 46 had more than four times the likelihood of having used tanning beds.

The interesting thing is that tanning beds expose the salon customer to about the same proportion of UVA and UVB as the sun does. Yet melanoma rates for tanning bed users are much higher than outdoor sun worshipers. Why is this?

Most believe that it is because of the intensity of the tanning bed. Sitting under tanning bed lights for 10-15 minutes will theoretically produce more intense exposure to UVA and UVB than sitting outside during the mid-day sun for well over double that period of time.

The consideration that most do not make, however, is the exposure to the other electromagnetic fields these light systems produce. For example, a typical tanning bed at a salon with have from 20 to

60 lamps. Each of these lamps will utilize 100 to 200 watts. Each lamp will utilize phosphor excitation to produce the light. The excitation of atoms within the bulb, along with the current running through the bulb will produce a significant amount of magnetic fields. While the electronic portion of the alternating current may be shielded with dual cords to lower polarity, the magnetic fields will be proportionate to the magnetic bulb ballasts. Some tanning bed lights also emit x-rays. These present additional EMF exposure.

Using a conventional tanning bed is not such a good choice. Why not just step outside into the sun? For extreme or northern winters, cases of SAD and vitamin D deficiencies, tanning beds may have some value, assuming they are some of the more recent "healthier" tanning bed versions that utilize low-magnetic ballasts. Some of these tanning beds also produce red light, blue light and infrared light. Red light is known to increase relaxation while suppressing melatonin (some say it reduces wrinkles but this appears to be anecdotal). This can be helpful in cases of phase-shift sleep disorders. Blue light therapy has been shown in some cases to reduce acne, specifically cases due to certain types of bacteria.

Any tanning bed and salon can be tested for EMR with a meter prior to its use. At any case, do not fall asleep in a tanning bed. Set an alarm and make sure the maximum dose is not exceeded. This should generally be no more than about 10 minutes.

Cell Phones

We can limit our cell phone use to urgent or important calls, talk briefly, and use a headset or better yet, the cell phone's speaker. Just about every new cell phone has a speaker now. Bluetooth headsets emit 2.4 GHz short-range radiofrequencies. Though non-ionizing, there is little research on the long-term effects of this technology. Headset wires can also emit magnetic fields, although a properly shielded, double-strand speaker and microphone wire will emit little in the way of magnetic fields.

Some cell phones emit more radiofrequencies and magnetic fields than others. These specifications can be found in the phone's manual and may also be on the phone's body (although not always).

The Cellular Telecommunications Industry Association (CTIA) has developed a standard measurement, called the SAR or *specific absorption rate*. The association states that this is *"a way of measuring the quantity of radio frequency (RF) energy that is absorbed by the body."*

SAR ratings have two general standards: The European standard and the North American standard. Both utilize watts per kilograms of body tissue. However they differ by whether they use a one-gram or a 10-gram average volume:

North American Standard: The SAR cell phone limit for public use is 1.6 watts per kilogram (W/kg). This is averaged over one grams of body tissue.

European Standard: The SAR cell phone limit for public use is 2.0 watts per kilogram (W/kg). This is averaged over ten grams of body tissue.

These standards can be used to compare phones side by side. One standard measurement cannot be compared to another phone with a different standard measurement. Using the European standard, commercial cell phones can range from about 0.18 W/kg to about 2.2 W/kg. Cell phones in the U.S. can range from about .26 W/kg to about 1.8 W/kg using the North American standard. Most levels will range below both standards, however.

Obviously, choosing a phone with a lower SAR is a good idea. This may not be possible, however, as the phone we want or need may have a higher rating. See the EMR shield section for information on reducing SAR levels in your phone.

Measuring EMFs

A TriField® EMF meter can be used to measure workplace, home, phone, vehicle and other environments. We can use this to determine safe levels of magnetic fields, radiofrequencies and electrical pulses.

To use, simply turn the dial to the desired test (RF, mag or elect) and place or hold the meter at the location of the body's proximity to the appliance. For most small household appliances, there will be little or no electric potential, and little RF if any: Certainly in the safe zone.

Magnetic fields may be a different matter, however. A small household appliance, as we've illustrated earlier, can have a significant magnetic field emission at close proximity. Depending upon our sensitivity, magnetic field levels over 5-6 mG can cause concern—especially for any length of time. We might consider standing back from the appliance at or near these levels.

Field Canceling Equipment

There are a number of field canceling devices on the market. While lead and nickel aprons and garments have been shown to protect against EMR doses in clinical settings, the effects of bio-wave products on the market have been more controversial.

Some, however, present small laboratory studies to back up their value. Without naming brands, the author has seen laboratory testing that has shown that EMR levels are reduced well over 75% of their field strength. These results are worth considering. The author has experienced a noticeable effect while wearing one in close proximity to electronics.

Some of these devices are very reasonably priced, and present little or no risk of side effects. Wearing an EMR canceling device on the wrist or on a pendant around the neck should be considered by electricians, those who fly frequently, or those who are otherwise in close proximity to electrical appliances for an extended period. There is certainly little risk involved in wearing one.

The costs for some of these devices are ridiculously inexpensive for the level of risk reduction they can offer. SAR shield devices are typically very small–the size of a dime or nickel. They adhere to the back of the phone as one might apply a small decal sticker: Very convenient and simple for the extent of shielding provided.

EMF shield devices are available from a number of vendors of varying reputation and credibility. Closely examining the laboratory data and reputation of the company before spending money is not a bad idea. Consider buying from a manufacturer who can provide laboratory and clinical data specific to the device. A return policy is also not a bad idea.

Wellness Self-Assessments

We can also judge whether our EMR dose might be burdensome by assessing how we are feeling when we are using these devices. Do we feel dizzy? Tired? Do we have brain fog? Does part of our body located closest to the device feel hot or feverish? These symptoms can lead to more serious health concerns later, and can be responded to immediately by turning off the device or standing back from it. Other biowave enforcement strategies discussed below can also be considered.

Self-assessments require placebos in order to safely judge their accuracy. As was found in RF tower research, it is very easy to feel more sensitive to RFs if we know a cell tower is near.

Thus, we need to self-assess before we know the levels (and proximity with respect to cell towers) of our possible EMR sources. This should be done with a small notepad or chart listing:

DATE TIME LOCATION OBSERVATIONS COMMENTS
("observations" would refer to how we are feeling).

So we note the time and place, and describe any mysterious ill effects we might feel at any point during the day or night over a period of time. The chart should cover at least a month or two in order for us to be able to see a reasonable trend. Here is an example of a possible entry into the above-mentioned categories:

July 12, 2010/12:30pm/Desk/Brain fog/Working on computer.

In terms of assessing levels or distances, we might utilize a partner or friend to qualify proximity or levels using the TriField® meter once we are finished with at least 45 days of our assessment.

As we ponder synthetic radiation in our work or home environment, we should also consider that extreme focus or attention on the issue—especially if emotions are involved—could serve to increase our negative EMF responses. The mechanism here is that our minds can lower our biowave strength and thereby increase our susceptibility to synthetic radiation. Better to perform periodic self-assessments and tactfully become aware of any other similar complaints among those in the same environment.

It's probably better to approach the topic without too much urgency. This can be interpreted incorrectly, as others may see our concern as unnecessary. It may also alert people unnecessarily to a problem that does not exist for everyone. It may well be that we have more sensitivity to synthetic EMFs than most. In this or in any case, we can take practical steps to reduce our exposure and increase our EMF resistance by increasing our biowave strength. Let's discuss this strategy in more detail:

Conducting Nature's Biowaves

Our body's biowaves resonate with the earth, moon, stars, oceans, rivers, soils, rocks, sky, colors, plants and so many elements within nature. After millions of years of entrainment, the human organism is tuned into these waves. Should we connect with these elements on a regular basis, we will help maintain our body's internal waves and rhythms. Regular contact with nature's elements, exercise, whole foods, fresh water and quality sleep can considerably strengthen our biowaves. They can also increase our body's threshold for synthetic electromagnetic radiation. Let's look at some specifics on how we can strengthen our biowaves by aligning with nature's array biowaves.

Our modern-day indoor lifestyles have disconnected most of us from nature's biowaves generated by the sun, the earth, the atmosphere, wind, water and so on. As a result, many people—especially those in first world countries—suffer from weakened immunity, allergies, food sensitivities, lethargy, fibromyalgia, cancer, autoimmune disorders, insomnia and other degenerating issues. Our indoor habitats are replete with electromagnetic influences that disrupt nature's geomagnetic fields. Are these necessarily the sole cause of these issues? We can surely state that at the very least, our indoor lifestyles prevent many of the preventative and healing properties that these (clean) elements supply.

The only way to participate fully with the electromagnetic waveform flows of nature is to be outside where they directly influence our bodies without the interference caused by wiring circuits, air conditioning, appliances, insulation, siding, sheet rock, and hydrocarbon roofing material. These "skins" effectively alter most of the rhythms and electromagnetic fields that nature is circulating. Otherwise, we can bring nature's elements into our indoor lifestyles.

Becoming Grounded

Grounding is just as critical for our electromagnetic body as it is for a house circuit or electrical grid. Grounding is essential for maintaining the appropriate polarity within our body's vast array of biowaves.

We can most efficiently become grounded by connecting with the biomagnetic flows of the earth. There are several methods for accomplishing this:

Walking barefoot: By walking barefoot on the ground or beach, we reorient our biowaves to align to the polarity of the earth's geomagnetic waves. Walking barefoot on rocks, grass fields, beaches and gardens can be an exhilarating experience. Natural wood or stone floors in our house can also be effective if they are built upon a slab foundation without a basement. Even still, these will not be as powerful as directly walking directly on the ground.

Sitting and lying on the ground: If we aren't walking, we can sit down on the grass or on a rock when we are outside. We can also sleep outside on the ground. Going camping and sleeping in a tent on the ground is an incredible experience—nothing like sleeping in a camper van or recreation vehicle. Air mattresses placed on the ground are also effective, as they (and waterbeds) conduct the earth's geofields quite well.

Working in the garden: Gardening is a great way to become grounded because we can stick our hands and fingers directly into the soil as we plant and weed our garden. Gardening provides other natural biowave contact as well, as our body can absorb sunshine, breathe fresh air, and be in intimate contact with plant life. As we'll discuss, these all work together to increase our body's biowave strength.

Thermal stones: A great way to align with the earth's fields is to use hot thermal stones. This is an ancient method used by the Polynesians (called *lomi lomi*), by Ayurvedic practitioners (called *shila abhyanga*) and by North American Indians. These therapies each utilize smooth flat, hand-sized stones. The stones can be heated in hot water or heated in the mid-day sun by laying them on the ground for an hour or two. This will transfer the sun's radiation to the stone as it absorbs additional geomagnetic fields. The stones can be stroked over the skin with massage oil or they can simply be laid upon key areas (on the *chakras,* acupuncture points or sore areas) until they cool off.

Crystals

Humans have been utilizing crystals for healing and energizing for thousands of years. The *Ebers Papyrus* documents the use of crystals by Egyptian healers several thousand years ago. Crystal therapy was used extensively in ancient India and China by healers that understood the crystal's ability to resonate with the *chakra*s, *nadis and meridians.*

Crystals are electromagnetic conductors, as we discussed earlier with regard to their ability to conduct radiowaves. The original cat's whisker crystal diode rectifier utilized galena crystals, which are composed of lead sulfite. This crystal was the original semiconductor that effectively conducted radiowaves into the thin bronze wire called the cat's whisker. Quartz crystals are also used in many appliances, as their silicon dioxide crystalline structure conducts a variety of electromagnetic waveforms.

Crystals have been instrumental in humanity's development of modern technology. Ubiquitous digital appliances now utilize crystalline semiconductors such as silicon. The first laser, developed by scientists from the Bell Laboratory, utilized the ruby crystal to focus the laser beams. Photonic crystals have been responsible for much of the advancement with today's fiber-optic cabling technologies. Photonic crystals are grown from colloidal crystals and arranged with layered semiconductor crystals. Many of today's LED devices utilize gallium arsenide crystals to convey their micro-laser information displays.

Holography has also been developed through the use of crystals. In the 1980s, Philips Research Labs utilized lithium niobate crystals to disperse duplicative light through a demonstration movie.

Today, most semiconductors are synthetically produced (or "grown"). Silicon is such a blended, "grown" crystal. Because these synthetic crystals are grown, they still maintain the lattice, crystalline structures that resonate with nature's waveforms. The crystalline structure interacts with particular waveforms, allowing for a filtering or tuning process to take place.

As we've discussed, the body is full of crystalline molecules. Neurotransmitters, hormones, enzymes, DNA/RNA and many ions are semiconducting crystals, as they conduct and filter information biowaves as they vibrate through the body. Neurons also function as semiconductors. The retinal photoreceptors are semiconductors. The list goes on.

The body's biowave currents that circulate through the *meridians*, *nadis* and *chakra*s can thus be focused and amplified by the application of natural crystal gems. The gems that resonate with the waveforms of a particular *chakra, nadi* or *meridian* will modify and amplify those waveforms as they circulate through the body. This amplification can balance that elemental plane with its presiding biowaves. At the same time, any of the crystals that resonate with any of the *chakras* can strengthen and balance (or tune) all of the body's biowaves if applied with care and humility.

The dominant crystal gems and systems that resonate with each *chakra* include:

First chakra gems: The crystals that most resonate with this *chakra* include the onyx, the ruby, the garnet and the red jasper gems. Their trigonal crystal system and rhombohedral lattice structure resonates with this *chakra*.

Second chakra gems: The second *chakra* as we move up the spine, resonates with the hematite, the moonstone, the camelian and the orange zincite gems. The cubic crystal system, with its isometric (or cubical) shape resonates more closely with the biowaves of this *chakra*.

Third chakra gems: This third *chakra*, positioned along the spine around the solar plexus, resonates with the topaz, the citrine and the amber gems. Their hexagonal crystal system, made of hexagonal lattice shapes, resonates with this *chakra*.

Fourth chakra gems: This heart *chakra* resonates most with the rose quartz and the Chinese fluorite gems. The tetragonal crystal system, with its seven lattice points, resonates with this *chakra*.

Fifth chakra gems: This *chakra*, oriented at the throat level of the spine, resonates best with the turquoise blue lace stone and the agate gem. Their orthorhombic crystal system, with its stretched cubic lattice shapes, harmonically aligns with this *chakra*.

Sixth chakra gems: This *chakra* is also referred to as the third eye, and resonates with the sapphire, the turquoise and the lapiz gems. The monoclinic crystal system, with its rectangular prisms, most closely resonate with the sixth *chakra*.

Seventh chakra gems: This is the crown *chakra*, which resonates with the amethyst and clear quartz crystals. Their triclinic crystal system and orthorhombic lattice structure resonates best with this most important *chakra*, according to *Ayurveda.*

In order to utilize these gems to increase the body's biowave strength, we first need to select the gem(s) appropriate to our bio-wave weaknesses. Each type of gem will amplify the strength and output of the particular *chakra* it resonates with. We can accomplish this by examining the *chakra* section in Chapter Four and self-assessing our general weaknesses. If we are unsure, we can select whatever gem we seem to resonate best with. It is hard to make a mistake here.

For example, if a person is finding that when they are around RF of EMF radiation, they get a headache, they might consider rubbing or holding a turquoise or agate stone at the base of their occipital region (back of the skull). We can simply hold it against the skin or rotate it in a clockwise rotation around the area.

Likewise, nausea or digestive problems resulting from EMF exposure can be responded to by rubbing a topaz or citrine around the spine behind the solar plexus and over the abdomen.

Another way to use crystals is to hold one between the thumb and forefinger up to the sun, and let the sunshine pass through the crystal and diffract onto the body. This is thought to have more effects when someone else holds the crystal up to the sun, while letting the spectrum of light hit either our *chakra* areas (best) or parts of our body that are adversely affected.

Alternatively, we can set a crystal on a table nearby and allow the light to be dispersed around the room. This effect can be increased by hanging the crystal on a string next to a window to let the sunlight from the window enter and diffract through the crystal into the room.

A useful strategy might be to purchase gems for all seven of the *chakra*, and place them around our room or office. We can also place them near the respective *chakra* or have our mate gently rub them into the location.

We can also wear these gems on our body. Most gem experts agree that this was why the ancients began wearing gems as jewelry—as healing therapies. As gem knowledge was lost, the tradition continued.

For example, wearing a rose quartz or Chinese fluorite on a gold or silver chain around the neck with the crystal hanging in the heart region will strengthen the heart *chakra* throughout the day.

Remember that strengthening one *chakra* will also strengthen the others. *Chakra*s are not independent of each other. Strengthening one will not weaken the other, as often happens with synthetic western medical therapies.

We also do not necessarily have to put the appropriate stone on or around the *chakra* in order for it to be therapeutic. This is because the biowaves of that *chakra* will also be circulating throughout the body, unless blocked somewhere. (Blockages can also be cleared with the application of crystals). Putting the gem on the *chakra* more directly increases the strength of that *chakra*.

Crystals are significantly useful during periods of brain fog that may be stimulated by synthetic EMF exposure. A quartz can be placed on the forehead or top of the head to increase clarity, for example.

In *Ayurveda*, crystals were also connected with particular planets and houses. Thus, a person might choose a particular crystal that most closely resonated with their birthday. In addition, particular times of the day are linked with particular crystals, and years will have governing crystals. The Ayurvedic science of crystals was complex to say the least.

This complexity is reflected by modern technology's use of crystals in laser technology, fiber-optic communications, semiconducting and digital electronics. Consider that these technologies are currently some of science's greatest achievements: And they all utilize crystals in their processes.

Finding crystals to use should not be hard. Raw mined stores that are manually cut provide the clearest conductance. Jewelry versions of these stones can be ground or otherwise processed to a point where their ability to conduct EMFs can be slightly hampered. Raw stones that have been cut off mine walls or otherwise broken off larger stones are probably the best choices.

Solar Resonation

Radiation from the sun can significantly strengthen our body's biowaves and resistance to synthetic radiation. When our body absorbs the sun's rays, our own waves begin to resonate with the sun's radiation. This can be compared to striking a chord or tuning fork in a room full of instruments tuned to the same key. As the sound vibrates through the standing instruments, the chord begins to resonate through those instruments, due to their structure. The other instruments begin to vibrate at the same frequency.

This can also be seen with two tuning forks of the same key. As one is struck, the other begins to vibrate. Just being in the sun for a minimum of 20-30 minutes every day can reset and significantly retrain the body's biowaves.

Sun gazing during sunrise and sunset can refresh our biowaves. Many traditional medicines including Ayurvedic, North American Indian, Mayan and Greek disciplines have recommended sun gazing for a number of ailments. The particles in the earth's atmosphere will filter the sun's ultraviolet waves as the sun approaches the horizon. Both the ultraviolet and the infrared spectrum are almost completely blocked 15 minutes before the sunset and 15 minutes after sunrise. These times are typically safe to look directly at the sun. We can also check our local weather station website, the newspaper or the NOAA weather service for the hourly ultraviolet index.

Near the end of the day—at around dusk—the sky can have an array of colors, reflecting the rays of the sun reflecting through more of the atmosphere. The post-sunset sky can turn purple, violet, and even indigo. As discussed earlier, these colors can influence spiritual insight and thoughts of higher consciousness, as we ponder the meaning of our lives and our purpose. We may also experience increased reflective and meditative feelings—as darkness begins to fall and the sky becomes increasingly violet and indigo.

Sunset or sunrise gazing is best accompanied by consistent blinking and looking away at other natural images in the distance. Initially we can point the eyes and face at the setting or rising sun with eyes closed. After doing this for a few days or weeks, the eyes can gradually be opened, while blinking frequently. After 10-15 seconds, the eyes can then wander over other images until the image of the sun has disappeared from the eyelids. We can gradually increase our gazing time to a comfortable 5-10 minutes. Consult with your eye specialist prior to undertaking gazing.

It is not appropriate to stare at the sun 15 minutes after sunrise or fifteen minutes before sunset. If the sun is rising or setting upon the water this limit can be shortened to 10 minutes. Retinal damage can result if we stare at the sun when it is too high. This also applies to solar eclipses as well. Staring at a solar eclipse can damage our eyes as much as looking directly at the mid-day sun.

Sunbathing can be done for just long enough to derive the sun's benefits without producing the damaging effects caused by too much exposure and the wrong kind of exposure.

Here are a few tips for healthy sunbathing:

Creams and Sunscreen: Sun exposure is best without any creams or lotions. Many lotions have toxic ingredients. Even the healthiest oils and lotions can become oxidized or otherwise degraded by the sun's rays, creating more free radicals and denatured molecules.

Gradual exposure: Reasonable sun exposure starts with taking walks, gardening or sitting outside while allowing the sun's rays to shine upon our heads, feet, arms, and hands. The fair-skinned can begin with a few minutes in the morning sun or late afternoons. Expose skin in stages: First the arms and legs; then the neck and shoulders; then the chest and back. Gradually, we can build up melanin content on each area. Melanin is evidenced by a light brown skin color. Skin type, previous sun exposure, time of day and location are determining factors for how much exposure is healthy.

We can also gradually expose new areas, such as the shoulders, neck, chest and back. Gradually increase time on previously exposed areas or add new areas each day. New areas will produce greater levels of vitamin D in the same amount of time.

Avoid erythema: In no case should the exposure result in a pink skin color. This should be considered sunburn. Sunburn is not advisable in any circumstance.

After this slow build-up, we should be able to spend 1-2 hours in morning or late afternoon sun without burning. Hat and clothing can be used if the skin begins to feel hot. Mid-day summer sun should be limited to about 10-15 minutes for a fair-skinned person and more for darker skinned persons. The mid-day sun will maximize our vitamin D production. For summertimes in latitudes below 42 degrees, the mid-day sun should be avoided.

Cloudy or sunny, we still receive the sun's waveforms. The sun's ultraviolet-A and ultraviolet-B waves will penetrate cloud cover at about 50%. This means that on a cloudy day we can still produce vitamin D. We can also still sunburn on a cloudy day.

Because vitamin D is stored in fat cells, we can store up enough vitamin D to get us through a few rainy, colder days. If we are north of latitude 42, we can head south every so often during the winter to replenish our vitamin D stores. Even north of latitude 42, getting out into the sun is still important for moods, energy, cognition and biomagnetism.

A vacation in the tropics, where the sun can be 5-10 times more intense, or an extended period outside may provide enough vitamin D for the next month or more. After the vacation, it is still important to be outside for the sun's other benefits.

North of latitude 34, the best time for winter sunbathing is during the mid-day. During the summer, mornings and late afternoons are best for sunbathing. South of latitude 34, mid-day sun should be avoided and mid-mornings and afternoons are best. For areas north of latitude 42, mid-day sun is best all year round. Little vitamin D is produced between November and February in these areas.

If we do not have enough time to spend outside on a particular day, or during winter sun (south of latitude 42, north of latitude 34), exposing our underbelly body parts can more quickly yield vitamin D production. 'Underbelly' parts include the backs of the arms, the armpits, the backs of the knees, the feet, the back of the neck, and of course the belly and butt (assuming privacy). Remember that these areas will burn faster too, so shorter durations or weaker sun positions are required for these parts.

We can still receive many of the sun's healthy waveforms with clothes on. These include radio, infrared and geomagnetic waves. As we've discussed, these waveforms invigorate the nervous system, calm the mind and stimulate hormone production.

For those who have trouble getting outside, the sun can be sought through a window at the appropriate time of day. The window may be better opened, however, to avoid an imbalance between

UV-A and UV-B rays. Glass blocks the sun's UV-B radiation, so we cannot produce vitamin D next to a window.

A healthy diet and good hydration is critical to healthy sun exposure. A primarily plant-based antioxidant-rich diet, rich in colorful foods and fiber, will allow increased sun exposure and vitamin D production. Research has showed that antioxidants reduce or eliminate the damaging effects of reasonable sun exposure. See the author's book, *Healthy Sun* for more information.

The healthiest sunscreen is a hat, clothing, and/or a shade tree. Chemical sunscreen should be avoided, unless cover and clothes are not possible. If we must wear sunscreen, we can choose "natural" versions, preferably without PABA and other chemicals. Sunscreen lotions with zinc and added vitamins and botanicals are now available. These added antioxidants may minimally help neutralize free radicals from sun exposure at the source. They will not replace dietary antioxidants, however.

Night Skies

Moon gazing and stargazing can also significantly strengthen our biowaves. The bodies of our nighttime skies generate electromagnetic radiation and geomagnetism. These resonate with our own bodies.

Finding a darkened place to spy at the distant galaxies, planets, and stars can provide us with a view that can humble even the most arrogant amongst us. Focusing and unfocusing into the depths of space also exercises the eyes. As in sun gazing, by peering in and out of the distances between and among the stars, our pupils enlarge and narrow, and along with it, our ciliary muscles, scleras, retinas, and zonular fibres all bend and flex with the changing focus. As we gaze, our eyes dart back and forth from star to star, the cavity of vitreous humour, optic disc and suspensory ligaments all adjust and resize with our focus.

Positive and Negative Ions

The electromagnetic interaction between water, atmospheric elements, and geomagnetism produces polarity within our local environment. This can radically affect our body's biowave strength.

Atmospheric ions are suspended in our atmosphere. They provide stability between the elements and their atmospheric effects. Humidity, smog, cities, buildings, weather, wind and of course, storms affect our local ions levels.

Outdoor ion counts in rural areas in good weather conditions can range from 200 to 4,000 negative ions, and 250 to 1500 positive ions per cubic centimeter. Positive ion count can increase to over five thousand ions per cubic centimeter ahead of an incoming storm front. This is due to the sudden increase in humidity within the storm front. Once the storm front hits, the level of positive ions falls quickly, and negative ion levels dramatically rise.

Smog and other pollutants dramatically reduce total ion count. This is thought to be because both positive and negative ions will attach to unstable pollutant particles.

Natural settings containing moisture can contain dramatically more negative ions. For example, a waterfall might have as much as 100,000 negative ions per cubic centimeter. Ion levels around crowded freeways tend to be quite low, on the other hand—often below 100 negative ions per cubic centimeter.

Numerous trials have indicated that indoor ion levels are slightly lower than outdoor levels in most areas. This is thought to be because outdoor ions tend to interact with greater levels of moisture, and thus last longer than do their indoor cousins. This also correlates with the existence of the various electromagnetic fields existing within the home due to the use of various electronic appliances.

Negative ions can form easily. One pass of the comb through the hair can create from 1000 to 10,000 ions per cubic centimeter. The living organism is a tremendous ion producer. Assuming adequate grounding onto the earth or a grounding metal, a typical human exhalation will contain from 20,000 to 50,000 ions per cubic centimeter. This correlates with the fluid levels in the body.

Positive ions are typically generated with a decrease of atmospheric pressure; an increase in wind and temperature; a decrease in humidity and a decrease in elevation. This is particularly noticeable in *Foehn winds*—warm winds that descend from mountainous areas down to areas of lower elevation.

Wind patterns considered Foehn include the dry southerly wind (meaning it comes from the south) blowing through the Alps, Switzerland and across southern Germany. The Sharav or Hamsin winds blowing though the desert of the Middle East are Foehns. The Sirocco that blows through Italy and the Mistral that blows through southern France are both considered Foehns. The Chinook winds of western Canada and NW United States, and the Santa Ana winds that blow through southern California from time to time are also considered Foehns. Foehn winds have also been occasionally spotted around various mountain ranges such as the Colorado Rocky Mountains and Tennessee's Smokey Mountains. Foehn winds tend to funnel between mountain ridges, which accelerate their gusting speeds to an excess of 50 miles per hour.

Foehn winds are known for their heat and ultralow humidity, and their propensity for causing erratic fires. They also can cause a number of negative physical and emotional effects in both humans and animals. For these various reasons, the Foehn is often referred culturally as an 'ill wind.' While some have disputed the effects of Foehn winds, both research and observation has indicated otherwise. Research performed by Sulman (*et al.* 1973-1980) indicated these winds are associated with headaches, heat stress, and irritability. Others have documented an increase in allergies and sinus ailments during Foehn winds.

Positive ions also correlate with these immediate changes in temperature, pressure, and humidity. Because positive ions are linked to Foehn winds, it is safe to assume that the various effects related to positive ions are also connected with the environmental effects of Foehn winds.

Not surprisingly, ions' effects upon health and behavior have been the subject of intense study for the past eighty years. This began in 1926, when Russian scientist Alexander Chizhevsky exposed animals to ionized air with negative ions and/or positive ions. In these studies, he found—as have many others such as Krueger and Reed (1976)—that living in positive ion conditions is associated with more illness and shorter life duration when compared with those living in areas with greater negative ion conditions.

Negative ions have been linked to health benefits among humans in a number of studies. Increased negative ions were associated with higher levels of cognition and memory by Delyukov and Didyk (1999), and by Baron (1987). Negative ions were linked with

236

lower levels of aggression by Baron as well. A lower incidence of asthma was observed by Ben-Dou (1983). Lower levels of irritability and higher serotonin levels were also linked with negative ions in two studies by Sulman (1984; 1980).

In Sulman's 1980 study, daily urine samples were taken from 1,000 volunteers one to two days before a storm's arrival during Feohn winds, and during normal weather conditions. The samples were analyzed for neurotransmitter and hormone levels, including serotonin, adrenaline, noradrenaline, histamine, and thyroxine metabolites. The results concluded that during positive ion conditions, an overproduction of serotonin levels resulted in irritability. In positive ion conditions, Sulman found increases in adrenal deficiency and early exhaustion. Positive ions were also associated with hyperthyroidism and subclinical "apathetic" thyroid symptoms.

There are a number of ways to now temporarily increase our negative ion count in our home. These include salt lamps, small indoor waterfalls, and house plants. Some ionizing machines apparently increase negative ions as well.

Beyond this, living in a rural or natural environment or at least frequenting such an environment might be considered to establish a predominantly negative ion local environment.

Natural Light

Many indoor office and lighting systems have poor quality fluorescent lamps. Older models with conventional ballasts tend to flicker at lower frequencies. Their blinking will range from 60-100 times per second. The newer technology of high frequency electronic-ballast compact fluorescent light bulbs have increased frequencies in the 20-40 kilohertz range—over 2000 times faster than the older models. Higher-speed flickering seems to have a far less negative affect.

Remember the research headed up by Professor Dr. Fritz Hollwich published a study in 1979. This showed that people who worked under white fluorescent tube lighting produced higher levels of stress hormones such as adrenocorticortropic hormone and cortisol. He also found that exposure to natural light lowered these levels, and lowered the stress of the subjects.

There are a number of strategies to consider. These begin with working outside, working next to windows, and minimizing our nighttime work efforts. We can also utilize candles, fires, filament bulbs, or full-spectrum bulbs. If fluorescent lights are needed, high-speed ballast or compact fluorescent lights are preferred to conventional ballast bulbs. It can also help to properly shield or filter lights to the greatest degree possible, rather than allow the direct bulk access to our eyes.

Incandescent bulbs are more like fire, because the atoms are radiating from heat. The filament (such as tungsten) wire is sealed within the bulb filled with gas. As electrons are pumped (conducted) through the wire, the wire is heated, producing light. The upper band of the reacting atoms emits visible light, but the lower bands produce primarily heat in the form of infrared radiation. For this reason, incandescent bulbs are not very economical when it comes to energy conservation.

The conventional fluorescent bulb is a tube containing a gas such as argon, together with a small amount of mercury with electrodes on both ends that emit electrons. The compact fluorescent bulb (also called the spiral tube fluorescent, invented by General Electric engineer Edward Hammer) is more efficient because most of the atoms are emitting light through the excitation of the energy orbitals of the atoms within the bulb. Phosphors, or rare earth metals, are used as illuminating factors. In other words, they produce luminescence. The new CFLs utilize newer phosphors that tend to radiate more light per watt of energy. This produces their energy savings.

CFLs also use the newest types of ballasts, which contain electronic rectifiers and transistors within the bulb base. This produces an extremely high emission rate, which is less stressful upon the body than the conventional fluorescent light. It also produces less noise.

Even so, CFLs are still more stressful than natural sunlight.

If we cannot go outside, using natural window light is far better than indoor lighting. Keeping our windows unshaded throughout the day is therefore critical. Demand a window location from your employer. You can quote some of the research quoted here to prove that window lighting improves productivity among workers.

If we are reading or working at our computer during the day— or otherwise working inside—we can consider looking out the window every few minutes.

Sunglasses: The ability to stimulate biowave resonation with nature's pallet of color instantly vanishes with one innocent act: putting on a pair of sunglasses. Sunglasses can modulate a significant part of the visible spectrum. Sunglasses block important light rays from reaching our eyes. They also polarize or diffract light. They mute color as well. Sunglasses can create a depressive state because they limit exposure of light to our pineal gland, changing our output of important energy and mood hormones and neurotransmitters (such as GABA, dopamine and serotonin). If we must wear sunglasses during driving or boating to prevent glare, they can be taken off periodically. Also, consider non-glare sunglasses that polarize with minimal darkening.

While sunglasses are protective when it comes to glare reflecting off cars or water, there is a negative side effect as well: Sunglasses refract, polarize and diffuse light rays. They bring to the eyes unnatural and unreal colors. While some sunglasses may appear to brighten the colors around us, others remove light and colors and thus dampen color. Depressing color will depress our moods and cognition. Artificially brightening and changing the color pallet around us renders an ungrounded, almost eerie mood.

Darker sunglasses can bring about even darker physiological and psychological effects, which serve to increase our sensitivity to synthetic EMR. Darken light exposure depresses the pineal gland, which suppresses serotonin and dopamine availability. These two important neurochemicals are critical to our moods and behavior. Depressing these can result in feeling fatigued, depressed, and lethargic. Dark glasses can unnaturally raise melatonin levels. Increased melatonin stimulates sleepiness and lethargy. In the middle of the day—particularly while driving—this is not a good idea.

Worse are automatic darkening eyeglasses. Eyeglasses that automatically darken with increased light are convenient, and we can appreciate the advances in glass colorimetry. However, the problem with wearing automatically-darkening eyeglasses is that not only are we robbed of much of the light needed to stimulate important hormones and neurotransmitters and cheated of the benefit of natural colors: We are also entraining our bodies, nervous system and endocrine glands to a world of dampened color and reduced light. This entrainment might be compared to sending a person to live in a cave. After awhile, they cannot deal with going outside into the light.

Nature's Colors

Throughout the day, we are provided with nature's rainbow of changing colors, which stimulate and strengthen our body's biowaves. At daybreak, we can see the coming sun with a red-orange-amber hue, stimulating our physical energy. Through the later morning, the yellows of the sun's radiation increase our focus and energy by stimulating cortisol levels. The glowing mid-day sun balances our mood levels as cortisol levels fall. It is important to journey outside for at least a few minutes during the middle of the day to receive these colors.

Nature's colors strengthen our biowaves because they resonate with the radiative energy of our cells, starting with our skin and retinal cells. Different colors stimulate different moods through the effects upon our brainwaves and neurotransmitters.

The colors of our rooms, our houses, our cars, and our clothing can all affect the strength of our metabolic biowaves. Therefore, we can pick the right colors for our surroundings and circumstances.

The walls of our rooms can significantly affect our biowaves and cognition levels. Studies have shown that color photographs with natural scenery are remembered more than black and white photos, though unnaturally colored photos are remembered no better than black and white photos. Therefore, to enhance learning and memory, we can pick natural colors and images in our surroundings with as much natural context as possible. Natural imagery might include, for example, a large picture window to a natural setting, an array of indoor plants, and/or a photograph of a waterfall on the wall. A selection of nature's greens, blues, oranges and yellows can enhance our moods and promote relaxation. This in turn reduces the stress load upon the body.

Our clothing colors can also influence our biowaves and the biowaves of those around us. If we are going to a negotiation where we want to project a calm, cool approach, we might want to wear dark blue. Should we want to convey increased energy and better moods amongst our associates, we might wear an orange tie or scarf. Should we be seeking balance with our environment and relationships, we might consider wearing some green.

Natural Food Colors

A significant amount of research has confirmed that the same pigments providing the color in foods also give those foods nutritional and therapeutic value. Colors are produced from pigments that result from the plant's reception of the sun's EMR combined with nutrition from the soil and water. These colored pigments resonate within our cells and strengthen our biowaves.

For example, curcumin—a color pigment giving turmeric its yellow color—has been shown to enhance the immune system. Curcumin, for example, has been reported to stimulate the production of T cells, B cells, macrophages, neutrophils, and natural killer cells. Curcumin also downgrades inflammatory cytokines (Jagetia and Aggarwal 2007).

Color pigments are produced by plants from the sun and nutrients from the soil. Plants produce most of their color pigments as part of their immune response to viruses, bacteria and other challenges. Many pigments protect the plant from ultraviolet rays. They also provide great benefit to humans. Here are a few:

Red foods including tomatoes, watermelon, apples, strawberries, red raspberries and pink grapefruit contain nutrients such as lycopene and astaxanthin. These biochemical pigments have been associated with cancer prevention, healthy lungs, cardiovascular health, and prostrate health.

Orange foods including squash, carrots, oranges, papaya and mango contain alpha- and beta-carotenes as well as cryptoxanthins. These components convert and support nerve and sensory cells. They also stimulate enzyme processes, provide strong antioxidant activity and increase metabolism. For example, vitamin A is a frequent component in orange foods, which promotes metabolism, nerve transduction, and retinal cell health.

Yellow foods including yellow pears, bananas, corn and summer squash contain limonenes, luteins, carotenes and zeaxanthins—

pigments that guard against cancer growth, assist in detoxification, provide antioxidants, inhibit atherosclerosis, and assist in cellular metabolism.

Green foods including wheat grass, mustard, onions, leafy greens, cruciferous vegetables and spirulina contain zeaxanthins, sulforaphanes, isoiocyanates, allyl sulfides, amino acids and vitamins such as K and C—which assist with liver function, DNA repair, cell metabolism, and cancer prevention among others.

Purple foods including grapes, cherries, cabbage, eggplant and various berries contain ellagic acid, anthocyanins, pomeratrol, pycnogenol and other polyphenols. These elements work conjunctively to inhibit bacteria growth, increase detoxification, prevent cancer growth and balance hormones.

Brown foods including whole grains, nuts and legumes contain good levels of amino acids, fatty acids, vitamin E and isoflavones such as lignans and phytoestrogens. They thus help modulate and regulate hormones, increase immune function, build proteins, nourish cell membranes and provide fiber. They also provide complex carbohydrates—precursors to serotonin and melatonin production.

Saunas

The waveforms of infrared radiation can cleanse and heal our bodies. They also increase our biowave strength. Heat from the sun or fire promotes sweating and detoxification. Heat also raises body core temperature. Our body's thermal circulation can provide healing mechanisms for many illnesses. It can also increase immunity to prevent illness.

Many healthy cultures have used saunas to speed up healing. Traditional saunas used fires and hot stones in an outdoor environment such as a tent or wooden room. The North American Indians have used sweat lodges, and the Finnish used fired furnaces in this fashion. Modern versions usually include a wooden room with an electric heating filament, some with hot stones for pouring water.

The modern *filament sauna* is the least desirable, because the dry alternating current output heats up the body's dermal layer faster than the epidermis and inner tissues. This imbalance can stress the body. For this reason, filament saunas can cause dizziness, fainting and cardiovascular events. Used with caution, this sauna can still successfully produce detoxification.

The filament sauna can also emit tremendous EMR. This can be counterproductive to the activity of detoxification, especially if the time in the sauna is considerable. Heat a filament sauna to 120-130 degrees F before entering. Then a fairly short sauna period of 10-15 minutes is suggested, followed by going outside if possible to balance the alternating current EMR.

The *sweat lodge* is a wonderful sauna strategy because it is outdoors, and utilizes the natural thermal radiation from fire, which heats the body more gradually, and utilizes some of nature's most powerful biowave rhythms.

To make a sweat lodge, simply dig a fire pit and begin a fire with some larger, easy-to-lift stones sitting close to the fire. Erect a small building frame or teepee close by, using sticks from the surrounding environment if possible. In the middle of the framework, dig a small pit and cover pit and ground inside with sage or similar aromatic plants from surrounding area (eucalyptus is nice too). Drape some heavy blankets over the frame. Place rocks at the bottom ends to seal the lodge. After the fire has gone on for a few hours, the stones will be sufficiently hot. Find a sturdy cloth or piece of wood to roll the hot (not fiery) stones onto, and carry into the covered lodge. Enclose the lodge. With ten large stones or many smaller stones, the lodge can get nice and hot. Keep fire smoke out of the lodge, however. Smoke inhalation can be deadly.

The *far-infrared sauna* provides a great form of thermal therapy during colder winter weather. It is good for chronic pain, fatigue, congestion, muscle aches and certainly for over-toxicity. Because it improves circulation, the infrared sauna stimulates the body's healing response. This is because the infrared waveforms more easily pierce through our dermal and epidermal layers, immediately expanding blood vessels and micro-capillaries to stimulate healing, relax muscles and soothe nerves. This immediate effect is quite noticeable, and for this reason, infrared saunas, and infrared massage tools have become extremely popular and effective for detoxification and stimulating circulation.

The far-infrared system uses a series of infrared lamps placed around the sauna room to heat the skin directly. Some can produce a reasonable amount of magnetic radiation (4-5 milligauss) if sitting too close to the bulbs. It would thus be best to position at least 6 inches from any of the bulbs.

A cool or cold bath after any sauna can stimulate the immune system, improve cardiovascular function, and increase lymphatic circulation. Increased water intake is vital during and directly following any sauna. It is best to take at least a half-gallon of water into any sauna. These are all critical for biowave strengthening.

The *sun sauna:* The sun, of course, emits the best infrared radiation. The sun's infrared radiation is tuned to the body's cells. Therefore, the specific waveforms of the sun's thermal infrared waves resonate deeply with the body, opening up micro-capillaries and tissue systems. There is little resistance or stress from the body during heating by the sun. An infrared sauna may also have detoxifying infrared waveforms, but these will accompany subtle electromagnetic waveforms that are a product of alternating current—a modified or synthetic waveform.

The sun sauna simply consists of sitting outside in the direct mid-day sun with a hat, comfortable cotton or wool sweat pants and sweatshirt—allowing the body to sweat by trapping the sun's thermal radiation within the clothing. A hot summer's day is optimal for an outdoor sun sauna, but a sun sauna can work during any season's afternoon sun.

In cooler temperatures, simply put on more clothes until sweating is accomplished. Wearing gloves and lightly binding the edges of the clothing around the neck, arms and ankles will help more completely trap the heat within the clothing. Sun saunas can also be done with tents or sunrooms. A cloth army tent or other thick material tent that blocks ultraviolet is recommended to make the sun tent. A ventilated woodshed can also make a nice sun sauna room.

Music

Music strengthens our body's internal biowaves. How so?

The human ear will pick up air-pressure frequencies from 20 to 20,000 cycles per second, although sensitivity is most prevalent between 1,000 and 4,000 cycles per second. The higher the frequency, the higher the *pitch* the sound appears to our ears. Meanwhile, louder waves have greater amplitudes.

Prior to its entry into the ear canal, sound is a longitudinal wave. These waveforms undulate through air molecules without moving the medium. Longitudinal sound waves move through a matrix of resonating waveforms by interaction and interference. Wave pulses are transduced through the air molecules. It is a sort of hand-off mechanism—a conduction from one molecule to another. This conductance can be measured through pressure gradients, because the waveform interference modulates the density of waveforms within each microenvironment. This modulation of air pressure is what physically vibrates the eardrum.

A natural balance of sound waveforms is critical to the well-being of the body. Research on sound and stress has demonstrated that practically any mechanical sound over the 90 decibels level stresses the body and mind. This type of stress can rival the electromagnetic radiation that is produced by the machine. Sound vibration affects not only the tympanic membrane, ear bones, cilia and neural network, but also the entire body and mind.

Research has documented these effects. Automobile traffic noise levels are often sited as major threat to health, for example. Outdoor traffic noise levels between 55 and 65 dB(A) and considered stressful, and levels greater than 65 dB(A) are considered disruptive. The recommended exposure guidelines given by the *Occupational Health and Safety Association* defines a 90 dB(A) exposure for more than eight hours as hazardous to physical health and hearing. Consistent noise above these levels has been known to cause sleep disturbance and communication interference, create coordination problems, damage social behavior, and cause hearing loss.

A number of studies have cited that sustained levels of 90-95 dB(A) will cause hearing loss and otherwise damage hearing, and 125 dB(A) levels will cause painful hearing. 140 dB(A) is considered the top painful threshold of human hearing. A typical conversation is 55 to 65 dB. A washing machine is about 75 dB(A), while close-in city traffic can get up to 85 dB(A). A subway will have a maximum level of 112 db(A) inside and around subway platforms. A lawn mower might run up to 95 to 110 dB(A), while an average household hums at about 40 dB(A). A power saw will easily push out 110 dB(A), while a pneumatic riveter will easily create 125 dB(A) sound levels. The sound of a jet engine can easily top 150 dB(A).

Interestingly, we have a much greater tolerance for decibel ranges in music than for machinery noise. The typical concert piano ranges from 60-100 dB(A), while most classical instruments range from 85 dB(A) to over 100 dB(A). The trombone, clarinet, cello and oboe for example, can each reach 110 dB(A). Meanwhile a symphony might peak out at over 130 decibels, while a rock concert may easily reach 150 decibels. A walkman headset at mid-volume range will push some 94 dB(A), while a headset and digital music player will easily reach the 105 decibel level, often peaking at 110 decibels. Harmonic distortion in headsets can add 10 dB(A) to these levels, so the equivalent of 120 dB has been measured with personal digital music players.

Mechanical sounds, made of repetitious bursts of forceful pounding, are *monotonous*. Although music also has repetition, it is not monotonous. This is illustrated by the breakdown of the word "monotonous:" *mono*, meaning "single," and *tonus*, meaning "tone." In other words, mechanical sounds are not only repetitious, but they maintain a single tone.

In other words, the prime distinction between music and mechanical noise is variable harmony. The beat and tempo of music is based upon a harmonic—meaning that rhythms are expanded, yet maintain a fundamental tempo and beat. Tones also change, as different notes are blended into a particular tempo. Machine noise might also establish harmonic through repetition, but there is no variance of tempo and there is little or no tonal change. Machinery noise is monotonous due to repetition without tonal change.

Research by Garcia-Lazaro *et al.* (2006) at Oxford University's Laboratory of Physiology has determined that nature's sounds exhibit primarily $1/f$ spectra. The research also established that human subjects prefer melodies with $1/f$ distributions than $1/f0$ (slower) or $1/f2$ (faster) distributions of fluctuations in loudness and pitch. The researchers then tested the sound fluctuations with brain auditory cortex imaging, and found that the auditory cortex responded more positively to the $1/f$ distributions. The researchers concluded that a form of tuning existed between $1/f$ sounds and the brain's auditory cortex pathways.

Humans, plants and animals all respond similarly to certain kinds of music. Australian psychologist Manfried Klein conducted research testing hand-muscle responses to music around the world. He found that regardless of the language and cultural background—whether Japanese, Australian aboriginal, American or otherwise—the emotional response to the same music passages (indicated by hand-muscle tension) were identical. It didn't matter that the music had not been heard before. The emotional response was also the same regardless of whether that particular type of music was familiar (Ackerman 1990).

Music strengthens our biowaves because it resonates with our inner rhythms. This resonation creates the positive affects we relate to certain sounds. In other words, we like the music we like because it resonates with the music already playing within us.

This juxtaposes with unexpected sounds. A sudden loud or unexpected noise can cause *acoustic shock injury*. This injury can cause pain around the ear, phonophobia, vertigo, and tinnitus.

We are almost always prepared to hear music. A musical octave—also referred to as the *perfect octave*—is the interval occurring between notes with a doubling or halving of frequency between them. Another perfect octave will occur when the frequency is doubled or halved again. This is referred to as *equivalency*. The *diminished* or *augmented* octave has a slight variance from a precise doubling, forming a flat or sharp note.

A harmonic is accomplished when sound frequencies are whole integer multiples of a base frequency. The first four harmonics of a 200-hertz frequency are 400 hertz, 600 hertz, 800 hertz, and 1,000 hertz, for example. The whole integer multiple of a sound will harmonize with the first sound simply because its frequency is reflective. By reflective we mean that the successive sound mirrors the waveform of the first sound. This reflective waveform is typically referred to as the *fundamental frequency* in a harmonic sequence. If we look at the concept of harmonic from a broader perspective, we can understand that each harmonic is a reflective fraction or multiple of a fundamental frequency.

The *pitch* of a sound may be related to its frequency, but frequency is not the only characteristic of pitch. The pitch of a sound is its perceived frequency. Frequency is a two-dimensional measurement related to cycles per second. A sound's pitch will still incorporate a variety of *overtones* into the total sound. These include

247

changes in amplitude, tempo, and intonation. These qualities give the waveform informative variance. A sound may have a pitch that appears very much like a note of a particular frequency, yet the sound waveform may not have that precise frequency. The pure note *A,* for example, should have a frequency of 440 hertz. Most concert tuning forks are set to the A-440 frequency for this reason.

Flat or sharp notes move the pitch or frequency adjustment into the *enharmonic genus,* based on the Greek *tetra chord.* The tetra chord concept calls for notes to be tuned in intervals of *perfect fourths.* The four-stringed lyre was its early basis, but later the tetra chord concept was expanded into other instruments. The *diatonic and chromatic* interval systems are also part of the enharmonic system.

Pitch variances are measured in tones. A shift to flat or sharp may become a variance in *semitones, quartertones, duotones,* or even *microtones.* These shifts may also be represented as fractions. For example, a *ditone*—or third major tone—is 16/13 of a full note. The octave concept expressed in tetra chords would thus be a whole tone plus two tetra cords. The *chromatic scale* is a common scale used in music to denote the rise through a series of related notes. The chromatic scale is usually based upon the C note, but the B note and other notes may also be used as fundamental pitches as well. There are typically twelve total pitches in a tempered chromatic scale. Each of these pitches is a half step or semitone step from the prior pitch.

As music math further developed, the perfect fourth led way to the disjunctive *perfect fifth.* Also called the *diapente,* this is a music interval providing harmonious latitude with surrounding tones. On the piano keyboard, perfect fifths are separated by exactly seven keys. The perfect fifth also provides the root of the major and minor chords and their extensions. The *just fifth* provides a 3:2 ratio. The *perfect fifth* has seven semitones—two less than the just fifth.

When notes harmonize, they resonate together. An A-440 tuning fork will vibrate at the 440-hertz frequency, transferring this frequency through the air until it is interfered with by other waveforms. A concert tuning fork will typically be tuned to the violin's third string. As the violin is tuned, the tuning fork and the violin's third string will resonate together.

This occurs because of a facility within the violin's construction that allows it to become an *acoustic resonator.* An acoustic resonator is a point on an instrument or body that carries the vibration of a note for a period of time. In other words, it vibrates at the same frequency. On a violin, for example, the string, the bridge, and the body of the violin all facilitate this resonating system. When the tuning fork is struck and the *A* note resonates through the concert hall, a violin tuned to the *A* note will resonate with the tuning fork, forming a harmonic to tune by. This is the same mechanism occurring within our bodies as we listen to music or sounds we like.

Resonators appear throughout nature. A canyon resonates with the sounds of the wind, birds, trees, and animals. An ocean beach or bay is a resonator of the waves marching in from distant storms. Nautilus shells and conch shells resonate wind in such a way that they sound like the ocean. Garcia-Lazaro *et al.*'s 1/f spectra research confirms that our bodies resonate with nature's sounds. This implies also that the sounds of nature resonate within our bodies— from the largest roars to the smallest chirps.

Dr. Jacques Benveniste and his associates illustrated this directly when they found that biochemicals like hormones and neurotransmitters create tiny harmonic waveforms. They were able to digitally record these just as one might record a song. Like a song, the recorded frequencies could be played back in the presence of living tissue, and those frequencies stimulated effects identical to those stimulated by the biomolecules themselves.

For this reason, *sound therapy* has been remarkably successful for the treatment of a number of disorders. *Voice analysis therapy, Audio-Psycho-Phonology, Tomatis Method,* and various music therapies have all been observed to invoke healing responses.

Music therapy has a long tradition. Over two thousand years ago, Pythagoras and his students explored the relationships between music, the universe, and health quite extensively. His *Music of the Spheres* treatise, handed down by Pythagoras' students, illustrated the harmony existing within the universe; and how this harmony related to music. The writings of Aristotle and Plato describe healing with music. Homer prescribed music to counteract mental anguish, and Asclepiades of Bithynia is said to have prescribed Phrygian music for sciatica and other illnesses. Democritus prescribed various flute melodies, and Pythagoras is said to have clinically applied music for nervousness. The respected Roman physician Galen applied music to his healing repertoire. Among other therapies, Galen prescribed a *"medical bath"* inclusive of flute song for nerve pain. The famous sixteenth century Swiss physician Paracelsus was a strong believer in sound therapy as well. His recommendations included colors and natural sounds in addition to herbal remedies.

Modern western medicine rediscovered music therapy during the twentieth century—although the many classic composers had contributed a wealth of healing to their listeners over the centuries. Music therapy has become a credentialed, evidence-based healing modality. It is used in hospitals and therapy centers around the world. In the 1980s, the Certification Board for Music Therapists began to certify music therapists. Today this organization claims over 4,000 board certified music therapists.

Most researchers agree that a combination of harmony and tempo gives music its soothing effect. The music does not have to be slow to create this effect. Music with faster tempos and drumming beats can also provide calming, therapeutic results. EEG testing has shown many therapeutic relaxation methods do not produce the benefits that native music, Celtic music, and even certain rock and roll music can. Evidently, rhythmic beats provide a balancing effect between the left and right brainwaves. Flutes have also been shown to be particularly therapeutic. Research has also shown that live performances seem to provide more therapeutic results than do recordings. The right mix of therapeutic music increases deep breathing, lowers the heart rate, balances thermoregulation, and increases serotonin production.

Playing an instrument or percussion provides a special benefit to our biowave strength. Playing music will strengthen our inner rhythms. Melodies we play reflect the harmony we feel deep within. Most people can find at least one instrument they can play, even if it is just a makeshift drum of some sort.

Music with slower rhythms—slower than one's heart rate—tends to slow the pulse and increase sleep. Music with faster beats—faster than one's heart rate—tends to increase energy and stimulate activity. Familiar music from the past soothes anxiety and depression, especially among the elderly. These three effects can be combined as well. A tempo that is rhythmic enough to allow us to tap our feet, clap or even dance a little is particularly beneficial.

Studies in the 1960s by Dr. Georgi Lozanov demonstrated that learning and memorization increases with certain types of music. He also found that if information was repeated either every eight seconds or every twelve seconds, its memorization was higher than repetition at other rhythms or randomly. This led to memory comparisons between combinations of beat (frequency) and intonation, and eventually, to different forms of music.

Dr. Lozanov discovered that particular beats and melodies had greater effects upon the body than did others. In particular, he found that music playing around sixty beats per minute—close to the average human resting pulse—substantially relaxed the body. This also had the effect of calming and synchronizing breathing rates. More importantly, music at this tempo consistently increased memory retention, recall, and learning.

Dr. Lozanov's research found that Baroque-style music as composed by sixteenth, seventeenth, and eighteenth century composers such as Handel, Bach and Vivaldi had the greatest positive effects upon learning and memorization skills. These music forms seem to relax the body and focus the mind more than other types of music.

It is not simply the 60 beats-per-minute (or 3600 hertz) frequency rate that encourages this high cognition state—enabling better memorization and physical relaxation. It is the 4/4 or 4/3 tempo along with the various tonal and pitch variances. Numerous beats and intonations have been tested in this research. Few, however, have the effect of increasing learning and relaxation to the degree certain music can (Ostrander 1979).

In 1972, Dan Carlson, a student at the University of Minnesota, conducted research into stimulating plant growth with sound. His research led him to discover that the tiny pores on the leaf's surface that absorb nutrients—the *stomata*—appear to open further within an environment of sounds with particular frequencies. The sound frequencies causing the greatest stomata opening ranged from 3,000 cycles to 5,000 cycles per second—quite similar to the cycles produced by baroque music. As he investigated the frequency results further, Carlson discovered that the sounds were remarkably similar to the sounds of common morning songbirds. The songs of swallows, martins, and warblers appeared to provide the closest match. The songs of these birds stimulated the opening of the stomata the greatest.

Most of us have experienced the calming effect of listening to morning birds singing outside our window. Our own experiences and observations clearly indicate that natural melodies can induce a calming effect, together with a higher level of alertness and mental activity. Biofeedback research confirms that these moods are connected to a preponderance of alpha brainwaves.

In other words, listening to music and certain beats and frequencies will strengthen and support our internal biowaves. They will also sound good.

Touching

Our body resonates with other bodies. By touching each other—especially accompanied by affection and friendship—our body's biowave strength is increased. Why? Remember our discussion of coherence and constructive interference. When our body's biowaves comingle with another's—especially when we are friends or mates—they are reinforced, and will often increase in amplitude.

In the 1960s, a group of psychologists (Harlow 1962; 1964; 1965) studied the relationships between monkeys and their mothers. Some baby monkeys were pulled away from their mothers at birth and put in isolated cages. The scientists observed that these monkeys quickly became hostile, depressed, and unstable as compared with caged monkeys united with their mothers.

Some of the baby monkeys were left alone with wire-built frames made to look like the shape of a monkey. Some of these frames were even built with milk-bottle breasts so the monkey could feed from a pair of fake nipples. Although the baby monkeys tried to hug the fake monkeys and suck milk from the fake breasts, they also became hostile, depressed, and unstable. They simply did not receive the gratification brought on by a loving relationship between mother and child.

Some of the monkeys isolated or caged with wire surrogates were introduced to live monkey surrogates who were not their mothers. These monkeys immediately began to hug the surrogates, and these stressed and hostile monkeys gradually became "normal" (for being imprisoned in cages).

The instinctive exchange of a loving relationship with another living being is critical to the existence of every living being. Once baby monkeys were allowed to exchange a relationship with a living being, they normalized. This is because every living being needs to exchange loving relationships. Contact with a physical form without a living being inside of it (like the monkey wire frames) will not replace our need for a relationship with a living being. The inner self needs to connect with another living being. If we were all physical machines, there would be no need for loving other living beings. We would be fully satisfied with lifeless robots.

The case for our innate need for love is also made among human babies. Several peer-reviewed studies have compared preemie babies (preterm infants) who were held, stroked and/or massaged with preemies who were not. Preemie babies held more often, and were stroked or massaged, grew 47% faster; were significantly more alert; were less stressed and were more responsive to the world around them than preemies who were more isolated during incubation. The touched babies were also calmer and better adjusted later in their childhood than babies who were not touched as often (Field et al. 1986; Hayes 1998; Dieter et al. 2003). This result has been confirmed among lovingly stroked neonatal rats compared to those not stroked (Schanberg and Field 1987). Every organism hosts a love-seeking inner self.

The loving or nurturing touch is by far the most resonating, because we are all, beneath our desires, loving and caring beings. Reaching into this consciousness as we touch others resonates with the other person's deeper being. As our biowaves become connected, we can have a meeting of consciousness. This resonates throughout our natural biowave systems, strengthening them and increasing our tolerance of synthetic versions.

Breathing

Our body takes in oxygen, nitrogen and other elements from our atmosphere. The elements derived from fresh air resonate with our body's biowaves. This resonation heightens immunity and increases our tolerance of synthetic fields. The act of breathing in itself also increases our biowave strength.

Fresh air deep breathing is particularly healthy. Deeply breathing reinforces the conversion process among the body's *chakras* and *meridians*. This is because not only does the body utilize the air's molecules: The body also consumes the electromagnetic fields available within our atmosphere.

For this reason, breathing on a windless day will feel different than breathing on a windy day. Even if the air temperatures are the same, the air we breath in on a windy day will affect us differently. Depending upon the type of wind, breathing on a windy day may feel lighter on the lungs than the air of a still day. This is because wind changes the ion content of the atmosphere, which in turn changes the electromagnetic condition of the air we breathe in. This was also illustrated in the negative and positive ion research discussed earlier.

These polar ions, along with the other electromagnetic elements within our immediate atmosphere, are sucked into our lungs when we breathe. After that, they are channeled through our body's biowave broadcasting systems.

Breathing deeply reinforces the positive effects of the EMFs available in our immediate environment. Deep breathing exercises, including diaphragm breathing and abdominal breathing, are suggested. Deep breathing also helps settle and balance our body's metabolism, and this can help reduce mental and physical stress.

Plant Life

Plants provide a consistent source of resonating biowaves. The biowaves of plants in our immediate surrounding create a field strength quite simply because plants are alive. For this reason, being around plants, or surrounding our living environments with plants will help support and align our biowaves. If we cannot live in a rural area with lots of nature's plants and trees around us, we can bring plants and trees into our homes.

Many of our yards are covered with concrete. Concrete looks tidy, but too much of it is not healthy for our environment, our eyes or our biowave fields. Tucking some plants in between the concrete is an easy way to get more green color diffracting into and around our homes. Even those native plants some consider weeds can offer therapeutic EMFs—along with various medicinal properties. Look for native plants that need little water. Brightly flowering plants can offer additional color benefits.

Stress

As we illustrated on page 166, both physical and mental stress has been linked to a lack of being outside, within nature, where the sun and earth's biomagnetic waveforms can flow uninterrupted.

Anxiety and stress have a number of effects upon the body. One is a reduction in the body's immunity, as our body seeks to resolve a perceived threatening circumstance. When a person begins to focus his or her attention on such a stressor, the body's reserves begin to mount in anticipation of a physical response. This is because the body has been designed for physical response to stress. Initially, the body responds to anxiety with increases in adrenaline and acetylcholine. These stimulate the central nervous system, sensory organs, and the muscles used to leap into action. This state of readiness deprioritizes many metabolic activities, including digestion and immune response. It is like the "all hands on deck" order on a battleship. All the cells become ready for battle.

Our body's biowave broadcasting system corresponds to these biochemical and nerve responses. The body's biowave broadcasting system, which includes the *nadis*, *meridians* and *chakras*, focuses the body upon the physical responses necessary to defend the body. Even if the stressor is psychological, the body will still respond with survival instincts.

This response is intensified in an environment of stressors. There are mental stressors, and then there are physical stressors. Physical stressors include toxins, lack of water, a poor diet, and an environment of synthetic electromagnetic fields.

Consider this analogy. Let's say that we trapped a wolf and we put it in a cage inside a building lit with fluorescent lighting and a room full of noisy, blinking machines. How will the wolf react? The wolf will be freaked out. Why? Not only has the wolf been trapped in a little cage, but it is trapped inside an environment that is wholly unlike its normal, natural surroundings. Even after the wolf calms down from being captured, it will still be scared and anxious about its current surroundings. It doesn't know what to expect next. It doesn't know how it will survive in this new environment.

We are not that much different. For hundreds of thousands of years, our bodies adapted to the rhythms and environments of nature. Our bodies are thus finely tuned to the sun, the wind, the water and the food that grows on the planet. When we alter these inputs, our body becomes stressed. Why?

We can break nature's elements down to their fundamental waveforms. Our bodies need those waveforms. When the body does not get receive a healthy supply of these waveforms, it becomes stressed.

The blueness of the sky, the greenness of the forest, the motion of water, the heat of the sun, the whoosh of the wind and the chirping of the birds all stimulate our body's natural biowaves. They can also render calmness, because nature's waveforms resonate with the biowaves within our bodies.

The Biowave Diet

This discussion would require another book to properly cover. Let's summarize how diet can strengthen our biowaves.

We discussed the necessity of trace minerals as conductors within nerves, ion channels and throughout interstitial fluids. Therefore, a fundamental of the biowave diet is plenty of trace minerals.

The body uses in excess of 80 trace minerals for all of its various conducting and enzymatic processes. Sources of trace minerals include whole, unprocessed rock and sea salts, mineral and spring water, vegetables, greenfoods, roots such as beets and carrots, and seaweeds. A mineral rich diet will strengthen the immune system and give every cell plenty of ions for conducting purposes.

The rest of the biowave diet is oriented towards whole, unprocessed plant-based foods. Processing can change the molecular structures and subatomic bonding within the foods. These bonds are critical to the assimilability and the health-giving properties of the food. Considerable research supports the need for the nutrients bound to fibers. Removing fibers from our foods will expose those nutrients to oxygen, light and heat. These elements can denature and degrade those nutrients.

This is illustrated when wheat or rice bran is separated from the endosperm and the germ of a kernel of grain. Both the endosperm and the germ are loaded with nutrients. These nutrients are oxygen-, heat- and light-sensitive, however. When the bran is removed, many of the nutrients are lost or oxidized. We also lose the bran's soluble and insoluble fiber content—important for maintaining good digestion and healthy cholesterol levels.

This is just one example. Almost every other food is more nutritious in its raw, whole form. The reason nutrients are good for us is their unique molecular structure: This of course relates to their subatomic bonds, which are made up of electromagnetic orbitals.

By ingesting these special bonding structures, we are taking in nature's biowaves. Our body's biowaves resonate with the nutrients of nature's whole foods from nuts, seeds, vegetables and fruits. This has been shown in many studies on illness prevention.

It is especially important that we consume plenty of whole seeds. Seeds contain special molecular bonding structures that specifically nourish our *chakras*. This is because whole seeds contain genetic and enzymatic structures related to growth, procreation and survival. Their subatomic elements are converted and used by the body for healing, endocrine balance and genetic repair.

The Right House

When looking for a new place to live, the outside environment (and access to it) is just if not more important that the inside of the house. How many windows does it have? How many trees are around the house? Does it have a good potential for a garden? Look at the views from each window. The more nature can be viewed from inside the house the better. The less concrete the better. The fewer neighboring houses obscuring our views of nature the better. A house or apartment surrounded by nature can be our sanctuary. A house or apartment surrounded by urban noise, pollution, concrete and obstructed views, on the other hand, can become our place of stress. We choose.

The wiring of the house can also be considered. Make sure the wiring is made of copper. Many older houses have been wired with aluminum. Aluminum not a good idea. It can present fire hazards and leaking EMFs. It is also best if the wiring has been done within the last 20 years, as wiring standards have vastly improved. Newer wiring has less risk of being unshielded in places, not properly grounded, or otherwise producing external fields. Consider rewiring an older house or one with aluminum wiring.

Houses where most or all of the outlets have the third grounding plug are preferred. Appliances with ground plugs should plug into a grounded outlet. Using a converter is not recommended.

In bathrooms and kitchens, GFCI outlets should be used. GFCI or GFI means *ground-fault circuit interrupter*. A GFI protects us from electric shock caused by an overloading of current. This is especially important for any outlet that is located near rooms that use water. A GFCI outlet draws hot (electron-rich) current into a ground. It can also monitor the balance between the incoming current and the draw to ground. If the current becomes imbalanced, the switch trips and breaks the circuit (stops the flow of current).

If we were to be wet, we could become a "ground" and draw the current into our bodies. If the appliance is plugged into a GFCI outlet, the monitor will trip as soon as the grounding balance changes—preventing us from being electrocuted.

Speaking of grounding, be sure that the entire house circuit is properly grounded. This should be evident from the fuse box. The circuits should all have a neutral that is connected to a grounding pole. The grounding pole should be made of copper. It should also have a copper wire at the bottom and be inserted firmly into the ground. Often this is just below the fuse box.

We can consider, especially if there are children in the house, having our house inspected by a certified home inspector. Home inspectors are trained and certified to test for and recognize wiring problems. Even if we are renting the house, it makes sense to either hire one (typically $250-$350) or ask the owners for a copy of their inspection when they bought the house.

As detailed earlier (pages 208-210), radon is also an issue to consider. The house should sit on a solid concrete foundation, because concrete can shield incoming radon daughters. Houses with dirt basements and wood floors have been known to produce significantly more radon gas. Radon test kits are easy and quite inexpensive. The U.S. EPA recommends radon levels be no more than 4 pCi/L. Higher levels should be remedied by cementing exposed areas under the house or sealing foundation cracks. Radon ventilation systems can also be helpful. Keeping the house well-ventilated in general is also an important consideration, as radon daughters increase with reduced indoor circulation. This is especially the case during the nighttime or during the winter, when the house is hotter than the outside environment.

Conclusion

The easiest way for increasing our biowave strength is to spend a significant amount of time in an outdoor or semi-outdoor environment. This may mean developing an inviting patio environment where we can sit and eat or read. It also means opening our blinds and drapes as much as possible to let the light of the sun and the colors diffracted by nature into our living space. If our house or work building is not currently very accommodating in this respect, we can simply step outside and take a walk as much as possible. We can head to a nearby park to sit amongst the trees and do our reading. We can pack a little lunch and have a wonderful simple picnic outside. We can listen to the birds as we eat.

Outdoor environments boost cognition and stimulate creativity. We've shown research illustrating that learning increases in schoolrooms with increased natural light or outdoor seating. Behavior and moods are more balanced and relaxed in the outdoors as well.

Outside, we can gain perspective. We can better see the bigger picture—and prioritize things. Within a natural setting, we might just realize how unimportant our issues really are. We often find our best solutions while outside. We can also bring nature into our homes by using crystals, thermal stones, wood or stone floors, natural fabrics, house plants, and wood furniture.

The obvious take-away here is that the more contact we have with nature—as work, play, sit, walk, exercise, sleep and eat—the stronger our body's biowaves will be. The EMFs put out by the elements of the sun, stars, earth, wind, fresh air and water resonate with our bodies. This resonation effectively increases the amplitude of our body's internal rhythms and biowaves—which in turn increases our immunity and cognition, and our body's tolerance of the synthetic fields surrounding us.

So we can relax a bit, and take advantage of some of the benefits our technologies can offer. As in just about anything, moderation and balance is the key. We can be balanced in our approach to technology. We can minimize our exposure to cell phone EMFs by using the cell's speaker or headphones. We can also go for a walk or look out into nature as we talk on the phone. Keeping our cell phone calls to a reasonable length is also not a bad idea. It's a good way to reduce our cell phone bills as well.

As for other appliances, it makes sense to be as simple as possible. Some appliances replace manual labor. Are all of them necessary? The can-opener comes to mind. Why not give our wrists a little exercise? And how about raking rather than using the leaf blower? Raking and sweeping work the arms and hips quite nicely.

For most of us in the modern world, working our muscles outside of a gym is becoming a thing of the past. There is nothing wrong with a little "elbow grease" to get something done: It's better for our health and better for the planet (ergo conserving energy).

At the end of the day, wisdom is the most important component to be applied to our use of electromagnetic technologies. Consider for a moment those uses of technology that further our education, or communicate with our friends and loved ones. These uses have intangible value.

Consider using our television to learn about how to save whales from extinction. Consider using our cell phone to communicate our love to our spouse or family member halfway around the world. Are these uses of technology worth the risk of a slight disturbance to our biowaves? Surely most of us will say yes.

We might add that these uses of technology will likely also strengthen our biowaves. The exchange of loving emotions in the case of the phone call, or the learning experience we come away with in the case of the television documentary, both stimulate our internal biowaves. They might even counteract the biowave disturbance produced by the television and cell phone.

Technology offers some great benefits to each of us personally, and to our society in general. We simply have to wisely and moderately use our technologies for the greater purposes of life.

References and Bibliography

Abdou AM, Higashiguchi S, Horie K, Kim M, Hatta H, Yokogoshi H. Relaxation and immunity enhancement effects of gamma-aminobutyric acid GABA. *Biofactors.* 2006;26(3):201-8.

Ackerman D. *A Natural History of the Senses.* New York: Vintage, 1991.

Ainsleigh HG. Beneficial effects of sun exposure on cancer mortality. *Prev Med.* 1992;22:132-40.

Aissa J, Harran H, Rabeau M, Boucherie S, Brouilhet H, Benveniste J. Tissue levels of histamine, PAF-acether and lysopaf-acether in carrageenan-induced granuloma in rats. *Int Arch Allergy Immunol.* 1996 Jun;110(2):182-6.

Aissa J, Jurgens P, Litime M, Béhar I, Benveniste J. Electronic transmission of the cholinergic signal. *FASEB Jnl.* 1995;9: A683.

Aissa J, Litime M, Attias E, Allal A, Benveniste J. Transfer of molecular signals via electronic circuitry. *FASEB Jnl.* 1993;7: A602.

Aissa J, Nathan N, Arnoux B, Benveniste J. Biochemical and cellular effects of heparin-protamine injection in rabbits are partially inhibited by a PAF-acether receptor antagonist. *Eur J Pharmacol.* 1996 Apr 29;302(1-3):123-8.

Akbar-Khanzadeh F, Bitovski DK. Exposure of school employees to extremely low frequency magnetic fields. *Can J Public Health.* 2000 Jan-Feb;91(1):21-4.

Albrechtsen O. The influence of small atmospheric ions on human well-being and mental performance. *Intern. J. of Biometeorology.* 1978;22(4): 249-262.

Alexandre P, Darmanyan D, Yushen G, Jenks W, Burel L, Eloy D, Jardon P. Quenching of Singlet Oxygen by Oxygen- and Sulfur-Centered Radicals: Evidence for Energy Transfer to Peroxyl Radicals in Solution. *J. Am. Chem. Soc.,* 120 (2), 396 -403, 1998.

Amassian VE, Cracco RQ, Maccabee PJ. A sense of movement elicited in paralyzed distal arm by focal magnetic coil stimulation of human motor cortex. *Brain Res.* 1989 Feb 13;479(2):355-60.

Ammor MS, Michaelidis C, Nychas GJ. Insights into the role of quorum sensing in food spoilage. *J Food Prot.* 2008 Jul;71(7):1510-25.

Anderson DR, Huston AC, Schmitt KL, Linebarger DL, Wright JC. Early childhood television viewing and adolescent behavior: the recontact study. *Monogr Soc Res Child Dev.* 2001;66(1):I-VIII, 1-147.

Anderson GC, Moore E, Hepworth J, Bergman N. Early skin-to-skin contact for mothers and their healthy newborn infants. *Cochrane Database Syst Rev.* 2003;(2):CD003519.

Anderson MJ, Petros TV, Beckwith BE, Mitchell WW, Fritz S. Individual differences in the effect of time of day on long-term memory access. *Am J Psych.* 1991;104:241–255.

Anonymous. Cimetidine inhibits the hepatic hydroxylation of vitamin D. *Nutr Rev.* 1985;43:184-5.

Apperley FL. The relation of solar radiation to cancer mortality in North America. *Cancer Res.* 1941;1:191-96.

Armas LA, Hollis BW, Heaney RP. Vitamin D2 is much less effective than vitamin D3 in humans. *J Clin Endocrinol Metab.* 2004 Nov;89(11):5387-91.

Armstrong B, Thériault G, Guénel P, Deadman J, Goldberg M, Héroux P. Association between exposure to pulsed electromagnetic fields and cancer in electric utility workers in Quebec, Canada, and France. *Am J Epidemiol.* 1994 Nov 1;140(9):805-20.

Armstrong BK, Kricker A. Sun exposure and non-Hodgkin lymphoma. *Cancer Epidemiol Biomarkers Prev.* 2007 Mar;16(3):396-400.

Asimov I. *The Chemicals of Life.* New York: Signet, 1954.

Askeland D. *The Science and Engineering of Materials.* Boston: PWS, 1994.

Aspect A, Grangier P, Roger G. Experimental Realization of Einstein-Podolsky-Rosen-Bohm Gedankenexperiment: A New Violation of Bell's Inequalities. *Physical Review Letters.* 1982;49(2): 91-94.

Aton SJ, Colwell CS, Harmar AJ, Waschek J, Herzog ED. Vasoactive intestinal polypeptide mediates circadian rhythmicity and synchrony in mammalian clock neurons. *Nat Neurosci.* 2005 Apr;8(4):476-83.

Azar JA, Conroy T. Measuring the effectiveness of horticultural therapy at a veterans administration medical center: experimental design issues. In Relf, D. (ed) *The Role of Horticulture in Human Well-Being and Social Development: A National Symposium.* Portland: Timber Press. 1992:169-171.

Bachmann KA, Sullivan TJ, Jauregui L, Reese J, Miller K, Levine L. Drug interactions of H2-receptor antagonists. *Scand J Gastroenterol Suppl.* 1994;206:14-9.

Backster C. *Primary Perception: Biocommunication with Plants, Living Foods, and Human Cells.* Anza, CA: White Rose Millennium Press, 2003.

Bai H, Yu P, Yu M. Effect of electroacununcture on sex hormone levels in patients with Sjogren's syndrome. *Zhen Ci Yan Jiu.* 2007;32(3):203-6.

Baker DW. An introduction to the theory and practice of German electroacupuncture and accompanying medications. *Am J Acupunct.* 1984;12:327-332.

Ballentine RM. *Radical Healing.* New York: Harmony Books, 1999.

Banyo T. The role of electrical neuromodulation in the therapy of chronic lower urinary tract dysfunction. *Ideggyogy Sz.* 2003 Jan 20;56(1-2):68-71.

Baranauskas G, Nistri A. Sensitization of pain pathways in the spinal cord: cellular mechanisms. *Prog Neurobiol.* 1998 Feb;54(3):349-65.

Barker A. *Scientific Method in Ptolemy's Harmonics.* Cambridge: Cambridge University Press, 2000.

Baron RA. Effects of negative ions on interpersonal attraction: evidence for intensification. *J Pers Soc Psychol.* 1987 Mar;52(3):547-53.

Barron M. Light exposure, melatonin secretion, and menstrual cycle parameters: an integrative review. Biol Res Nurs. 2007 Jul;9(1):49-69.

Bastide M, Doucet-Jaboeuf M, Daurat V. Activity and chronopharmacology of very low doses of physiological immune inducers. *Immun Today.* 1985;6: 234-235.

Bastide M. Immunological examples on ultra high dilution research. In: Endler P, Schulte J (eds.): *Ultra High Dilution. Physiology and Physics.* Dordrech: Kluwer Academic Publishers, 1994:27-34.

Batmangheilidj F. Neurotransmitter histamine: an alternative view point, *Science in Medicine Simplified.* Falls Church, VA: Foundation for the Simple in Medicine, 1990.

Beauvais F, Bidet B, Descours B, Hieblot C, Burtin C, Benveniste J. Regulation of human basophil activation. I. Dissociation of cationic dye binding from histamine release in activated human basophils. *J Allergy Clin Immunol.* 1991 May;87(5):1020-8.

Beauvais F, Burtin C, Benveniste J. Voltage-dependent ion channels on human basophils: do they exist? *Immunol Lett.* 1995 May;46(1-2):81-3.

Beauvais F, Echasserieau K, Burtin C, Benveniste J. Regulation of human basophil activation; the role of Na+ and Ca2+ in IL-3-induced potentiation of IgE-mediated histamine release from human basophils. *Clin Exp Immunol.* 1994 Jan;95(1):191-4.

Beauvais F, Shimahara T, Inoue I, Hieblot C, Burtin C, Benveniste J. Regulation of human basophil activation. II. Histamine release is potentiated by K+ efflux and inhibited by Na+ influx.. *J Immunol.* 1992 Jan 1;148(1):149-54.

Becker R. *Cross Currents.* Los Angeles: Jeremy P. Tarcher, 1990.

Becker R. *The Body Electric.* New York: Morrow, Inc., 1985.

Beckerman H, Becher J, Lankhorst GJ. The effectiveness of vibratory stimulation in anejaculatory men with spinal cord injury. *Paraplegia.* 1993 Nov;31(11):689-99.

Beeson, C. The moon and plant growth. *Nature.* 1946;158:572–3.

Bell B, Defouw R. Concerning a lunar modulation of geomagnetic activity. *J Geophys Res.* 1964;69:3169-3174.

Benatuil L, Apitz-Castro R, Romano E. Ajoene inhibits the activation of human endothelial cells induced by porcine cells: implications for xenotransplantation. *Xenotransplantation.* 2003 Jul;10(4):368-73.

Bennet LW, Cardone S, Jarczyk J. Effects of therapeutic camping program on addiction recovery. *Journal of Substance Abuse Treatment.* 1998;15(5):469-474.

Bennett GJ, Update on the neurophysiology of pain transmission and modulation: focus on the NMDA-receptor. *J Pain Symptom Manage.* 2000;19 (suppl 1):S.:2-6.

Benor D. Healing Research. Volume 1. Munich, Germany: Helix Verlag, 1992.

Bensky D, Gable A, Kaptchuk T (transl.). *Chinese Herbal Medicine Materia Medica.* Seattle: Eastland Press, 1986.

Bentley E. *Awareness: Biorhythms, Sleep and Dreaming.* London: Routledge, 2000.

Benveniste J, Aïssa J, Guillonnet D. A simple and fast method for in vivo demonstration of electromagnetic molecular signaling (EMS) via high dilution or computer recording. *FASEB Jnl.* 1999;13: A163.

Benveniste J, Aïssa J, Guillonnet D. Digital Biology : Specificity of the digitized molecular signal. *FASEB Jnl.* 1998;12: A412.

Benveniste J, Aïssa J, Guillonnet D. The molecular signal is not functional in the absence of "informed" water. *FASEB Jnl.* 1999;13: A163.

Benveniste J, Aïssa J, Litime M, Tsangaris G, Thomas Y. Transfer of the molecular signal by electronic amplification. *FASEB J.* 1994;8:A398.

Benveniste J, Arnoux B, Hadji L. Highly dilute antigen increases coronary flow of isolated heart from immunized guinea-pigs. *FASEB J.* 1992;6:A1610.

Benveniste J, Davenas E, Ducot B, Spira A. Basophil achromasia by dilute ligand: a reappraisal. *FASEB Jnl.* 1991;5: A1008.

Benveniste J, Ducot B, Spira A. Memory of water revisited. *Nature.* 1994 Aug 4;370(6488):322.

Benveniste J, Guillonnet D. QED and digital biology. *Riv Biol.* 2004 Jan-Apr;97(1):169-72.

Benveniste J, Jurgens P, Aïssa J. Digital recording/transmission of the cholinergic signal. *FASEB Jnl.* 1996;10: A1479.

Benveniste J, Jurgens P, Hsueh W, Aïssa J. Transatlantic transfer of digitized antigen signal by telephone link. *Jnl Aller Clin Immun.* 1997;99: S175.

Benveniste J, Kahhak L, Guillonnet D. Specific remote detection of bacteria using an electromagnetic / digital procedure. *FASEB Jnl.* 1999;13: A852.

Benveniste J. Benveniste on Nature investigation. *Science.* 1988 Aug 26;241(4869):1028.

Benveniste J. Benveniste on the Benveniste affair. *Nature.* 1988 Oct 27;335(6193):759.

Benveniste J. Diagnosis of allergic diseases by basophil count and in vitro degranulation using manual and automated tests. *Nouv Presse Med.* 1981 Jan 24;10(3):165-9.

Benveniste J. Meta-analysis of homoeopathy trials. *Lancet.* 1998 Jan 31;351(9099):367.

Berk M, Dodd S, Henry M. Do ambient electromagnetic fields affect behaviour? A demonstration of the relationship between geomagnetic storm activity and suicide. *Bioelectromagnetics.* 2006 Feb;27(2):151-5.

Berk M, Sanders KM, Pasco JA, Jacka FN, Williams LJ, Hayles AL, Dodd S. Vitamin D deficiency may play a role in depression. *Med Hypotheses.* 2007;69(6):1316-9.

Berman S, Fein G, Jewett D, Ashford F. Luminance-controlled pupil size affects Landolt C task performance. *J Illumin Engng Soc.* 1993;22:150-165.

Berman S, Jewett D, Fein G, Saika G, Ashford F. Photopic luminance does not always predict perceived room brightness. *Light Resch and Techn.* 1990;22:37-41.

Bernardi D, Dini FL, Azzarelli A, Giaconi A, Volterrani C, Lunardi M. Sudden cardiac death rate in an area characterized by high incidence of coronary artery disease and low hardness of drinking water. *Angiology.* 1995;46:145-149.

Berry J. Work efficiency and mood states of electronic assembly workers exposed to full-spectrum and conventional fluorescent illumination. *Diss Abstr Internl.* 1983;44:635B.

Bertin G. *Spiral Structure in Galaxies: A Density Wave Theory.* Cambridge: MIT Press, 1996.

Besset A, Espa F, Dauvilliers Y, Billiard M, de Seze R. No effect on cognitive function from daily mobile phone use. *Bioelectromagnetics.* 2005 Feb;26(2):102-8.

Bhattacharjee C, Bradley P, Smith M, Scally A, Wilson B. Do animals bite more during a full moon? *BMJ.* 2000 December 23; 321(7276): 1559-1561.

Bickham DS, Rich M. Is television viewing associated with social isolation? Roles of exposure time, viewing context, and violent content. *Arch Pediatr Adolesc Med.* 2006 Apr;160(4):387-92.

Bierman DJ. Does Consciousness Collapse the Wave-Packet? *Mind and Matter.* 1993;1(1):45-57.

Bishop B. Pain: its physiology and rationale for management. Part III. Consequences of current concepts of pain mechanisms related to pain management. *Phys Ther.* 1980 Jan;60(1):24-37.

Bishop ID, Rohrmann B. Subjective responses to simulated and real environments: a comparison. *Landscape and Urban Planning.* 2003;65(4):261-277.

Bishop, C. Moon influence in lettuce growth. *Astrol J.* 1977;10(1):13-15.

Bitbol PL, Luisi PL. Autopoiesis with or without cognition: defining life at its edge. *J R Soc Interface.* 2004 Nov 22;1(1):99-107.

Blackman CF, Benane SG, House DE, Pollock MM. Action of 50 Hz magnetic fields on neurite outgrowth in pheochromocytoma cells. *Bioelectromagnetics.* 1993;14(3):273-86.

Bockemühl, J. *Towards a Phenomenology of the Etheric World.* New York: Anthroposophical Press, 1985.

Bodnar L, Simhan H. The prevalence of preterm birth varies by season of last menstrual period. *Am J Obst and Gyn.* 2003;195(6):S211-S211.

Bohay RN, Bencak J, Kavaliers M, Maclean D. A survey of magnetic fields in the dental operatory. *J Can Dent Assoc.* 1994 Sep;60(9):835-40.

Boivin DB, Czeisler CA. Resetting of circadian melatonin and cortisol rhythms in humans by ordinary room light. *Neuroreport.* 1998 Mar 30;9(5):779-82.

Boivin DB, Duffy JF, Kronauer RE, Czeisler CA. Dose-response relationships for resetting of human circadian clock by light. *Nature.* 1996 Feb 8;379(6565):540-2.

Bollani L, Dolci C, Gerola O, Montaruli A, Rondini G, Carandente F. The early maturation of the circadian system in newborns. *Chronobiologia.* 1994 Jan-Jun;21(1-2):105-8.

Boray P, Gifford R, Rosenblood L. Effects of warm white, cool white and full-spectrum fluorescent lighting on simple cognitive performance, mood and ratings of others. J Environl Psychol. 1989;9:297-308.

Boscoe FP, Schymura MJ. Solar ultraviolet-B exposure and cancer incidence and mortality in the United States, 1993-2002. BMC Cancer. 2006 Nov 10;6:264.

Bose J. *Response in the Living and Non-Living.* New York: Longmans, Green & Co., 1902.

Boston University. Effects Of Vitamin D And Skin's Physiology Examined. ScienceDaily. 2008 February 24. Retrieved February 24, 2008, from http://www.sciencedaily.com/releases/2008/02/080220161707.htm. Accessed: 2008 Nov.

Bottorff JL. The use and meaning of touch in caring for patients with cancer. *Oncol Nurs Forum.* 1993 Nov-Dec;20(10):1531-8.

Boyce P, Rea M. A field evaluation of full-spectrum, polarized lighting. Paper presented at the 1993 Annual Convention of the Illuminating Engineering Society of North America, Houston, TX. 1993 Aug.

Boyce P. Investigations of the subjective balance between illuminance and lamp colour properties. *Light Resch and Technol.* 1977;9:11-24.

Brainard GC, Kavet R, Kheifets LI. The relationship between electromagnetic field and light exposures to melatonin and breast cancer risk: a review of the relevant literature. *J Pineal Res.* 1999 Mar;26(2):65-100.

Brasseur JG, Nicosia MA, Pal A, Miller LS. Function of longitudinal vs circular muscle fibers in esophageal peristalsis, deduced with mathematical modeling. *World J Gastroenterol.* 2007 Mar 7;13(9):1335-46.

Braunstein G, Labat C, Brunelleschi S, Benveniste J, Marsac J, Brink C. Evidence that the histamine sensitivity and responsiveness of guinea-pig isolated trachea are modulated by epithelial prostaglandin E2 production. *Br J Pharmacol.* 1988 Sep;95(1):300-8.

Brenner D, Hall E. Computed Tomography — An Increasing Source of Radiation Exposure. *NE J Med.* 2007;357(22):2277-2284.

Breton ME, Montzka DP. Empiric limits of rod photocurrent component underlying a-wave response in the electroretinogram. *Doc Ophthalmol.* 1992;79(4):337-61.

Britt R. Hole Drilled to Bottom of Earth's Crust, Breakthrough to Mantle Looms. *LiveScience.* 2005. 07 Apr. http://www.livescience.com/ technology/050407_earth_drill.html. Acc. 2006 Nov.

Brodeur P. *Currents of Death.* New York: Simon and Schuster, 1989.

Brosseau LU, Pelland LU, Casimiro LY, Robinson VI, Tugwell PE, Wells GE. Electrical stimulation for the treatment of rheumatoid arthritis. *Cochrane Database Syst Rev.* 2002;(2):CD003687.

Brown FA, Chow CS. Lunar-Correlated variations in water uptake by bean seeds. *Biol B.* 1973 145:265-278.

Brown, F. The rhythmic nature of animals and plants. *Cycles.* 1960 Apr:81-92.

Brown, J. Stimulation-produced analgesia: acupuncture, TENS and alternative techniques. *Anaesthesia &intensive care medicine.* 2005 Feb;6(2):45-47.

Browne J. Developmental Care - Considerations for Touch and Massage in the Neonatal Intensive Care Unit. *Neonatatal Network.* 2000 Feb;19(1).

Brownstein D. *Salt: Your Way to Health.* West Bloomfield, MI: Medical Alternatives, 2006.

Buckley NA, Whyte IM, Dawson AH. There are days ... and moons. Self-poisoning is not lunacy. *Med J Aust.* 1993 Dec 6-20;159(11-12):786-9.

Buijs RM, Scheer FA, Kreier F, Yi C, Bos N, Goncharuk VD, Kalsbeek A. Organization of circadian functions: interaction with the body. *Prog Brain Res.* 2006;153:341-60.

Bulsing PJ, Smeets MA, van den Hout MA. Positive Implicit Attitudes toward Odor Words. *Chem Senses.* 2007 May 7.

Burikov AA, Bereshpolova YuI. The activity of thalamus and cerebral cortex neurons in rabbits during "slow wave-spindle" EEG complexes. *Neurosci Behav Physiol.* 1999 Mar-Apr;29(2):143-9.

Burnham K, Andersson D. *Model Selection and Inference. A Practical Information-Theoretic Approach.* New York: Springer, 1998

Burr H, Hovland C. Bio-Electric Potential Gradients in the Chick. *Yale Journal of Biology & Medicine.* 1937;9:247-258

Burr H, Lane C, Nims L. A Vacuum Tube Microvoltmeter for the Measurement of Bioelectric Phenomena. *Yale Journal of Biology & Medicine.* 1936;10:65-76.

Burr H, Smith G, Strong L. Bio-electric Properties of Cancer-Resistant and Cancer-Susceptible Mice. *American Journal of Cancer.* 1938;32:240-248

Burr H. *The Fields of Life.* New York: Ballantine, 1972.

Buzsaki G. Theta rhythm of navigation: link between path integration and landmark navigation, episodic and semantic memory. *Hippocampus.* 2005;15(7):827-40.

Cahill RT. A New Light-Speed Anisotropy Experiment: Absolute Motion and Gravitational Waves Detected. *Progress in Physics.* 2006; (4).

Cajochen C, Zeitzer JM, Czeisler CA, Dijk DJ. Dose-response relationship for light intensity and ocular and electroencephalographic correlates of human alertness. *Behav Brain Res.* 2000 Oct;115(1):75-83.

Caldwell MM, Bornman JF, Ballare CL, Flint SD, Kulandaivelu G. Terrestrial ecosystems, increased solar ultraviolet radiation, and interactions with other climate change factors. *Photochem Photobiol Sci.* 2007 Mar;6(3):252-66.

Callender ST, Spray GH. Latent pernicious anemia. *Br J Haematol* 1962;8:230-240.

Calvin W. *The Handbook of Brain Theory and Neural Networks.* Boston: MIT Press, 1995.

Campbell A. The role of aluminum and copper on neuroinflammation and Alzheimer's disease. *J Alzheimers Dis.* 2006 Nov;10(2-3):165-72.

Cantor KP, Stewart PA, Brinton LA, Dosemeci M. Occupational exposures and female breast cancer mortality in the United States. *J Occup Environ Med.* 1995 Mar;37(3):336-48.

Capitani D, Yethiraj A, Burnell EE. Memory effects across surfactant mesophases. *Langmuir.* 2007 Mar 13;23(6):3036-48.

Carlsen E, Olsson C, Petersen JH, Andersson AM, Skakkebaek NE. Diurnal rhythm in serum levels of inhibin B in normal men: relation to testicular steroids and gonadotropins. *J Clin Endocrinol Metab.* 1999 May;84(5):1664-9.

Cavalli-Sforza L, Feldman M. *Cultural Transmission and Evolution: A quantitative approach.* Princeton: Princeton UP, 1981.

REFERENCES AND BIBLIOGRAPHY

Celec P, Ostaniková D, Skoknová M, Hodosy J, Putz Z, Kúdela M. Salivary sex hormones during the menstrual cycle. *Endocr J.* 2009 Jun;56(3):521-3.

Celec P, Ostatníková D, Hodosy J, Putz Z, Kúdela M. Increased one week soybean consumption affects spatial abilities but not sex hormone status in men. *Int J Food Sci Nutr.* 2007 Sep;58(6):424-8.

Celec P, Ostatníková D, Hodosy J, Skoknová M, Putz Z, Kúdela M. Infradian rhythmic variations of salivary estradioland progesterone in healthy men. *Biol Res.* 2006;37(1): 37-44.

Celec P, Ostatníková D, Putz Z, Hodosy J, Burský P, Stárka L, Hampl R, Kúdela M. Circatrigintan Cycle of Salivary Testosterone in Human Male. *Biol Rhythm Res.* 2003;34(3): 305-315.

Celec P, Ostatnikova D, Putz Z, Kudela M. The circalunar cycle of salivary testosterone and the visual-spatial performance. *Bratisl Lek Listy.* 2002;103(2):59-69.

Celec P. Analysis of rhythmic variance - ANORVA. A new simple method for detecting rhythms in biological time series. *Biol Res.* 2004;37:777-782.

Cengel YA, *Heat Transfer: A Practical Approach.* Boston: McGraw-Hill, 1998.

Chapman, S. Fear of frying: power lines and cancer. *BMJ* 2001;322:682.

Chen HY, Shi Y, Ng CS, Chan SM, Yung KK, Zhang QL. Auricular acupuncture treatment for insomnia: a systematic review. *J Altern Complement Med.* 2007 Jul-Aug;13(6):669-76.

Chen-Goodspeed M, Cheng Chi Lee. Tumor suppression and circadian function. *J Biol Rhythms.* 2007 Aug;22(4):291-8.

Chirkova E. Mathematical methods of detection of biological and heliogeophysical rhythms in the light of developments in modern heliobiology: A platform for discussion. *Cybernet Sys.* 2000;31(6):903-918.

Chirkova EN, Suslov LS, Avramenko MM, Krivoruchko GE. Monthly and daily biorhythms of amylase in the blood of healthy men and their relation with the rhythms in the external environment. *Lab Delo.* 1990;(4):40-4.

Chong AS, Boussy IA, Jiang XL, Lamas M, Graf LH Jr. CD54/ICAM-1 is acostimulator of NK cell-mediated cytotoxicity. *Cell Immunol.* 1994 Aug;157(1):92-105.

Chong NW, Codd V, Chan D, Samani NJ. Circadian clock genes cause activation of the human PAI-1 gene promoter with 4G/5G allelic preference. *FEBS Lett.* 2006 Aug 7;580(18):4469-72.

Christophersen, A. G., Jun, H., Jørgensen, K., and Skibsted, L. H. Photobleaching of astaxanthin and canthaxanthin: quantum-yields dependence of solvent, temperature, and wavelength of irradiation in relation to packageing and storage of carotenoid pigmented salmonoids. *Z. Lebensm. Unters. Forsch.,* 1991;192:433-439.

Chu Q, Wang L, Liu GZ. Clinical observation on acupuncture for treatment of diabetic nephropathy. *Zhongguo Zhen Jiu.* 2007 Jul;27(7):488-90.

Churchill G, Doerge R. Empirical threshold values for quantitative trait mapping. *Genetics* 1994;138:963-971.

Chwirot B, Kowalska M, Plóciennik N, Piwinski M, Michniewicz Z, Chwirot S. Variability of spectra of laser-induced fluorescence of colonic mucosa: Its significance for fluorescence detection of colonic neoplasia. *Indian J Exp. Biol.* 2003;41(5):500-510.

Chwirot WB, Popp F. White-light-induced luminescence and mitotic activity of yeast cells. *Folia Histochemica et Cytobiologica.* 1991;29(4):155.

Cimetidine inhibits the hepatic hydroxylation of vitamin D. *Nutr Rev.* 1985;43:184-5.

Citro M, Endler PC, Pongratz W, Vinattieri C, Smith CW, Schulte J. Hormone effects by electronic transmission. *FASEB J.* 1995:Abstract 12161.

Citro M, Smith CW, Scott-Morley A, Pongratz W, Endler PC. Transfer of information from molecules by means of electronic amplification, in P.C. Endler, J. Schulte (eds.): *Ultra High Dilution. Physiology and Physics.* Dordrecht: Kluwer Academic Publishers. 1994;209-214.

Clark D. The use of electrical current in the treatment of nonunions. *Vet Clin North Am Small Anim Pract.* 1987 Jul;17(4):793-8.

Cochran ES, Vidale JE, Tanaka S. Earth tides can trigger shallow thrust fault earthquakes. *Science.* 2004 Nov 12;306(5699):1164-6.

Cocilovo A. Colored light therapy: overview of its history, theory, recent developments and clinical applications combined with acupuncture. *Am J Acupunct.* 1999;27(1-2):71-83.

Cohen S, Popp F. Biophoton emission of the human body. *J Photochem & Photobio.* 1997;B 40:187-189.

Cohen S, Popp F. Low-level luminescence of the human skin. *Skin Res Tech.* 1997;3:177-180.

Cohen S, Popp FA. Biophoton emission of the human body. *J Photochem Photobiol B.* 1997 Sep;40(2):187-9.

Coles JA, Yamane S. Effects of adapting lights on the time course of the receptor potential of the anuran retinal rod. *J Physiol.* 1975 May;247(1):189-207.

Coll AP, Farooqi IS, O'Rahilly S. The hormonal control of food intake. *Cell.* 2007 Apr 20;129(2):251-62.

Collins RL, Elliott MN, Berry SH, Kanouse DE, Kunkel D, Hunter SB, Miu A. Watching sex on television predicts adolescent initiation of sexual behavior. *Pediatrics.* 2004 Sep;114(3):e280-9.

Contreras D, Steriade M. Cellular basis of EEG slow rhythms: a study of dynamic corticothalamic relationships. *J Neurosci.* 1995 Jan;15(1 Pt 2):604-22.

Cook J, The Therapeutic Use of Music. *Nursing Forum.* 1981;20:3: 253-66.

Cook N, Freeman S. Report of 19 cases of photoallergic contact dermatitis to sunscreens seen at the Skin and Cancer Foundation. *Australas J Dermatol.* 2001 Nov;42(4):257-9.

Corkin S, Amaral DG, González RG, et al: H. M.'s medial temporal lobe lesion: findings from magnetic resonance imaging. *J Neurosci.* 1997;17:3964-3979.

Council Recommendation on the Limitation of Exposure of the General Public to Electromagnetic Fields (0 Hz to 300 GHz). *Official Journal of the European Communities.* 1999. July 12.

Cranney A, Horsley T, O'Donnell S, Weiler H, Puil L, Ooi D, Atkinson S, Ward L, Moher D, Hanley D, Fang M, Yazdi F, Garritty C, Sampson M, Barrowman N, Tsertsvadze A, Mamaladze V. Effectiveness and safety of vitamin D in relation to bone health. *Evid Rep Technol Assess.* 2007 Aug;(158):1-235.

Crawley J. *The Biorhythm Book.* Boston: Journey Editions, 1996.

Creinin MD, Keverline S, Meyn LA. How regular is regular? An analysis of menstrual cycle regularity. *Contraception.* 2004 Oct;70(4):289-92.

Crofford LJ. Neuroendocrine abnormalities in fibromyalgia and related disorders. *Am J Med Sci.* 1998;315:359-66.

Cruccu G, Aziz TZ, Garcia-Larrea L, Hansson P, Jensen TS, Lefaucheur JP, Simpson BA, Taylor RS. EFNS guidelines on neurostimulation therapy for neuropathic pain. *Eur J Neurol.* 2007 Sep;14(9):952-70.

Cuppari L, Garcia-Lopes MG. Hypovitaminosis D in chronic kidney disease patients: prevalence and treatment. *J Ren Nutr.* 2009 Jan;19(1):38-43.

Cuthbert SC, Goodheart GJ Jr. On the reliability and validity of manual muscle testing: a literature review. *Chiropr Osteopat.* 2007 Mar 6;15:4.

Dalmose A, Bjarkam C, Vuckovic A, Sorensen JC, Hansen J. Electrostimulation: a future treatment option for patients with neurogenic urodynamic disorders? *APMIS Suppl.* 2003;(109):45-51.

D'Angelo S, Ingrosso D, Migliardi V, Sorrentino A, Donnarumma G, Baroni A, Masella L, Tufano MA, Zappia M, Galletti P. Hydroxytyrosol, a natural antioxidant from olive oil, prevents protein damage induced by long-wave ultraviolet radiation in melanoma cells. *Fr Rad Bio Med.* 2005 Apr 1;38(7):908-19.

Darby S, Hill D, Auvinen A, Barros-Dios JM, Baysson H, Bochicchio F, Doll R, *et al.* Radon in homes and risk of lung cancer: collaborative analysis of individual data from 13 European case-control studies. *BMJ.* 2005 Jan 29;330(7485):223.

Darrow K. *The Renaissance of Physics.* New York: Macmillan, 1936.

Davenas E, Beauvais F, Amara J, Oberbaum M, Robinzon B, Miadonna B, Tedeschi A, Pomeranz B, Fortner P, Belon P, Sainte-Laudy J, Poitevin B, Benveniste J. Human basophil degranulation triggered by very dilute antiserum against IgE. *Nature.* 1988;333: 816-818.

Davenas E, Poitevin B, Benveniste J. Effect on mouse peritoneal macrophages of orally administered very high dilutions of silica. *European Journal of Pharmacology.* 1987;135: 313-319.

Davidson T. *Rhinology: The Collected Writings of Maurice H. Cottle, M.D.* San Diego, CA: American Rhinologic Society, 1987.

Davies G. *Timetables of Medicine.* New York: Black Dog & Leventhal, 2000.

DaVinci L. (Dickens E. ed.) *The Da Vinci Notebooks.* London: Profile, 2005.

Davis GE Jr, Lowell WE. Chaotic solar cycles modulate the incidence and severity of mental illness. *Med Hypotheses.* 2004;62(2):207-14.

Davis GE Jr, Lowell WE. Solar cycles and their relationship to human disease and adaptability. *Med Hypotheses.* 2006;67(3):447-61.

Davis GE Jr, Lowell WE. The Sun determines human longevity: teratogenic effects of chaotic solar radiation. *Med Hypotheses.* 2004;63(4):574-81.

Davis RL, Mostofi FK. Cluster of testicular cancer in police officers exposed to hand-held radar. *Am J Ind Med.* 1993 Aug;24(2):231-3.

Davis S, Kaune WT, Mirick DK, Chen C, Stevens RG. Residential magnetic fields, light-at-night, and nocturnal urinary 6-sulfatoxymelatonin concentration in women. *Am J Epidem.* 2001 Oct 1;154(7):591-600.

Davis S, Mirick DK, Stevens RG. Night shift work, light at night, and risk of breast cancer. *J Natl Cancer Inst.* 2001 Oct 17;93(20):1557-62.

Davis-Berman J, Berman DS. The widlerness therapy program: an empirical study of its effects with adolescents in an outpatient setting. *Journal of Contemporary Psychotherapy.* 1989;19 (4):271-281.

de Vries E, Coebergh JW, van der Rhee H. Trends, causes, approach and consequences related to the skin-cancer epidemic in the Netherlands and Europe. *Ned Tijdschr Geneeskd.* 2006 May 20;150(20):1108-15.

Dean E, Mihalasky J, Ostrander S, Schroeder L. *Executive ESP.* Englewood Cliffs, NJ: Prentice-Hall, 1974.

Dean E. Infrared measurements of healer-treated water. In: Roll W, Beloff J, White R (Eds.): *Research in parapsychology 1982.* Metuchen, NJ: Scarecrow Press, 1983:100-101.

REFERENCES AND BIBLIOGRAPHY

Defrin R, Ohry A, Blumen N, Urca G. Sensory determinants of thermal pain. *Brain.* 2002 Mar;125(Pt 3):501-10.

Deitel M. Applications of electrical pacing in the body. *Obes Surg.* 2004 Sep;14 Suppl 1:S3-8.

Del Giudice E, Preparata G, Vitiello G. Water as a free electric dipole laser. *Phys Rev Lett.* 1988;61:1085-1088.

Del Giudice E. Is the 'memory of water' a physical impossibility?, in P.C. Endler, J. Schulte (eds.): *Ultra High Dilution. Physiology and Physics.* Dordrecht: Kluwer Academic Publishers, 1994:117-120.

Delyukov A, Didyk L. The effects of extra-low-frequency atmospheric pressure oscillations on human mental activity. *Int J Biometeorol.* 1999 Jul;43(1):31-7.

Delcomyn F. *Foundations of Neurobiology.* New York: W.H. Freeman and Co., 1998.

Dement W, Vaughan C. *The Promise of Sleep.* New York: Dell, 1999.

Demers PA, Thomas DB, Rosenblatt KA, Jimenez LM, McTiernan A, Stalsberg H, Stemhagen A, Thompson WD, Curnen MG, Satariano W, et al. Occupational exposure to electromagnetic fields and breast cancer in men. *Am J Epidemiol.* 1991 Aug 15;134(4):340-7.

Dennett D. *Brainstorms: Philosophical Essays on Mind & Psychology.* Cambridge: MIT Press., 1980.

Dennett D. *Consciousness Explained.* London: Little, Brown and Co., 1991.

Deorah S, Lynch CF, Sibenaller ZA, Ryken TC. Trends in brain cancer incidence and survival in the US: Surveillance, Epidemiology, and End Results, 1973 to 2001. *Neurosrg Foc.* 2006 Apr 15;20(4):E1.

Depue BE, Banich MT, Curran T. Suppression of emotional and nonemotional content in memory: effects of repetition on cognitive control. *Psychol Sci.* 2006 May;17(5):441-7.

Dere E, Kart-Teke E, Huston JP, De Souza Silva MA. The case for episodic memory in animals. *Neurosci Biobehav Rev.* 2006;30(8):1206-24.

Devulder J, Crombez E, Mortier E. Central pain: an overview. *Acta Neurol Belg.* 2002 Sep;102(3):97-103.

Dhond RP, Kettner N, Napadow V. Neuroimaging acupuncture effects in the human brain. *J Altern Complement Med.* 2007 Jul-Aug;13(6):603-16.

Diamond WJ, Cowden WL, Goldberg B. *Cancer Diagnosis: What to Do Next.* Tiburon, CA: AlternMed, 2000.

Dimbylow PJ, Mann SM. SAR calculations in an anatomically realistic model of the head for mobile communication transceivers at 900 MHz and 1.8 GHz. *Phys Med Biol.* 1994 Oct;39(10):1537-53.

Dimitriadis GD, Raptis SA. Thyroid hormone excess and glucose intolerance. *Exp Clin Endocrinol Diabetes.* 2001;109 Suppl 2:S225-39.

Dobrowolski J, Ezzahir A, Knapik M. Possibilities of chemiluminescence application in comparative studies of animal and cancer cells with special attention to leucemic blood cells. In: Jezowska-Trzebiatowska, B., *et al.* (eds.). *Photon Emission from Biological Systems.* Singapore: World Scientific Publ, 1987:170-183.

Dolcos F, LaBar KS, Cabeza R. Interaction between the amygdala and the medial temporal lobe memory system predicts better memory for emotional events. *Neuron.* 2004 Jun 10;42(5):855-63.

Dotolo Institute. *The Study of Colon Hydrotherapy.* Pinellas Park, FL: Dotolo, 2003.

Dudley M. *Microwaved water and plants.* 2006; http://www.execonn.com/sf/. Accessed: 2007 Dec.

Duke M. *Acupuncture.* New York: Pyramid, 1973.

Dunlop KA, Carson DJ, Shields MD. Hypoglycemia due to adrenal suppression secondary to high-dose nebulized corticosteroid. *Pediatr Pulmonol.* 2002 Jul;34(1):85-6.

Dunne B, Jahn R, Nelson R. Precognitive Remote Perception. Princeton Engineering Anomalies *Res Lab Rep.* Princeton. 1983 Aug.

Dunstan JA, Roper J, Mitoulas L, Hartmann PE, Simmer K, Prescott SL. The effect of supplementation with fish oil during pregnancy on breast milk immunoglobulin A, soluble CD14, cytokine levels and fatty acid composition. *Clin Exp Allergy.* 2004 Aug;34(8):1237-42.

Durlach J, Bara M, Guiet-Bara A. Magnesium level in drinking water: its importance in cardiovascular risk. In: Itokawa Y, Durlach J: *Magnesium in Health and Disease.* London: J.Libbey, 1989:173-182.

Dwivedi S, Agarwal MP. Antianginal and cardioprotective effects of Terminalia arjuna, an indigenous drug, in coronary artery disease. *J Assoc Physicians India.* 1994 Apr;42(4):287-9.

Ebbesen F, Agati G, Pratesi R. Phototherapy with turquoise versus blue light. *Arch Dis Child Fetal Neonatal Ed.* 2003 Sep;88(5):F430-1.

Eden D, Feinstein D. *Energy Medicine.* New York: Penguin Putnam, 1998.

Edwards B. *Drawing on the Right Side of the Brain.* Los Angeles, CA: Tarcher, 1979.

Edwards R, Ibison M, Jessel-Kenyon J, Taylor R. Light emission from the human body. *Comple Med Res.* 1989;3(2):16-19.

Edwards R, Ibison M, Jessel-Kenyon J, Taylor R. Measurements of human bioluminescence. *Acup Elect Res, Intl Jnl,* 1990;15:85-94.

Edwards, L. *The Vortex of Life, Nature's Patterns in Space and Time.* Floris Press, 1993.

Egan KM, Sosman JA, Blot WJ. Sunlight and reduced risk of cancer: is the real story vitamin D? *J Natl Cancer Inst.* 2005 Feb 2;97(3):161-3.

Egon G, Chartier-Kastler E, Denys P, Ruffion A. Spinal cord injury patient and Brindley neurostimulation. *Prog Urol.* 2007 May;17(3):535-9.

Einstein In Need Of Update? Calculations Show The Speed Of Light Might Change. *Science Daily.* 2001 Feb 12. www.sciencedaily.com/releases/ 2001/02/010212075309.htm. Accessed: 2007 Oct.

Electromagnetic fields: the biological evidence. *Science.* 1990;249:1378-1381.

Electronic Evidence of Auras, Chakras in UCLA Study. *Brain/Mind Bulletin.* 1978;3:9 Mar 20.

Elias S, van Noord P, Peeters P, den Tonkelaar I, Kaaks R, Grobbee D. Menstruation during and after caloric restriction: The 1944-1945 Dutch famine. *Fertil Steril.* 2007 Jun 1.

Eltiti S, Wallace D, Ridgewell A, Zougkou K, Russo R, Sepulveda F, et al. Does Short-Term Exposure to Mobile Phone Base Station Signals Increase Symptoms in Individuals who Report Sensitivity to Electromagnetic Fields? *Environ Health Perspect.* 2007;115(11):1603-1608.

Elwood PC. Epidemiology and trace elements. *Clin Endocrinol Metab.* 1985 Aug;14(3):617-28.

EN 50360. *Product Standard to Demonstrate the Compliance of Mobile Phones with the Basic Restrictions Related to Human Exposure to Electromagnetic Fields (300 MHz 3GHz).* Brussels: CENELEC, 2001.

Endler PC, Pongratz W, Smith CW, Schulte J. Non-molecular information transfer from thyroxine to frogs with regard to 'homoeopathic' toxicology, *J Vet Hum Tox.* 1995:37:259-260.

Endler PC, Pongratz W, Van Wijk R, Kastberger G, Haidvogl M. Effects of highly diluted sucussed thyroxine on metamorphosis of highland frogs, *Berlin J Res Hom.* 1991;1:151-160.

Endler PC, Schulte, J. *Ultra High Dilution. Physiology and Physics.* Dordrecht: Kluwer Academic Publ, 1994.

Erdelyi R. MHD waves and oscillations in the solar plasma. Introduction. *Philos Transact A Math Phys Eng Sci.* 2006 Feb 15;364(1839):289-96.

Eschenhagen T, Zimmermann WH. Engineering myocardial tissue. *Circ Res.* 2005 Dec 9;97(12):1220-31.

Evans P, Forte D, Jacobs C, Fredhoi C, Aitchison E, Hucklebridge F, Clow A. Cortisol secretory activity in older people in relation to positive and negative well-being. *Psychoneuroendocrinology.* 2007 Aug 7.

Ezzo JM, Richardson MA, Vickers A, Allen C, Dibble SL, Issell BF, Lao L, Pearl M, Ramirez G, Roscoe J, Shen J, Shivnan JC, Streitberger K, Treish I, Zhang G. Acupuncture-point stimulation for chemotherapy-induced nausea or vomiting. *Cochrane Database Syst Rev.* 2006 Apr 19;(2):CD002285.

Fallen EL, Kamath MV, Tougas G, Upton A. Afferent vagal modulation. Clinical studies of visceral sensory input. *Auton Neurosci.* 2001 Jul 20;90(1-2):35-40.

Fan X, Zhang D, Zheng J, Gu N, Ding A, Jia X, Qing H, Jin L, Wan M, Li Q. Preparation and characterization of magnetic nano-particles with radiofrequency-induced hyperthermia for cancer treatment. *Sheng Wu Yi Xue Gong Cheng Xue Za Zhi.* 2006 Aug;23(4):809-13.

Federal Communications Commission.. *Evaluating Compliance with FCC Guidelines for Human Exposure to Radio Frequency Electromagnetic Fields.* Washington, DC: Supplement C to OET Bulletin 65 (01), 1997.

Fecher LA, Cummings SD, Keefe MJ, Alani RM. Toward a molecular classification of melanoma. *J Clin Oncol.* 2007 Apr 20;25(12):1606-20.

Fehring RJ, Schneider M, Raviele K. Variability in the phases of the menstrual cycle. *J Obstet Gynecol Neonatal Nurs.* 2006 May-Jun;35(3):376-84.

Felton JS, Fultz E, Dolbeare FA, Knize MG. Effect of microwave pretreatment on heterocyclic aromatic amine mutagens/carcinogens in fried beef patties. *Food Chem Toxicol.* 1994 Oct;32(10):897-903.

Field RW, Krewski D, Lubin JH, Zielinski JM, Alavanja M, Catalan VS, Klotz JB, Letourneau EG, Lynch CF, Lyon JL, Sandler DP, Schoenberg JB, Steck DJ, Stolwijk JA, Weinberg C, Wilcox HB. An overview of the North American residential radon and lung cancer case-control studies. *J Toxicol Environ Health A.* 2006 Apr;69(7):599-631.

Fischer JL, Mihelc EM, Pollok KE, Smith ML. Chemotherapeutic selectivity conferred by selenium: a role for p53-dependent DNA repair. *Mol Cancer Ther.* 2007 Jan;6(1):355-61.

Fraga CG. Relevance, essentiality and toxicity of trace elements in human health. Mol Aspects Med. 2005 Aug-Oct;26(4-5):235-44.

Freeman HL, Stansfield SA. Psychosocial effects of urban environments, noise, and crowding. In Lundberg, A. (ed) *Environment and Mental Health.* London: Lawrence Erlbaum. 1998:147-173.

Freeman W. *The Physiology of Perception. Sci. Am.* 1991 Feb.

Frey A. Electromagnetic field interactions with biological systems. *FASEB Jnl.* 1993;7:272-28.

Fu XH. Observation on therapeutic effect of acupuncture on early peripheral facial paralysis. *Zhongguo Zhen Jiu.* 2007 Jul;27(7):494-6.

Fukada Y, Okano T. Circadian clock system in the pineal gland. *Mol Neurobiol.* 2002 Feb;25(1):19-30.

Fuster JM. Prefrontal neurons in networks of executive memory. *Brain Res Bull.* 2000 Jul 15;52(5):331-6.

Gabriel S, Schaffner S, Nguyen H, Moore J, Roy J. The structure of haplotype blocks in the human genome. *Science.* 2002;296:2225-2229.

Galaev, YM. The Measuring of Ether-Drift Velocity and Kinematic Ether Viscosity within Optical Wave Bands. *Spacetime & Substance.* 2002;3(5): 207-224.

Galaev, YM. The Measuring of Ether-Drift Velocity and Kinematic Ether Viscosity within Optical Wave Bands. *Spacetime & Substance*. 2002;3(5):207-224.

Gambini JP, Velluti RA, Pedemonte M. Hippocampal theta rhythm synchronizes visual neurons in sleep and waking. *Brain Res.* 2002 Feb 1;926(1-2):137-41.

Gandhi T, Weingart S, Borus J, Seger A, Peterson J, Burdick E, Seger D, Shu K, Federico F, Leape L, Bates D. Adverse drug events in ambulatory care. *N Engl J Med.* 2003 Apr 17;348(16):1556-64.

Gange R. UVA sunbeds - are there longterm hazards. In Cronley-Dillon J, Rosen E, Marshall J (Eds.):*Hazards of Light, Myths and Realities*. Oxford, U.K.: Pergamon Press, 1986.

García AM, Sisternas A, Hoyos SP. Occupational exposure to extremely low frequency electric and magnetic fields and Alzheimer disease: a meta-analysis. *Int J Epidemiol.* 2008 Apr;37(2):329-40.

Garcia-Lazaro JA, Ahmed B, Schnupp JW. Tuning to natural stimulus dynamics in primary auditory cortex. *Curr Biol.* 2006 Feb 7;16(3):264-71.

Gardner CD, Fortmann SP, Krauss RM. Association of small low-density lipoprotein particles with the incidence of coronary artery disease in men and women. *JAMA*. 1996 Sep 18;276(11):875-81.

Garland CF, Gorham ED, Mohr SB, Grant WB, Giovannucci EL, Lipkin M, Newmark H, Holick MF, Garland FC. Vitamin D and prevention of breast cancer: pooled analysis. *J Steroid Biochem Mol Biol.* 2007 Mar;103(3-5):708-11.

Gauger J.R. Household appliance magnetic field survey. IEEE PAS-104, No.9:2436-2445, 1985.

Gerber R. *Vibrational Healing*. Sante Fe: Bear, 1988.

Gesler WM. Therapeutic landscapes: medical issues in light of the new cultural geography. *Soc Sci Med.* 1992 Apr;34(7):735-46.

Ghadioungui P. (transl.) *The Ebers Papyrus*. Academy of Scientific Research. Cairo, 1987.

Giovannucci E. The epidemiology of vitamin D and cancer incidence and mortality: *Cancer Causes Control.* 2005 Mar;16(2):83-95.

Gisler GC, Diaz J, Duran N. Observations on Blood Plasma Chemiluminescence in Normal Subjects and Cancer Patients. *Arq Biol Tecnol.* 1983;26(3):345-352.

Glover J. *The Philosophy of Mind*. Oxford University Press, 1976.

Goldstein LS, Dewhirst MW, Repacholi M, Kheifets L. Summary, conclusions and recommendations: adverse temperature levels in the human body. *Int J Hyperthermia.* 2003 May-Jun;19(3):373-84.

Goldstein N, Arshavskaya TV. Is atmospheric superoxide vitally necessary? Accelerated death of animals in a quasi-neutral electric atmosphere. *Z Naturforsch.* 1997. May-Jun;52(5-6):396-404.

Golub E. *The Limits of Medicine*. New York: Times Books, 1994.

Gomes A, Fernandes E, Lima JL. Fluorescence probes used for detection of reactive oxygen species. *J Biochem Biophys Methods.* 2005 Dec;65(2-3):45-80.

Gomez-Abellan P, Hernandez-Morante JJ, Lujan JA, Madrid JA, Garaulet M. Clock genes are implicated in the human metabolic syndrome. *Int J Obes.* 2007 Jul 24.

Gorham ED, Mohr SB, Garland CF, Chaplin G, Garland FC. Do sunscreens increase risk of melanoma in populations residing at higher latitudes? *Ann Epidemiol.* 2007 Dec;17(12):956-63.

Grad B, Dean E. Independent confirmation of infrared healer effects. In: White R, Broughton R (Eds.): *Research in parapsychology 1983*. Metuchen, NJ: Scarecrow Press, 1984:81-83.

Grad B. A Telekinetic Effect on Plant Growth. *Intl Jnl Parapsy.* 1964;6: 473.

Grad B. A telekinetic effect on plant growth: II. Experiments involving treatment of saline in stoppered bottles. *Internl J Parapsychol.* 1964;6:473-478, 484-488.

Grad B. The 'Laying on of Hands': Implications for Psychotherapy, Gentling, and the Placebo Effect. *Jnl Amer Soc for Psych Res.* 1967 Oct;61(4):286-305.

Grad, B. A telekinetic effect on plant growth: II. Experiments involving treatment of saline in stoppered bottles. *Internl J Parapsychol.* 1964;6:473-478, 484-488.

Graham C, Sastre A, Cook MR, Kavet R, Gerkovich MM, Riffle DW. Exposure to strong ELF magnetic fields does not alter cardiac autonomic control mechanisms. *Bioelectromagnetics.* 2000 Sep;21(6):413-21.

Grant WB, Garland CF. The association of solar ultraviolet B (UVB) with reducing risk of cancer: multifactorial ecologic analysis of geographic variation in age-adjusted cancer mortality rates. *Anticancer Res.* 2006 Jul-Aug;26(4A):2687-99.

Grant WB, Holick MF. Benefits and requirements of vitamin D for optimal health: a review. *Altern Med Rev.* 2005 Jun;10(2):94-111.

Grant WB. An estimate of premature cancer mortality in the U.S. due to inadequate doses of solar ultraviolet-B radiation. *Cancer.* 2002 Mar 15;94(6):1867-75.

Grant WB. Solar ultraviolet irradiance and cancer incidence and mortality. *Adv Exp Med Biol.* 2008;624:16-30.

Grasmuller S, Irnich D. Acupuncture in pain therapy. *MMW Fortschr Med.* 2007 Jun 21;149(25-26):37-9.

Grasso F, Grillo C, Musumeci F, Triglia A, Rodolico G, Cammisuli F, Rinzivillo C, Fragati G, Santuccio A, Rodolico M. Photon emission from normal and tumour human tissues. *Experientia.* 1992;48:10-13.

Grasso F, Musumeci F, Triglia A, Rodolico G, Cammisuli F, Rinzivillo C, Fragati G, Santuccio A, Rodolico M. In Stanley P, Kricka L (ed). *Ultraweak Luminescence from Cancer Tissues. In Bioluminescence and Chemiluminescence - Current Status.* New York: J Wiley & Sons. 1991:277-280.

Grasso F, Musumeci F, Triglia A. Yanbastiev M. Borisova, S. Self-irradiation effect on yeast cells. *Photochemistry and Photobiology.* 1991;54(1):147-149.

Grissom C. Magnetic field effects in biology: A survey of possible mechanisms with emphasis on radical pair recombination. *Chem. Rev.* 1995;95:3-24.

Grobstein P. Directed movement in the frog: motor choice, spatial representation, free will? *Neurobiology of motor programme selection.* Pergamon Press, 1992.

Gronfier C, Wright KP Jr, Kronauer RE, Czeisler CA. Entrainment of the human circadian pacemaker to longer-than-24-h days. *Proc Natl Acad Sci U S A.* 2007 May 22;104(21):9081-6.

Guager, James, Household Appliance Magnetic Field Data, provided by T.Dan Bracken, Inc., Lockheed Martin Energy Systems, Inc., and IIT Research Institute. 1997 June 24.

Guidelines for Limiting Exposure to Time-Varying Electric, Magnetic, and Electromagnetic Fields (up to 300 GHz). Munich, Germany: Internl. Comm. Non-Ionizing Radiation Protection (ICNIRP). 1998.

Guo J. Chronic fatigue syndrome treated by acupuncture and moxibustion in combination with psychological approaches in 310 cases. *J Tradit Chin Med.* 2007 Jun;27(2):92-5.

Gupta A, Rash GS, Somia NN, Wachowiak MP, Jones J, Desoky A. The motion path of the digits. J Hand *Surg.* 1998; 23A:1038-1042.

Haarala C, Bergman M, Laine M, Revonsuo A, Koivisto M, Hamalainen H. Electromagnetic field emitted by 902 MHz mobile phones shows no effects on children's cognitive function. *Bioelectromagnetics.* 2005;Suppl 7:S144-50.

Haas M, Cooperstein R, Peterson D. Disentangling manual muscle testing and Applied Kinesiology: critique and reinterpretation of a literature review. Chiropr Osteopat. 2007 Aug 23;15:11.

Hadji L, Arnoux B, Benveniste J. Effect of dilute histamine on coronary flow of guinea-pig isolated heart. Inhibition by a magnetic field. *FASEB Jnl.* 1991;5: A1583.

Hagins WA, Penn RD, Yoshikami S. Dark current and photocurrent in retinal rods. *Biophys J.* 1970 May;10(5):380-412.

Hagins WA, Robinson WE, Yoshikami S. Ionic aspects of excitation in rod outer segments. *Ciba Found Symp.* 1975;(31):169-89.

Hagins WA, Yoshikami S. Ionic mechanisms in excitation of photoreceptors. *Ann N Y Acad Sci.* 1975 Dec 30;264:314-25.

Hagins WA, Yoshikami S. Proceedings: A role for Ca2+ in excitation of retinal rods and cones. *Exp Eye Res.* 1974 Mar;18(3):299-305.

Hagins WA. The visual process: Excitatory mechanisms in the primary receptor cells. *Annu Rev Biophys Bioeng.* 1972;1:131-58.

Halliday GM, Agar NS, Barnetson RS, Ananthaswamy HN, Jones AM. UV-A fingerprint mutations in human skin cancer. *Photochem Photobiol.* 2005 Jan-Feb;81(1):3-8.

Halpern S. *Tuning the Human Instrument.* Palo Alto, CA: Spectrum Research Institute, 1978.

Hamel P. *Through Music to the Self: How to Appreciate and Experience Music.* Boulder: Shambala, 1979.

Hameroff SR, Penrose R. Conscious events as orchestrated spacetime selections. *J Consc Studies.* 1996;3(1):36-53.

Hameroff SR, Penrose R. Orchestrated reduction of quantum coherence in brain microtubules: A model for consciousness. In: Hameroff SN, Kaszniak A, Scott AC (eds.): *Toward a Science of Consciousness - The First Tucson Discussions and Debates.* Cambridge: MIT Press, 1996.

Hameroff SR, Smith, S, Watt.R. Nonlinear electrodynamics in cytoskeletal protein lattices. In: Adey W, Lawrence A (eds.), *Nonlinear Electrodynamics in Biological Systems.* 1984:567-583.

Hameroff SR, Watt, R. Information processing in microtubules. *J Theor Biology.* 1982;98:549-561.

Hameroff SR. Coherence in the cytoskeleton: Implications for biological information processing. In: Fröhlich H. (ed.): *Biological Coherence and Response to External Stimuli.* Springer, Berlin-New York 1988, pp.242-264.

Hameroff SR. Light is heavy: Wave mechanics in proteins - A microtubule hologram model of consciousness. *Proceedings 2nd. International Congress on Psychotronic Research.* Monte Carlo, 1975:168-169.

Hameroff SR. *Ultimate Biocomputing - Biomolecular Consciousness and Nanotechnology.* Amsterdam: Elsevier, 1987.

Hameroff, SR. Ch'i: A neural hologram? Microtubules, bioholography and acupuncture. *Am J Chin Med.* 1974;2(2):163-170.

Hamilton-Miller JM. Probiotics and prebiotics in the elderly. London: Department of Medical Microbiology, Royal Free and University College Medical School, 2004.

REFERENCES AND BIBLIOGRAPHY

Hammermeister J, Brock B, Winterstein D, Page R. Life without TV? cultivation theory and psychosocial health characteristics of television-free individuals and their television-viewing counterparts. *Health Commun.* 2005;17(3):253-64.

Hammitt WE. The relation between being away and privacy in urban forest recreation environments. *Environment and Behaviour.* 2000;32 (4):521-540.

Hancox RJ, Milne BJ, Poulton R. Association of television viewing during childhood with poor educational achievement. *Arch Pediatr Adolesc Med.* 2005 Jul;159(7):614-8.

Handwerk B. Lobsters Navigate by Magnetism, Study Says. *Natl Geogr News.* 2003 Jan 6.

Hanifin JP, Stewart KT, Smith P, Tanner R, Rollag M, Brainard GC. High-intensity red light suppresses melatonin. *Chronobiol Int.* 2006;23(1-2):251-68.

Hans J. *The Structure and Dynamics of Waves and Vibrations.* New York:.Schocken and Co., 1975.

Hardin P. Transcription regulation within the circadian clock: the E-box and beyond. *J Biol Rhythms.* 2004 Oct;19(5):348-60.

Harkins T, Grissom C. Magnetic Field Effects on B12 Ethanolamine Ammonia Lyase: Evidence for a Radical Mechanism. *Science.* 1994;263:958-960.

Harkins T, Grissom C. The Magnetic Field Dependent Step in B12 Ethanolamine Ammonia Lyase is Radical-Pair Recombination. *J. Am. Chem. Soc.* 1995;117:566-567.

Harland JD, Liburdy RP. Environmental magnetic fields inhibit the antiproliferative action of tamoxifen and melatonin in a human breast cancer cell line. *Bioelectromagnetics.* 1997;18(8):555-62.

Haye-Legrand I, Norel X, Labat C, Benveniste J, Brink C. Antigenic contraction of guinea pig tracheal preparations passively sensitized with monoclonal IgE: pharmacological modulation. *Int Arch Allergy Appl Immunol.* 1988;87(4):342-8.

Heckman JD, Ingram AJ, Loyd RD, Luck JV Jr, Mayer PW. Nonunion treatment with pulsed electromagnetic fields. *Clin Orthop Relat Res.* 1981 Nov-Dec;(161):58-66.

Heerwagen JH. The psychological aspects of windows and window design'. In Selby, R. I., Anthony, K. H., Choi, J. and Orland, B. (eds) *Proceedings of 21st Annual Conference of the Environmental Design Research Association.* Champaign-Urbana, Illinois, 1990 April:6-9.

Heinrich H. Assessment of non-sinusoidal, pulsed, or intermittent exposure to low frequency electric and magnetic fields. *Health Phys.* 2007 Jun;92(6):541-6.

Heinrich U, Gärtner C, Wiebusch M, Eichler O, Sies H, Tronnier H, Stahl W. Supplementation with beta-carotene or a similar amount of mixed carotenoids protects humans from UV-induced erythema. *J Nutr.* 2003 Jan;133(1):98-101.

Helms JA, Farnham PJ, Segal E, Chang HY. Functional demarcation of active and silent chromatin domains in human HOX loci by noncoding RNAs. *Cell.* 2007 Jun 29;129(7):1311-23.

Henderson SI, Bangay MJ. Survey of RF exposure levels from mobile telephone base stations in Australia. *Bioelectromag.* 2006 Jan;27(1):73-6.

Henshaw DL, Ross AN, Fews AP, Preece AW. Enhanced deposition of radon daughter nuclei in the vicinity of power frequency electromagnetic fields. *Int J Radiat Biol.* 1996 Jan;69(1):25-38.

Herbert V. Vitamin B12: Plant sources, requirements, and assay. *Am J Clin Nutr.* 1988;48:852-858.

Hess AF. *Rickets.* London: Henry Kimpton, 1930.

Heyers D, Manns M, Luksch H, Gü¨ntu¨rku¨n O, Mouritsen H. A Visual Pathway Links Brain Structures Active during Magnetic Compass Orientation in Migratory Birds. *PLoS One.* 2007;2(9):e937. 2007.

Hietanen M, Hamalainen AM, Husman T. Hypersensitivity symptoms associated with exposure to cellular telephones: no causal link. *Bioelectromagnetics.* 2002 May;23(4):264-70.

Hillecke T, Nickel A, Bolay HV. Scientific perspectives on music therapy. *Ann N Y Acad Sci.* 2005 Dec;1060:271-82.

Hirayama J, Sahar S, Grimaldi B, Tamaru T, Takamatsu K, Nakahata Y, Sassone-Corsi P. CLOCK-mediated acetylation of BMAL1 controls circadian function. *Nature* 450, 1086-1090 (13 December 2007)

Hjollund NH, Bonde JP, Skotte J. Semen analysis of personnel operating military radar equipment. *Reprod Toxicol.* 1997 Nov-Dec;11(6):897.

Ho MW. Assessing Food Quality by Its After-Glow. *Inst. Sci in Society.* Press release. 2004 May 1.

Hobbs C. *Stress & Natural Healing.* Loveland, CO: Interweave Press, 1997.

Holick MF. Photobiology of vitamin D. In: Feldman D, Pike JW, Glorieux FH, eds. *Vitamin D*, Second Edition, Volume I. Burlington, MA: Elsevier, 2005.

Holick MF. Sunlight and vitamin D for bone health and prevention of autoimmune diseases, cancers, and cardiovascular disease. *Am J Clin Nutr.* 2004 Dec;80(6 Suppl):1678S-88S.

Holick MF. Vitamin D status: measurement, interpretation, and clinical application. Ann Epidemiol. 2009 Feb;19(2):73-8.

Holick MF. Vitamin D. In: Shils ME, Shike M, Ross AC, Caballero B, Cousins RJ, eds. *Modern Nutrition in Health and Disease*, 10th ed. Philadelphia: Lippincott Williams & Wilkins, 2006.

Holick MF. Vitamin D: importance in the prevention of cancers, type 1 diabetes, heart disease, and osteoporosis. *Am J Clin Nutr.* 2004 Mar;79(3):362-71.

Hollfoth K. Effect of color therapy on health and wellbeing: colors are more than just physics. *Pflege.Z* 2000;53(2):111-112.

Hollwich F, Dieckhues B, Schrameyer B. The effect of natural and artificial light via the eye on the hormonal and metabolic balance of man. *Klin Monbl Augenheilkd.* 1977 Jul;171(1):98-104.

Hollwich F, Dieckhues B. Effect of light on the eye on metabolism and hormones. *Klin Monbl Augenheilkd.* 1989 Nov;195(5):284-90.

Hollwich F. Hartmann C. Influence of light through the eyes on metabolism and hormones. Ophtalmologie. 1990;4(4):385-9.

Hollwich F. *The influence of ocular light perception on metabolism in man and in animal.* NY: Springer-Verlag, 1979.

Holly EA, Aston DA, Ahn DK, Smith AH. Intraocular melanoma linked to occupations and chemical exposures. *Epidemiology.* 1996 Jan;7(1):55-61.

Holman CD, Armstrong BK, Heenan PJ. Relationship of cutaneous malignant melanoma to individual sunlight-exposure habits. *J Natl Cancer Inst.* 1986 Mar;76(3):403-14.

Holmquist G. Susumo Ohno left us January 13, 2000, at the age of 71. *Cytogenet and Cell Genet.* 2000;88:171-172.

Honeyman MK. Vegetation and stress: a comparison study of varying amounts of vegetation in countryside and urban scenes. In Relf, D. (ed) *The Role of Horticulture in Human Well-Being and Social Development: A National Symposium.* Portland: Timber Press. 1992:143-145.

Hood W, Nicholas J, Butler G, Lackland D, Hoel D, Mohr L. Magnetic field exposure of commercial airline pilots. *Annals of Epidemiology* 2000 Oct 1;10(7):479.

Horne JA, Donlon J, Arendt J. Green light attenuates melatonin output and sleepiness during sleep deprivation. *Sleep.* 1991 Jun;14(3):233-40.

Hoskin M.(ed.). *The Cambridge Illustrated History of Astronomy.* Cambridge: Cambridge Press, 1997.

Hoyle F. *Evolution from Space.* Londong: JM Dent, 1981.

Hu X, Wu B, Wang P. Displaying of meridian courses travelling over human body surface under natural conditions. *Zhen Ci Yan Jiu.* 1993;18(2):83-9.

Huesmann LR, Moise-Titus J, Podolski CL, Eron LD. Longitudinal relations between children's exposure to TV violence and their aggressive and violent behavior in young adulthood: 1977-1992. *Dev Psychol.* 2003 Mar;39(2):201-21.

Huffman C. Archytas of Tarentum: *Pythagorean, philosopher and Mathematician King.* Cambridge: Cambridge University Press, 2005.

Hunt V. *Infinite Mind: Science of the Human Vibrations of Consciousness.* Malibu: Malibu Publ. 2000.

Hur YM, Rushton JP. Genetic and environmental contributions to prosocial behaviour in 2- to 9-year-old South Korean twins. *Biol Lett.* 2007 Aug 28.

Ikeda M, Toyoshima R, Inoue Y, Yamada N, Mishima K, Nomura M, Ozaki N, Okawa M, Takahashi K, Yamauchi T. Mutation screening of the human Clock gene in circadian rhythm sleep disorders. *Psychiatry Res.* 2002 Mar 15;109(2):121-8.

Ikonomov OC, Stoynev AG. Gene expression in suprachiasmatic nucleus and circadian rhythms. *Neurosci Biobehav Rev.* 1994 Fall;18(3):305-12.

Inaba H. INABA Biophoton. Exploratory Research for Advanced Technology. *Japan Science and Technology Agency.* 1991. http://www.jst.go.jp/erato/project/isf_P/isf_P.html. Acc. 2006 Nov.

Itokawa Y. Magnesium intake and cardiovascular disease. *Clin Calcium.* 2005 Feb;15(2):154-9.

Ivanovic-Zuvic F, de la Vega R, Ivanovic-Zuvic N, Renteria P. Affective disorders and solar activity. *Actas Esp Psiquiatr.* 2005 Jan-Feb;33(1):7-12.

Ivry GB, Ogle CA, Shim EK. Role of sun exposure in melanoma. *Dermatol Surg.* 2006 Apr;32(4):481-92.

Iwase T, Kajimura N, Uchiyama M, Ebisawa T, Yoshimura K, Kamei Y, Shibui K, Kim K, Kudo Y, Katoh M, Watanabe T, Nakajima T, Ozeki Y, Sugishita M, Hori T, Ikeda M, Toyoshima R, Inoue Y, Yamada N, Mishima K, Nomura M, Ozaki N, Okawa M, Takahashi K, Yamauchi T. Mutation screening of the human Clock gene in circadian rhythm sleep disorders. *Psychiatry Res.* 2002 Mar 15;109(2):121-8.

Ji Y, Liu YB, Zheng LY, Zhang XQ. Survey of studies on tissue structures and biological characteristics of channel lines. *Zhongguo Zhen Jiu.* 2007 Jun;27(6):427-32.

Jin CN, Zhang TS, Ji LX, Tian YF. Survey of studies on mechanisms of acupuncture and moxibustion in decreasing blood pressure. *Zhongguo Zhen Jiu.* 2007 Jun;27(6):467-70.

Johansen C. Electromagnetic fields and health effects—epidemiologic studies of cancer, diseases of the central nervous system and arrhythmia-related heart disease. *Scand J Work Env Hlth.* 2004;30 Spl 1:1-30.

Johari H. *Ayurvedic Massage: Traditional Indian Techniques for Balancing Body and Mind.* Roch: Healing Arts, 1996.

Johari H. *Chakras.* Rochester, VT: Destiny, 1987.

Johnston A. A spatial property of the retino-cortical mapping. *Spatial Vision.* 1986;1(4):319-331.

REFERENCES AND BIBLIOGRAPHY

Johnston RE. Pheromones, the vomeronasal system, and communication. From hormonal responses to individual recognition. *Ann N Y Acad Sci.* 1998 Nov 30;855:333-48.

Jovanovic-Ignjatic Z, Rakovic D. A review of current research in microwave resonance therapy: novel opportunities in medical treatment. *Acupunct Electrother Res.* 1999; 24:105-125.

Jovanovic-Ignjatic Z. Microwave Resonant Therapy: Novel Opportunities in Medical Treatment. *Acup. & Electro-Therap. Res., The Int. J.* 1999;24(2):105-125.

Kahhak L, Roche A, Dubray C, Arnoux C, Benveniste J. Decrease of ciliary beat frequency by platelet activating factor: protective effect of ketotifen. *Inflamm Res.* 1996 May;45(5):234-8.

Kalsbeek A, Perreau-Lenz S, Buijs RM. A network of (autonomic) clock outputs. *Chronobiol Int.* 2006;23(1-2):201-15.

Kamide Y. We reside in the sun's atmosphere. *Biomed Pharmacother.* 2005 Oct;59 Suppl 1:S1-4.

Kamycheva E, Jorde R, Figenschau Y, Haug E. Insulin sensitivity in subjects with secondary hyperparathyroidism and the effect of a low serum 25-hydroxyvitamin D level on insulin sensitivity. *J Endocrinol Invest.* 2007 Feb;30(2):126-32.

Kandel E, Siegelbaum S, Schwartz J. *Synaptic transmission. Principles of Neural Science.* New York: Elsevier, 1991.

Kang Y, Li M, Yan W, Li X, Kang J, Zhang Y. Electroacupuncture alters the expression of genes associated with lipid metabolism and immune reaction in liver of hypercholesterolemia mice. *Biotechnol Lett.* 2007 Aug 18.

Kaplan R. The psychological benefits of nearby nature. In: Relf, D. (ed) *The Role of Horticulture in Human Well-Being and Social Development: A National Symposium.* Portland: Timber Press. 1992:125-133.

Kaplan S. A model of person - environment compatibility. *Environment and Behaviour* 1983;15:311-332.

Kaplan S. The restorative environment: nature and human experience. In: Relf, D. (ed) *The Role of Horticulture in Human Well-Being and Social Development: A National Symposium.* Portland: Timber Press. 1992:134-142.

Karis TE, Jhon MS. Flow-induced anisotropy in the susceptibility of a particle suspension. *Proc Natl Acad Sci USA.* 1986 Jul;83(14):4973-4977.

Karnstedt J. Ions and Consciousness. *Whole Self.* 1991 Spring.

Karpin VA, Kostriukova NK, Gudkov AB. Human radiation action of radon and its daughter disintegration products. *Gig Sanit.* 2005 Jul-Aug;(4):13-7.

Kato Y, Kawamoto T, Honda KK. Circadian rhythms in cartilage. *Clin Calcium.* 2006 May;16(5):838-45.

Keil J, Stevenson I. Do cases of the reincarnation type show similar features over many years? A study of Turkish cases. *J. Sci. Exploration.* 1999;13(2) 189-198.

Kelly TL, Neri DF, Grill JT, Ryman D, Hunt PD, Dijk DJ, Shanahan TL, Czeisler CA. Nonentrained circadian rhythms of melatonin in submariners scheduled to an 18-hour day. *J Biol Rhythms.* 1999 Jun;14(3):190-6.

Kent ST, McClure LA, Crosson WL, Arnett DK, Wadley VG, Sathiakumar N. Effect of sunlight exposure on cognitive function among depressed and non-depressed participants: a REGARDS cross-sectional study. *Environ Health.* 2009 Jul 28;8:34.

Kerr CC, Rennie CJ, Robinson PA. Physiology-based modeling of cortical auditory evoked potentials. *Biol Cybern.* 2008 Feb;98(2):171-84.

Kheifets L, Monroe J, Vergara X, Mezei G, Afifi AA. Occupational electromagnetic fields and leukemia and brain cancer: an update to two meta-analyses. *J Occup Environ Med.* 2008 Jun;50(6):677-88.

Kiecolt-Glaser JK, Graham JE, Malarkey WB, Porter K, Lemeshow S, Glaser R. Olfactory influences on mood and autonomic, endocrine, and immune function. *Psychoneuroendocrinology.* 2008 Apr;33(3):328-39.

Kinoshameg SA, Persinger MA. Suppression of experimental allergic encephalomyelitis in rats by 50-nT, 7-Hz amplitude-modulated nocturnal magnetic fields depends on when after inoculation the fields are applied. *J Neulet.*2004;08:18.

Kirlian SD, Kirlian V. Photography and Visual Observation by Means of High-Frequency Currents. *J Sci Appl Photogr.* 1963;6(6).

Kleffmann J. Daytime Sources of Nitrous Acid (HONO) in the Atmospheric Boundary Layer. *Chemphyschem.* 2007 Apr 10;8(8):1137-1144.

Klein R, Armitage R. Rhythms in human performance: 1 1/2-hour oscillations in cognitive style. *Science.* 1979 Jun 22;204(4399):1326-8.

Klima H, Haas O, Roschger P. Photon emission from blood cells and its possible role in immune system regulation. In: Jezowska-Trzebiatowska B., *et al.* (eds.): *Photon Emission from Biological Systems.* Singapore: World Scientific, 1987:153-169.

Kloss J. *Back to Eden.* Twin Oaks, WI: Lotus Press, 1939-1999.

Koch C. Debunking the Digital Brain. *Sci. Am.* 1997 Feb.

Kollerstrom N, Staudenmaier G. Evidence for Lunar-Sidereal Rhythms in Crop Yield: A Review. *Biolog Agri & Hort.* 2001;19:247–259.

Kollerstrom N, Steffert B. Sex difference in response to stress by lunar month: a pilot study of four years' crisis-call frequency. *BMC Psychiatry.* 2003 Dec 10;3:20.

Köpcke W, Krutmann J. Protection from sunburn with beta-Carotene—a meta-analysis. *Photochem Photobiol.* 2008 Mar-Apr;84(2):284-8.

Krause R, Buhring M, Hopfenmuller W, Holick MF, Sharma AM. Ultraviolet B and blood pressure. *Lancet.* 1998 Aug 29;352(9129):709-10.

Krueger AP, Reed EJ. Biological impact of small air ions. *Science.* 1976 Sep 24;193(4259):1209-13.

Küller R, Laike T. The impact of flicker from fluorescent lighting on well-being, performance and physiological arousal. *Ergonomics.* 1998 Apr;41(4):433-47.

Kuo FF, Kuo JJ. *Recent Advances in Acupuncture Research, Institute for Adnanced Research in Asian Science and Medicine.* Garden City, New York. 1979.

Kuribayashi M, Wang J, Fujiwara O, Doi Y, Nabae K, Tamano S, Ogiso T, Asamoto M, Shirai T. Lack of effects of 1439 MHz electromagnetic near field exposure on the blood-brain barrier in immature and young rats. *Bioelectromagnetics.* 2005 Oct;26(7):578-88.

Kuuler R, Ballal S, Laike T Mikellides B, Tonello G. The impact of light and colour on psychological mood: a cross-cultral study of indoor work environments. Ergonomics. 2006 Nov 15;49(14):1496.

Lad V. *Ayurveda: The Science of Self-Healing.* Twin Lakes, WI: Lotus Press.

Lafrenière, G. The material Universe is made purely out of Aether. *Matter is made of Waves.* 2002. http://www.glafreniere.com/matter.htm. Acc. 2007 June.

Lakin-Thomas PL. Transcriptional feedback oscillators: maybe, maybe not. *J Bio Rhyth.* 2006 Apr;21(2):83-92.

Lam F, Jr, Tsuei JJ, Zhao Z. Studies on the bioenergetic measurement of acupuncture points for determination of correct dosage of allopathic or homeopathic medicine in the treatment of diabetes mellitus. *Am J Acupunct.* 1990;18:127-33.

Lambing K. Biophoton Measurement as a Supplement to the Conventional Consideration of Food Quality. In: Popp F, Li K, Gu Q (eds.). *Recent Advances in Biophoton Research.* Singapore: World Scientific Publ. 1992:393-413.

Lancranjan I, Maicanescu M, Rafaila E, Klepsch I, Popescu HI. Gonadic function in workmen with long-term exposure to microwaves. *Health Phys.* 1975;29:381–383.

Larsen AI, Olsen J, Svane O. Gender-specific reproductive outcome and exposure to high-frequency electromagnetic radiation among physiotherapists. *Scand J Work Environ Health.* 1991;17:324–329.

Larsen AI, Skotte J. Can exposure to electromagnetic radiation in diathermy operators be estimated from interview data? A pilot study. *Am J Ind Med* 1991;19:51–57.

Larsen AI. Congenital malformations and exposure to high-frequency electromagnetic radiation among Danish physiotherapists. *Scand J Work Environ Health.* 1991;17:318–323.

Latour E. Functional electrostimulation and its using in neurorehabilitation. *Ortop Traumatol Rehabil.* 2006 Dec 29;8(6):593-601.

Laura AG, Armas, B, Heaney H, Heaney R. Vitamin D_2 Is Much Less Effective than Vitamin D_3 in Humans. *J Clin Endocr & Metab.* 2004;89(11):5387-5391.

Laverty WH, Kelly IW. Cyclical calendar and lunar patterns in automobile property accidents and injury accidents. *Percept Mot Skills.* 1998 Feb;86(1):299-302.

Leder D. Spooky actions at a distance: physics, psi, and distant healing. *J Altern Complement Med.* 2005 Oct;11(5):923-30.

Lefort J, Sedivy P, Desquand S, Randon J, Coeffier E, Maridonneau-Parini I, Floch A, Benveniste J, Vargaftig BB. Pharmacological profile of 48740 R.P., a PAF-acether antagonist. *Eur J Pharmacol.* 1988 Jun 10;150(3):257-68.

Lehmann B. The vitamin D3 pathway in human skin and its role for regulation of biological processes. *Photochem Photobiol.* 2005 Nov-Dec;81(6):1246-51.

Lenn NJ, Beebe B, Moore RY (1977) Postnatal development of the suprachiasmatic nucleus of the rat. *Cell Tissue Res.* 178:463-475.

Lewis WH, Elvin-Lewis MPF. *Medical Botany: Plants Affecting Man's Health.* New York: Wiley, 1977.

Li DK, Odouli R, Wi S, Janevic T, Golditch I, Bracken TD, Senior R, Rankin R, Iriye R. A population-based prospective cohort study of personal exposure to magnetic fields during pregnancy and the risk of miscarriage. *Epidemiology.* 2002 Jan;13(1):9-20.

Li KH. Bioluminescence and stimulated coherent radiation. *Laser und Elektrooptik 3.* 1981:32-35.

Li N, Wang DL, Wang CW, Wu B. Discussion on randomized controlled trials about clinical researches of acupuncture and moxibustion medicine. *Zhongguo Zhen Jiu.* 2007 Jul;27(7):529-32.

Li Q, Gandhi OP. Calculation of magnetic field-induced current densities for humans from EAS countertop activation/deactivation devices that use ferromagnetic cores. *Phys Med Biol.* 2005 Jan 21;50(2):373-85.

Liao H, Xi P, Chen Q, Yi L, Zhao Y. Clinical study on acupuncture moxibustion, acupuncture plus moxibustion at Weiwanxiashu (EX-B3) for treatment of diabetes. *Zhongguo Zhen Jiu.* 2007 Jul;27(7):482-4.

REFERENCES AND BIBLIOGRAPHY

Lieber AL. Human aggression and the lunar synodic cycle. *J Clin Psychiatry.* 1978 May;39(5):385-92.

Lipkind M. Can the vitalistic Entelechia principle be a working instrument ? (The theory of the biological field of Alexander G.Gurvich). In: Popp F, Li K, Gu Q (eds.). *Recent Advances in Biophoton Research.* Singapore: World Sci Publ, 1992:469-494.

Lipkind M. Registration of spontaneous photon emission from virus-infected cell cultures: development of experimental system. *Indian J Exp Biol.* 2003 May;41(5):457-72.

Litime M, Aïssa J, Benveniste J. Antigen signaling at high dilution. *FASEB Jnl.* 1993;7: A602.

Litscher G. Bioengineering assessment of acupuncture, part 5: cerebral near-infrared spectroscopy. *Crit Rev Biomed Eng.* 2006;34(6):439-.

Livanova L, Levshina I, Nozdracheva L, Elbakidze MG, Airapetiants MG. The protective action of negative air ions in acute stress in rats with different typological behavioral characteristics. *Zh Vyssh Nerv Deiat Im I P Pavlova.* 1998 May-Jun;48(3):554-7.

Lloyd D, Murray D. Redox rhythmicity: clocks at the core of temporal coherence.*BioEss.* 2007;29(5):465-473.

Lloyd JU. *American Materia Medica, Therapeutics and Pharmacognosy.* Portland, OR: Eclect Med Publ, 1989-1983.

Lorenz I, Schneider EM, Stolz P, Brack A, Strube J. Sensitive flow cytometric method to test basophil activation influenced by homeopathic histamine dilutions. *Forsch Komplementarmed Klass Naturheilkd.* 2003 Dec;10(6):316-24.

Lovejoy S, Pecknold S, Schertzer D. Stratified multifractal magnetization and surface geomagnetic fields-I. Spectral analysis and modeling. *Geophysical Journal International.* 2001 145(1):112-126.

Lovelock, J. *Gaia: A New Look at Life on Earth.* Oxford: Oxford Press, 1979.

Lovely RH. Recent studies in the behavioral toxicology of ELF electric and magnetic fields. *Prog Clin Biol Res.* 1988;257:327-47.

Loving RT, Kripke DF, Knickerbocker NC, Grandner MA. Bright green light treatment of depression for older adults. *BMC Psychiatry.* 2005 Nov 9;5:42.

Lu J, Cui Y, Shi R. *A Practical English-Chinese Library of Traditional Chinese Medicine: Chinese Acupuncture and Moxibustion.* Shanghai: Publishing House of the Shanghai College of Traditional Chinese Medicine, 1988.

Lydic R, Schoene WC, Czeisler CA, Moore-Ede MC. Suprachiasmatic region of the human hypothalamus: homolog to the primate circadian pacemaker? *Sleep.* 1980;2(3):355-61.

Lynch M, Walsh B. *Genetics and Analysis of Quantitative Traits.* Sunderland, MA: Sinauer, 1998

Lythgoe JN. Visual pigments and environmental light. *Vision Res.* 1984;24(11):1539-50.

Lytle CD, Sagripanti JL. Predicted inactivation of viruses of relevance to biodefense by solar radiation. *J Virol.* 2005 Nov;79(22):14244-52.

Maas J, Jayson, J. K.. & Kleiber, D. A. Effects of spectral differences in illumination on fatigue. *J Appl Psychol.* 1974;59:524-526.

Maccabee PJ, Amassian VE, Cracco RQ, Cracco JB, Eberle L, Rudell A. Stimulation of the human nervous system using the magnetic coil. *J Clin Neurophysiol.* 1991 Jan;8(1):38-55.

Magnusson A, Stefansson JG. Prevalence of seasonal affective disorder in Iceland. *Arch Gen Psychiatry.* 1993 Dec;50(12):941-6.

Maier R, Greter SE, Maier N. Effects of pulsed electromagnetic fields on cognitive processes - a pilot study on pulsed field interference with cognitive regeneration. *Acta Neurol Scand.* 2004 Jul;110(1):46-52.

Maier T, Korting HC. Sunscreens - which and what for? *Skin Pharmacol Physiol.* 2005 Nov-Dec;18(6):253-62.

Marks C. *Commissurotomy, Consciousness, and Unity of Mind.* Cambridge: MIT Press, 1981.

Marks L. *The Unity of the Senses: Interrelations among the Modalities.* New York: Academic Press, 1978.

Matsumura Y, Nishigori C, Yagi T, Imamura S, Takebe H. Characterization of p53 gene mutations in basal-cell carcinomas: comparison between sun-exposed and less-exposed skin areas. *Int J Cancer.* 1996 Mar 15;65(6):778-80.

Matutinovic Z, Galic M. Relative magnetic hearing threshold. *Laryngol Rhinol Otol.* 1982 Jan;61(1):38-41.

Mayron L, Ott J, Nations R, Mayron E. Light, radiation and academic behaviour: Initial studies on the effects of full-spectrum lighting and radiation shielding on behaviour and academic performance of school children. *Acad Ther.* 1974;10, 33-47.

Mayron L. Hyperactivity from fluorescent lighting - fact or fancy: A commentary on the report by O'Leary, Rosenbaum and Hughes. *J Abnorm Child Psychol.* 1978;6:291-294.

McColl SL, Veitch JA. Full-spectrum fluorescent lighting: a review of its effects on physiology and health. *Psychol Med.* 2001 Aug;31(6):949-64.

McConnel JV, Cornwell PR, Clay M. An apparatus for conditioning Planaria. *Am J Psychol.* 1960 Dec;73:618-22.

McCulloch M, Jezierski T, Broffman M, Hubbard A, Turner K, Janecki T. Diagnostic accuracy of canine scent detection in early- and late-stage lung and breast cancers. *Integr Cancer Ther.* 2006 Mar;5(1):30-9.

McLay RN, Daylo AA, Hammer PS. No effect of lunar cycle on psychiatric admissions or emergency evaluations. *Mil Med.* 2006 Dec;171(12):1239-42.

McTaggart L. *The Field.* New York: Quill, 2003.

Meinecke FW. Sequelae and rehabilitation of spinal cord injuries. *Curr Opin Neurol Neurosurg.* 1991 Oct;4(5):714-9.

Melzack R, Coderre TJ, Katz J, Vaccarino AL. Central neuroplasticity and pathological pain. *Ann N Y Acad Sci.* 2001 Mar;933:157-74.

Melzack R, Wall PD. Pain mechanisms: a new theory. *Science.* 1965 Nov 19;150(699):971-9.

Melzack R. Evolution of the neuromatrix theory of pain. The prithvi raj lecture: presented at the third world congress of world institute of pain, barcelona 2004. *Pain Pract.* 2005 Jun;5(2):85-94.

Melzack R. Pain: past, present and future. *Can J Exp Psychol.* 1993 Dec;47(4):615-29.

Melzack R. Pain—an overview. *Acta Anaesthesiol Scand.* 1999 Oct;43(9):880-4.

Miles LE, Raynal DM, Wilson MA. Blind man living in normal society has circadian rhythms of 24.9 hours. *Science.* 1977 Oct 28;198(4315):421-3.

Miller GT. *Living in the Environment.* Belmont, CA: Wadsworth, 1996.

Miller JD, Morin LP, Schwartz WJ, Moore RY. New insights into the mammalian circadian clock. *Sleep.* 1996 Oct;19(8):641-67.

Mishkin M, Appenzeller T. The Anatomy of Memory. *Sci. Am.* 1987 June.

Mishkin M. Memory in monkeys severely impaired by combined but not by separate removal of amygdala and hippocampus. *Nature.* 1978;273: 297-298.

Modern Biology. Austin: Harcourt Brace, 1993.

Mohr SB, Garland CF, Gorham ED, Grant WB, Garland FC. Is ultraviolet B irradiance inversely associated with incidence rates of endometrial cancer: an ecological study of 107 countries. *Prev Med.* 2007 Nov;45(5):327-31.

Mohr SB. A brief history of vitamin d and cancer prevention. *Ann Epidemiol.* 2009 Feb;19(2):79-83.

Moore RY, Speh JC. Serotonin innervation of the primate suprachiasmatic nucleus. *Brain Res.* 2004 Jun 4;1010(1-2):169-73.

Moore RY. Neural control of the pineal gland. *Behav Brain Res.* 1996;73(1-2):125-30.

Moore RY. Organization and function of a central nervous system circadian oscillator: the suprachiasmatic hypothalamic nucleus. *Fed Proc.* 1983 Aug;42(11):2783-9.

Morick H. *Introduction to the Philosophy of Mind: Readings from Descartes to Strawson.* Glenview, Ill: Scott Foresman, 1970.

Morton C. *Velocity Alters Electric Field.* www.amasci.com/ freenrg/ morton1.html. Accessed: 2007 July.

Moshe M. Method and apparatus for predicting the occurrence of an earthquake by identifying electromagnetic precursors. US Patent Issued on May 28, 1996. Number 5521508.

Motoyama H. Acupuncture Meridians. *Science & Medicine.* 1999 July/August.

Motoyama H. Before Polarization Current and the Acupuncture Meridians. *Journal of Holistic Medicine.* 1986;8(1&2).

Motoyama H. Deficient/ Excessive Patterns Found in Meridian Functioning in Cases of Liver Disease. *Subtle Energy & Energy Medicine.* 2000; 11(2).

Motoyama H. Energetic Medicine: new science of healing: An interview with A. Jackson. www.shareintl.org/archives/health-healing/hh_adjenergetic.html. Acc. 2007 Oct.

Motoyama H. Smith, W. Harada T. Pre-Polarization Resistance of the Skin as Determined by the Single Square Voltage Pulse. *Psychophysiology.* 1984;21(5).

Mumby DG, Wood ER, Pinel J. Object-recognition memory is only mildly impaired in rats with lesions of the hippocampus and amygdala. *Psychobio.* 1992;20: 18-27.

Murchie G. *The Seven Mysteries of Life.* Boston: Houghton Mifflin Company, 1978.

Murphy R. *Organon Philosophy Workbook.* Blacksburg, VA: HANA, 1994.

Musaev AV, Nasrullaeva SN, Zeïnalov RG. Effects of solar activity on some demographic indices and morbidity in Azerbaijan with reference to A. L. Chizhevsky's theory. *Vopr Kurortol Fizioter Lech Fiz Kult.* 2007 May-Jun;(3):38-42.

Muzzarelli L, Force M, Sebold M. Aromatherapy and reducing preprocedural anxiety: A controlled prospective study. *Gastroenterol Nurs.* 2006 Nov-Dec;29(6):466-71.

Myss C. *Anatomy of the Spirit.* New York: Harmony, 1996.

Nadkarni AK, Nadkarni KM. *Indian Materia Medica.* (Vols 1 and 2). Bombay: Popular Pradashan, 1908, 1976.

Nakamura K, Urayama K, Hoshino Y. Lumbar cerebrospinal fluid pulse wave rising from pulsations of both the spinal cord and the brain in humans. *Spinal Cord.* 1997 Nov;35(11):735-9.

Nakatani K, Yau KW. Calcium and light adaptation in retinal rods and cones. *Nature.* 1988 Jul 7;334(6177): 69-71.

REFERENCES AND BIBLIOGRAPHY

Natarajan E, Grissom C. The Origin of Magnetic Field Dependent Recombination in Alkylcobalamin Radical Pairs. *Photochem Photobiol.* 1996;64: 286-295.

Navarro Silvera SA, Rohan TE. Trace elements and cancer risk: a review of the epidemiologic evidence. *Cancer Causes Control.* 2007 Feb;18(1):7-27.

Nestel PJ. Adulthood - prevention: Cardiovascular disease. *Med J Aust.* 2002 Jun 3;176(11 Suppl):S118-9.

Nestor PJ, Graham KS, Bozeat S, Simons JS, Hodges JR. Memory consolidation and the hippocampus: further evidence from studies of autobiographical memory in semantic dementia and frontal variant frontotemporal dementia. *Neuropsychologia.* 2002;40(6):633-54.

Newton PE. The Effect of Sound on Plant Grwoth. *JAES.* 1971 Mar;19(3): 202-205.

Nicholas JS, Lackland DT, Butler GC, Mohr LC Jr, Dunbar JB, Kaune WT, Grosche B, Hoel DG. Cosmic radiation and magnetic field exposure to airline flight crews. *Am J Ind Med.* 1998 Dec;34(6):574-80.

Nielsen LR, Mosekilde L. Vitamin D and breast cancer. *Ugeskr Laeger.* 2007 Apr 2;169(14):1299-302.

Nievergelt CM, Kripke DF, Remick RA, Sadovnick AD, McElroy SL, Keck PE Jr, Kelsoe JR. Examination of the clock gene Cryptochrome 1 in bipolar disorder: mutational analysis and absence of evidence for linkage or association. *Psychiatr Genet.* 2005 Mar;15(1):45-52.

Niggli H. Temperature dependence of ultraweak photon emission in fibroblastic differentiation after irradiation with artificial sunlight. *Indian J Exp Biol.* 2003 May;41:419-423.

Nishigori C, Hattori Y, Toyokuni S. Role of reactive oxygen species in skin carcinogenesis. *Antioxid Redox Signal.* 2004 Jun;6(3):561-70.

North J. *The Fontana History of Astronomy and Cosmology.* London: Fontana Press, 1994.

NRPB 2003. Health Effects from Radiofrequency Electromagnetic Fields. Report of an Independent Advisory Group on Non-ionising Radiation. Chilton, Didcot, *UK:National Radiation Protection Board.*

Núñez S, Pérez Méndez L, Aguirre-Jaime A. Moon cycles and violent behaviours: myth or fact? *Eur J Emerg Med.* 2002 Jun;9(2):127-30.

O'Dwyer JJ. *College Physics.* Pacific Grove, CA: Brooks/Cole, 1990.

O'Connor J., Bensky D. (ed). *Shanghai College of Traditional Chinese Medicine: Acupuncture: A Comprehensive Text.* Seattle: Eastland Press, 1981.

Oh CK, Lücker PW, Wetzelsberger N, Kuhlmann F. The determination of magnesium, calcium, sodium and potassium in assorted foods with special attention to the loss of electrolytes after various forms of food preparations. *Mag.-Bull.* 1986;8:297-302.

Okamura H. Clock genes in cell clocks: roles, actions, and mysteries. *J Biol Rhythms.* 2004 Oct;19(5):388-99.

Okayama Y, Begishvili TB, Church MK. Comparison of mechanisms of IL-3 induced histamine release and IL-3 priming effect on human basophils. *Clin Exp Allergy.* 1993 Nov;23(11):901-10.

Ole D. Rughede, On the Theory and Physics of the Aether. *Progress in Physics.* 2006; (1).

O'Leary KD, Rosenbaum A, Hughes PC. Fluorescent lighting: a purported source of hyperactive behavior. *J Abnorm Child Psychol.* 1978 Sep;6(3):285-9.

Olney JW. Excitotoxins in foods. *Neurotoxicology.* 1994;15:535-44.

Oosterga M, ten Vaarwerk IA, DeJongste MJ, Staal MJ. Spinal cord stimulation in refractory angina pectoris—clinical results and mechanisms. *Z Kardiol.* 1997;86 Suppl 1:107-13.

Ostrander S, Schroeder L, Ostrander N. *Super-Learning.* New York: Delta, 1979.

Otani S. Memory trace in prefrontal cortex: theory for the cognitive switch. *Biol Rev Camb Philos Soc.* 2002 Nov;77(4):563-77.

Otsu A, Chinami M, Morgenthale S, Kaneko Y, Fujita D, Shirakawa T. Correlations for number of sunspots, unemployment rate, and suicide mortality in Japan. *Percept Mot Skills.* 2006 Apr;102(2):603-8.

Ott J. Color and Light: Their Effects on Plants, Animals, and People (Series of seven articles in seven issues). *Internl J Biosoc Res.* 1985-1991.

Ott J. *Health and Light: The Effects of Natural and Artificial Light on Man and Other Living Things.* Self published, 1973,

Otto SJ, van Houwelingen AC, Hornstra G. The effect of supplementation with docosahexaenoic and arachidonic acid derived from single cell oils on plasma and erythrocyte fatty acids of pregnant women in the second trimester. *Prost Leuk Essent Fatty Acids.* 2000 Nov;63(5):323-8.

Ouellet-Hellstrom R, Stewart WF. Miscarriages among female physical therapists who report using radio- and microwave-frequency electromagnetic radiation. *Am J Epidemiol.* 1993 Nov 15;138(10):775-86.

Owen C, Tarantello C, Jones M, Tennant C. Lunar cycles and violent behaviour. *Aust-NZ J Psych.*1998 Aug;32(4):496-9.

Paavonen EJ, Pennonen M, Roine M, Valkonen S, Lahikainen AR. TV exposure associated with sleep disturbances in 5- to 6-year-old children. J Sleep Res. 2006 Jun;15(2):154-61.

Pacione M. Urban environmental quality and human wellbeing-a social geographical perspective. *Landscape and Urban Planning* 2003;986:1-12.

Palm TA. The geographical distribution and aetiology of rickets. *Practitioner.* 1890;45:270-90, 321-42.

Palumbo A. Gravitational and geomagnetic tidal source of earthquake triggering. *Ital Phys.* 1989 Nov;12(6).

Park AE, Fernandez JJ, Schmedders K, Cohen MS. The Fibonacci sequence: relationship to the human hand. *J Hand Surg.* 2003 Jan;28(1):157-60.

Partonen T, Haukka J, Nevanlinna H, Lönnqvist J. Analysis of the seasonal pattern in suicide. *J Affect Disord.* 2004 Aug;81(2):133-9.

Partonen T, Haukka J, Viilo K, Hakko H, Pirkola S, Isometsä E, Lönnqvist J, Särkioja T, Väisänen E, Räsänen P. Cyclic time patterns of death from suicide in N. Finland. *J Affect Disord.* 2004 Jan;78(1):11-9.

Partonen T. Magnetoreception attributed to the efficacy of light therapy. *Med Hypoth.* 1998 Nov;51(5):447-8.

Pedemonte M, Rodríguez-Alvez A, Velluti RA. Electroencephalographic frequencies associated with heart changes in RR interval variability during paradoxical sleep. *Auton Neurosci.* 2005 Dec 30;123(1-2):82-6.

Penn RD, Hagins WA. Kinetics of the photocurrent of retinal rods. *Biophys J.* 1972 Aug;12(8):1073-94.

Penn RD, Hagins WA. Signal transmission along retinal rods and the origin of the electroretinographic a-wave. *Nature.* 1969 Jul 12;223(5202):201-4.

Penson RT, Kyriakou H, Zuckerman D, Chabner BA, Lynch TJ Jr. Teams: communication in multidisciplinary care. *Oncologist.* 2006 May;11(5):520-6.

Pérez-López FR. Vitamin D and its implications for musculoskeletal health in women: an update. *Maturitas.* 2007 Oct 20;58(2):117-37.

Perreau-Lenz S, Kalsbeek A, Van Der Vliet J, Pevet P, Buijs RM. In vivo evidence for a controlled offset of melatonin synthesis at dawn by the suprachiasmatic nucleus in the rat. *Neuroscience.* 2005;130(3):797-803.

Perrin RN. Lymphatic drainage of the neuraxis in chronic fatigue syndrome: a hypothetical model for the cranial rhythmic impulse. *J Am Osteopath Assoc.* 2007 Jun;107(6):218-24.

Persinger M.A. Psi phenomena and temporal lobe activity: The geomagnetic factor. In L.A. Henkel & R.E. Berger (Eds.), *Research in parapsychology.* (121- 156). Metuchen, NJ: Scarecrow Press, 1989.

Persinger M.A., Krippner S. Dream ESP experiments and geomagnetic activity. *Journal of the American Society of Psychical Research.* 1989;83:101- 106.

Pert C. *Molecules of Emotion.* New York: Scribner, 1997.

Petiot JF, Sainte-Laudy J, Benveniste J. Interpretation of results on a human basophil degranulation test. *Ann Biol Clin (Paris).* 1981;39(6):355-9.

Piluso LG, Moffatt-Smith C. Disinfection using ultraviolet radiation as an antimicrobial agent: a review and synthesis of mechanisms and concerns. *PDA J Pharm Sci Technol.* 2006 Jan-Feb;60(1):1-16.

Pitt-Rivers R, Trotter WR. *The Thyroid Gland.* London: Butterworth Publisher, 1954.

Plotnikoff G, Quigley J. Prevalence of Severe Hypovitaminosis D in Patients With Persistent, Nonspecific Musculoskeletal Pain. *Mayo Clin Proc.* 2003;78:1463-1470.

Ponsonby AL, McMichael A, van der Mei I. Ultraviolet radiation and autoimmune disease: insights from epidemiological research. *Toxicology.* 2002 Dec 27;181-182:71-8.

Pont AR, Charron AR, Brand RM. Active ingredients in sunscreens act as topical penetration enhancers for the herbicide 2,4-dichlorophenoxyacetic acid. *Toxicol Appl Pharmacol.* 2004 Mar 15;195(3):348-54.

Pool R. Is there an EMF-Cancer connection? *Science.* 1990;249: 1096-1098.

Popp F Chang J. Mechanism of interaction between electromagnetic fields and living organisms. *Science in China.* 2000 Series C;43(5):507-518.

Popp F, Chang J, Herzog A, Yan Z, Yan Y. Evidence of non-classical (squeezed) light in biological systems. *Physics Lett.* 2002;293:98-102.

Popp F, Yan Y. Delayed luminescence of biological systems in terms of coherent states. *Phys.Lett.* 2000;293:91-97.

Popp F. Molecular Aspects of Carcinogenesis. In Deutsch E, Moser K, Rainer H, Stacher A (eds.). *Molecular Base of Malignancy.* Stuttgart: G.Thieme, 1976:47-55.

Popp F. Properties of biophotons and their theoretical implications. *Indian J Exper Biology.* 2003 May;41:391-402.

Popper KR, Eccles, JC. *The Self and Its Brain.* London: Routledge, 1983.

Poulos LM, Toelle BG, Marks GB. The burden of asthma in children: an Australian perspective. *Paediatr Respir Rev.* 2005 Mar;6(1):20-7.

Prato FS, Frappier JR, Shivers RR, Kavaliers M, Zabel P, Drost D, Lee TY. Magnetic resonance imaging increases the blood-brain barrier permeability to 153-gadolinium diethylenetriaminepentaacetic acid in rats. *Brain Res.* 1990 Jul 23;523(2):301-4.

Preisinger E, Quittan M. Thermo- and hydrotherapy. *Wien Med Wochenschr.* 1994;144(20-21):520-6.

Pribram K. *Brain and perception: holonomy and structure in figural processing.* Hillsdale, N. J.: Lawrence Erlbaum Assoc., 1991.

Pronina TS. Circadian and infradian rhythms of testosterone and aldosterone excretion in children. *Probl Endokrinol.* 1992 Sep-Oct;38(5):38-42.

Protheroe WM, Captiotti ER, Newsom GH. *Exploring the Universe.* Columbus, OH: Merrill, 1989,

Puthoff H, Targ R, May E. Experimental Psi Research: Implication for Physics. AAAS Proceedings of the 1979 Symposium on the Role of Consciousness in the Physical World. 1981.

Puthoff H, Targ R. A Perceptual Channel for Information Transfer Over Kilometer distances: Historical Perspective and Recent Research. Proc. *IEEE.* 1976;64(3):329-254.

Radin D. *The Conscious Universe.* San Francisco: HarperEdge, 1997.

Raloff J. Ill Winds. *Science News:* 2001;160(14):218.

Regel SJ, Negovetic S, Roosli M, Berdinas V, Schuderer J, Huss A, *et al.* UMTS base station-like exposure, well-being, and cognitive performance. *Environ Health Perspect.* 2006 Aug;114(8):1270-5.

Reger D, Goode S, Mercer E. *Chemistry: Principles & Practice.* Fort Worth, TX: Harcourt Brace, 1993.

Reichrath J. The challenge resulting from positive and negative effects of sunlight: how much solar UV exposure is appropriate to balance between risks of vitamin D deficiency and skin cancer? *Prog Biophys Mol Biol.* 2006 Sep;92(1):9-16.

Reiffenberger DH, Amundson LH. Fibromyalgia syndrome: a review. *Am Fam Physician.* 1996;53:1698-704.

Reilly T, Stevenson I. An investigation of the effects of negative air ions on responses to submaximal exercise at different times of day. *J Hum Ergol.* 1993 Jun;22(1):1-9.

Reiter RJ, Garcia JJ, Pie J. Oxidative toxicity in models of neurodegeneration: responses to melatonin. *Restor Neurol Neurosci.* 1998 Jun;12(2-3):135-42.

Reiter RJ, Tan DX, Korkmaz A, Erren TC, Piekarski C, Tamura H, Manchester LC. Light at night, chrono-disruption, melatonin suppression, and cancer risk: a review. *Crit Rev Oncog.* 2007;13(4):303-28.

Reiter RJ, Tan DX, Manchester LC, Qi W. Biochemical reactivity of melatonin with reactive oxygen and nitrogen species: a review of the evidence. *Cell Biochem Biophys.* 2001;34(2):237-56.

Retallack D. *The Sound of Music and Plants.* Marina Del Rey, CA: Devorss, 1973.

Robert AM, Groult N, Six C, Robert L. The effect of procyanidolic oligomers on mesenchymal cells in culture II-Attachment of elastic fibers to the cells. *Pathol Biol.* 1990 Jun;38(6):601-7.

Robert AM, Tixier JM, Robert L, Legeais JM, Renard G. Effect of procyanidolic oligomers on the permeability of the blood-brain barrier. *Pathol Biol.* 2001 May;49(4):298-304.

Roberts JE. Light and immunomodulation. *Ann N Y Acad Sci.* 2000;917:435-45.

Robilliard DL, Archer SN, Arendt J, Lockley SW, Hack LM, English J, Leger D, Smits MG, Williams A, Skene DJ, Von Schantz M. The 3111 Clock gene polymorphism is not associated with sleep and circadian rhythmicity in phenotypically characterized human subjects. *J Sleep Res.* 2002 Dec;11(4):305-12.

Robinson TN. Television viewing and childhood obesity. *Pediatr Clin North Am.* 2001 Aug;48(4):1017-25.

Rodermel SR, Smith-Sonneborn J. Age-correlated changes in expression of micronuclear damage and repair in Paramecium tetraurelia. *Genetics.* 1977 Oct;87(2):259-74.

Rodgers JT, Puigserver P. Fasting-dependent glucose and lipid metabolic response through hepatic sirtuin 1. *Proc Natl Acad Sci USA.* 2007 Jul 31;104(31):12861-6.

Rodriguez E, Valbuena MC, Rey M, Porras de Quintana L. Causal agents of photoallergic contact dermatitis diagnosed in the national institute of dermatology of Colombia. *Photodermatol Photoimmunol Photomed.* 2006 Aug;22(4):189-92.

Rollier A. *Le Pansement Solaire.* Paris: Payot, 1916.

Rosenthal N, Blehar M (Eds.). *Seasonal affective disorders and phototherapy.* New York: Guildford Press, 1989.

Rostand SG. Ultraviolet light may contribute to geographic and racial blood pressure differences. *Hypertension.* 1997 Aug;30(2 Pt 1):150-6.

Routasalo P, Isola A. The right to touch and be touched. *Nurs Ethics.* 1996 Jun;3(2):165-76.

Roy M, Kirschbaum C, Steptoe A. Intraindividual variation in recent stress exposure as a moderator of cortisol and testosterone levels. Ann Behav Med. 2003 Dec;26(3):194-200.

Royal Society of Canada *A Review of the Potential Health Risks of Radiofrequency Fields from Wireless Telecommunication Devices.* Ottawa, Ontario: Royal Society of Canada. 1999.

Roybal K, Theobold D, Graham A, DiNieri JA, Russo SJ, Krishnan V, Chakravarty S, Peevey J, Oehrlein N, Birnbaum S, Vitaterna MH, Orsulak P, Takahashi JS, Nestler EJ, Carlezon WA Jr, McClung CA. Mania-like behavior induced by disruption of CLOCK. *Proc Natl Acad Sci USA* 2007;104(15):6406-6411.

Rubin E., Farber JL. *Pathology.* 3rd Ed. Philadelphia: Lippincott-Raven, 1999.

Rubin GJ, Hahn G, Everitt BS, Cleare AJ, Wessely S. Are some people sensitive to mobile phone signals? Within participants double blind randomised provocation study. *BMJ.* 2006 Apr 15;332(7546):886-91.

Russ MJ, Clark WC, Cross LW, Kemperman I, Kakuma T, Harrison K. Pain and self-injury in borderline patients: sensory decision theory, coping strategies, and locus of control. *Psychiatry Res.* 1996 Jun 26;63(1):57-65.

Russell IJ. Advances in fibromyalgia: possible role for central neurochemicals. *Am J Med Sci.* 1998;315:377-84.

Russo PA, Halliday GM. Inhibition of nitric oxide and reactive oxygen species production improves the ability of a sunscreen to protect from sunburn, immunosuppression and photocarcinogenesis. *Br J Dermatol.* 2006 Aug;155(2):408-15.

Saarijarvi S, Lauerma H, Helenius H, Saarilehto S. Seasonal affective disorders among rural Finns and Lapps. *Acta Psychiatr Scand.* 1999 Feb;99(2):95-101.

Sahar S, Sassone-Corsi P. Circadian clock and breast cancer: a molecular link. *Cell Cycle.* 2007 Jun 1;6(11):1329-31.

Sainte-Laudy J, Belon P. Analysis of immunosuppressive activity of serial dilutions of histamine on human basophil activation by flow cytometry. *Inflam Rsrch.* 1996 Suppl. 1: S33-S34.

Salama OE, Naga RM. Cellular phones: are they detrimental? *J Egypt Pub Hlth.* 2004;79(3-4):197-223.

Salford LG, Brun AE, Eberhardt JL, Malmgren L, Persson BR. Nerve cell damage in mammalian brain after exposure to microwaves from GSM mobile phones. *Environ Health Perspect.* 2003 Jun;111(7):881-3; discussion A408.

Sanders R. Slow brain waves play key role in coordinating complex activity. UC Berkeley News. 2006 Sep 14.

Sarah Janssen S, Solomon G, Schettler T. Chemical Contaminants and Human Disease:A Summary of Evidence. *The Collaborative on Health and the Environment.* 2006. http://www.healthandenvironment.org. Acc. 2007 Jul.

Saran, S., Gopalan, S. and Krishna, T. P. Use of fermented foods to combat stunting and failure to thrive. *Nutrition.* 2002;8:393-396.

Sarveiya V, Risk S, Benson HA. Liquid chromatographic assay for common sunscreen agents: application to in vivo assessment of skin penetration and systemic absorption in human volunteers. *J Chromatogr B Analyt Technol Biomed Life Sci.* 2004 Apr 25;803(2):225-31.

Sato TK, Yamada RG, Ukai H, Baggs JE, Miraglia LJ, Kobayashi TJ, Welsh DK, Kay SA, Ueda HR, Hogenesch JB. Feedback repression is required for mammalian circadian clock function. *Nat Genet.* 2006 Mar;38(3):312-9.

Savitz DA. Epidemiologic studies of electric and magnetic fields and cancer: strategies for extending knowledge. *Environ Health Perspect.* 1993 Dec;101 Suppl 4:83-91.

Schäfer A, Kratky KW. The effect of colored illumination on heart rate variability. *Forsch Komplementmed.* 2006 Jun;13(3):167-73.

Schirber M. Earth as a Giant Pinball Machine. *LiveScience.* 2004; 19 Nov 19. http://www.livescience.com/environment/041119_earth_layers.html. Acc. 2006 Nov.

Schirmacher A, Winters S, Fischer S, Goeke J, Galla HJ, Kullnick U, Ringelstein EB, Stögbauer F. Electromagnetic fields (1.8 GHz) increase the permeability to sucrose of the blood-brain barrier in vitro. *Bioelectromagnetics.* 2000 Jul;21(5):338-45.

Schlebusch KP, Maric-Oehler W, Popp FA. Biophotonics in the infrared spectral range reveal acupuncture meridian structure of the body. *J Altern Complement Med.* 2005 Feb;11(1):171-3.

Schlumpf M, Cotton B, Conscience M, Haller V, Steinmann B, Lichtensteiger W. In vitro and in vivo estrogenicity of UV screens. *Environ Health Perspect.* 2001 Mar;109(3):239-44.

Schmidt C, Collette F, Cajochen C, Peigneux P. A time to think: circadian rhythms in human cognition. *Cogn Neuropsychol.* 2007 Oct;24(7):755-89.

Schmidt H, Quantum processes predicted? *New Sci.* 1969 Oct 16.

Schmitt B, Frölich L. Creative therapy options for patients with dementia—a systematic review. *Fortschr Neurol Psychiatr.* 2007 Dec;75(12):699-707.

Schreiber, G.H., Swaen, G.M., Meijers, J.M.M., Slangen, J.J.M., and Sturmans, F. Cancer mortality and residence near electricity transmission equipment: A retrospective cohort study. *Int. J. Epidemiol.* 1993;22:9-15.

Schüz J, Mann S. A discussion of potential exposure metrics for use in epidemiological studies on human exposure to radiowaves from mobile phone base stations. *J Expo Anal Environ Epidemiol.* 2000 Nov-Dec;10(6 Pt 1):600-5.

Schwartz GG, Skinner HG. Vitamin D status and cancer: new insights. *Curr Opin Clin Nutr Metab Care.* 2007 Jan;10(1):6-11.

Schwartz S, De Mattei R, Brame E, Spottiswoode S. Infrared spectra alteration in water proximate to the palms of therapeutic practitioners. In: Wiener D, Nelson R (Eds.): *Research in parapsychology 1986.* Metuchen, NJ: Scarecrow Press, 1987:24-29.

Scott BO. The history of ultraviolet therapy. in Licht S. ed. *Therapeutic Electricity and Ultraviolet Radiation.* Phys Med Lib 4. Connecticut: Licht, 1967.

Scoville WB, Milner B. Loss of recent memory after bilateral hippocampal lesions. *J Neurol Neurosurg Psychiatry.* 1957;20:11-21.

Semenza C. Retrieval pathways for common and proper names. *Cortex.* 2006 Aug;42(6):884-91.

Senekowitsch F, Endler PC, Pongratz W, Smith CW. Hormone effects by CD record /replay. *FASEB J.* 1995:A12025.

Senior F. Fallout. *New York Mag.* 2003 Fall.

Serra-Valls A. Electromagnetic Industrion and the Conservation of Momentum in the Spiral Paradox. *Cornell University Library.* http://arxiv.org/ftp/physics/papers/0012/0012009.pdf. Accessed: 2007 July.

Serway R. *Physics For Scientists & Engineers.* Philadelphia: Harcourt Brace, 1992.

Shearman LP, Zylka MJ, Weaver DR, Kolakowski LF Jr, Reppert SM. Two period homologs: circadian expression and photic regulation in the suprachiasmatic nuclei. *Neuron.* 1997 Dec;19(6):1261-9.

Shen YF, Goddard G. The short-term effects of acupuncture on myofascial pain patients after clenching. *Pain Pract.* 2007 Sep;7(3):256-64.

Shevelev IA, Kostelianetz NB, Kamenkovich VM, Sharaev GA. EEG alpha-wave in the visual cortex: check of the hypothesis of the scanning process. *Int J Psychophysiol.* 1991 Aug;11(2):195-201.

Shivers RR, Kavaliers M, Teskey GC, Prato FS, Pelletier RM. Magnetic resonance imaging temporarily alters blood-brain barrier permeability in the rat. *Neurosci Lett.* 1987 Apr 23;76(1):25-31.

Shupak NM, Prato FS, Thomas AW. Human exposure to a specific pulsed magnetic field: effects on thermal sensory and pain thresholds. *Neurosci Lett.* 2004 Jun 10;363(2):157-62.

Shutov AA, Panasiuk IIa. Efficacy of rehabilitation of patients with chronic primary low back pain at the spa Klyuchi using balneopelotherapy and transcranial electrostimulation. *Vopr Kurortol Fizioter Lech Fiz Kult.* 2007 Mar-Apr;(2):16-8.

Sicher F, Targ E, Moore D, Smith H. A Randomized Double-Blind Study of the Effect of Distant Healing in a Population With Advanced AIDS. Western Journal of Medicine. 1998;169 Dec::356-363.

Siegfried J. Electrostimulation and neurosurgical measures in cancer pain. *Recent Results Cancer Res.* 1988;108:28-32.

Sies H, Stahl W. Nutritional protection against skin damage from sunlight. Annu Rev Nutr. 2004;24:173-200.

Sita-Lumsden A, Lapthorn G, Swaminathan R, Milburn HJ. Reactivation of tuberculosis and vitamin D deficiency: the contribution of diet and exposure to sunlight. *Thorax.* 2007 Nov;62(11):1003-7.

Skwerer RG, Jacobsen FM, Duncan CC, Kelly KA, Sack DA, Tamarkin L, Gaist PA, Kasper S, Rosenthal NE. Neurobiology of Seasonal Affective Disorder and Phototherapy. *J Biolog Rhyth.* 1988;3(2):135-154.

Sloan F and Gelband (ed). Cancer Control Opportunities in Low- and Middle-Income Countries. Committee on Cancer Control in Low- and Middle-Income Countries. 2007.

Smith CW. Coherence in living biological systems. *Neural Network World.* 1994:4(3):379-388.

Smith MJ. "Effect of Magnetic Fields on Enzyme Reactivity" in Barnothy M.(ed.), *Biological Effects of Magnetic Fields.* New York: Plenum Press, 1969.

Smith MJ. *The Influence on Enzyme Growth By the 'Laying on of Hands: Dimensions of Healing.* Los Altos, California: Academy of Parapsychology and Medicine, 1973.

Smith-Sonneborn J. Age-correlated effects of caffeine on non-irradiated and UV-irradiated Paramecium Aurelia. *J Gerontol.* 1974 May;29(3):256-60.

Snow WB. *The Therapeutics of Radiant Light and Heat and Convective Heat.* NY: Sci Auth Publ, 1909.

Snyder K. Researchers Produce Firsts with Bursts of Light: Team generates most energetic terahertz pulses yet, observes useful optical phenomena. *Press Release: Brookhaven National Laboratory.* 2007 July 24.

Soler M, Chandra S, Ruiz D, Davidson E, Hendrickson D, Christou G. A third isolated oxidation state for the Mn12 family of single molecule magnets. *ChemComm;* 2000; Nov 22.

Speed Of Light May Not Be Constant, Physicist Suggests. *Science Daily.* 1999 Oct 6. www.sciencedaily.com/releases/1999/10/991005114024.htm. Accessed: 2007 June.

Spence A. *Basic Human Anatomy.* Menlo Park, CA: Benjamin/Commings, 1986.

Spencer FA, Goldberg RJ, Becker RC, Gore JM. Seasonal distribution of acute myocardial infarction in the second National Registry of Myocardial Infarction. J Am Coll Cardiol. 1998 May;31(6):1226-33.

Squire LR, Zola-Morgan S. The medial temporal lobe memory system. *Science.* 1991;253(5026):1380-1386.

St Hilaire MA, Klerman EB, Khalsa SB, Wright KP Jr, Czeisler CA, Kronauer RE. Addition of a non-photic component to a light-based mathematical model of the human circadian pacemaker. *J Theor Biol.* 2007 Aug 21;247(4):583-99.

Stahl W, Heinrich U, Wiseman S, Eichler O, Sies H, Tronnier H. Dietary tomato paste protects against ultraviolet light-induced erythema in humans. *J Nutr.* 2001 May;131(5):1449-51.

Steck B. Effects of optical radiation on man. *Light Resch Techn.* 1982;14:130-141.

Stoebner-Delbarre A, Thezenas S, Kuntz C, Nguyen C, Giordanella JP, Sancho-Garnier H, Guillot B; Le Groupe EPI-CES. Sun exposure and sun protection behavior and attitudes among the French population. *Ann Dermatol Venereol.* 2005 Aug-Sep;132(8-9 Pt 1):652-7.

Stojanovic MP, Abdi S. Spinal cord stimulation. *Pain Physician.* 2002 Apr;5(2):156-66.

Stoupel E, Kalediene R, Petrauskiene J, Gaizauskiene A, Israelevich P, Abramson E, Sulkes J. Monthly number of newborns and environmental physical activity. *Medicina Kaunas.* 2006;42(3):238-41.

Stoupel E, Monselise Y, Lahav J. Changes in autoimmune markers of the anti-cardiolipin syndrome on days of extreme geomamagnetic activity. *J Basic Clin Physiol Pharmacol.* 2006;17(4):269-78.

Stoupel EG, Frimer H, Appelman Z, Ben-Neriah Z, Dar H, Fejgin MD, Gershoni-Baruch R, Manor E, Barkai G, Shalev S, Gelman-Kohan Z, Reish O, Lev D, Davidov B, Goldman B, Shohat M. Chromosome aberration and environmental physical activity: Down syndrome and solar and cosmic ray activity, Israel, 1990-2000. *Int J Biometeorol.* 2005 Sep;50(1):1-5.

Strange BA, Dolan RJ. Anterior medial temporal lobe in human cognition: memory for fear and the unexpected. *Cognit Neuropsychiatry.* 2006 May;11(3):198-218.

Streitberger K, Ezzo J, Schneider A. Acupuncture for nausea and vomiting: an update of clinical and experimental studies. *Auton Neurosci.* 2006 Oct 30;129(1-2):107-17.

Sugarman E. *Warning, The Electricity Around You May be Hazardous To Your Health.* NY: Sim & Schuster, 1992.

Sulman FG, Levy D, Lunkan L, Pfeifer Y, Tal E. New methods in the treatment of weather sensitivity. *Fortschr Med.* 1977 Mar 17;95(11):746-52.

Sulman FG. Migraine and headache due to weather and allied causes and its specific treatment. *Ups J Med Sci Suppl.* 1980;31:41-4.

Suppes P, Han B, Epelboim J, Lu ZL. Invariance of brain-wave representations of simple visual images and their names. *Proc Natl Acad Sci Psych-BS.* 1999;96(25):14658-14663.

Swislocki A, Orth M, Bales M, Weisshaupt J, West C, Edrington J, Cooper B, Saputo L, Islas M, Miaskowski C. A randomized clinical trial of the effectiveness of photon stimulation on pain, sensation, and quality of life in patients with diabetic peripheral neuropathy. *J Pain Symptom Manage.* 2010 Jan;39(1):88-99. Epub 2009 Nov 5.

Tahvanainen K, Nino J, Halonen P, Kuusela T, Alanko T, Laitinen T, Lansimies E, Hietanen M, Lindholm H. Effects of cellular phone use on ear canal temperature measured by NTC thermistors. *Clin Physiol Funct Imaging.* 2007 May;27(3):162-72.

Tanagho EA. Principles and indications of electrostimulation of the urinary bladder. *Urologe A.* 1990 Jul;29(4):185-90.

Tang G, Serfaty-Lacronsniere C, Camilo ME, Russell RM. Gastric acidity influences the blood response to a beta-carotene dose in humans. *Am J Clin Nutr.* 1996;64:622-6.

Taoka S, Padmakumar R, Grissom C, Banerjee R. Magnetic Field Effects on Coenzyme B-12 Dependent Enzymes: Validation of Ethanolamine Ammonia Lyase Results and Extension to Human Methylmalonyl CoA Mutase. *Bioelectromagnetics.* 1997;18: 506-513.

Taraban M, Leshina T, Anderson M, Grissom C. Magnetic Field Dependence and the Role of electron spin in Heme Enzymes: Horseradish Peroxidase. *J. Am. Chem. Soc.* 1997;119: 5768-5769.

Targ R, Puthoff H. Information transfer under conditions of sensory shielding. *Nature.* 1975;251:602-607.

Taskinen H, Kyyrönen P, Hemminki K. Effects of ultrasound, shortwaves, and physical exertion on pregnancy outcome in physiotherapists. *J Epidemiol Community Health.* 1990 Sep;44(3):196-201.

Taylor SL, Kaur M, LoSicco K, Willard J, Camacho F, O'Rourke KS, Feldman SR. Pilot study of the effect of ultraviolet light on pain and mood in fibromyalgia syndrome. *J Altern Complement Med.* 2009 Jan;15(1):15-23.

Tevini M, ed. *UV-B Radiation and Ozone Depletion: Effects on humans, animals, plants, microorganisms and materials.* Boca Raton: Lewis Pub, 1993.

Thaker JP, Patel MB, Jongnarangsin K, Liepa VV, Thakur RK. Electromagnetic interference with pacemakers caused by portable media players. *Heart Rhythm.* 2008 Apr;5(4):538-44.

Thakkar RR, Garrison MM, Christakis DA. A systematic review for the effects of television viewing by infants and preschoolers. *Pediatrics.* 2006 Nov;118(5):2025-31.

Thakur CP, Sharma D. Full moon and crime. *Br Med J.* 1984 December 22; 289(6460): 1789-1791.

Thaut MH. The future of music in therapy and medicine. *Ann N Y Acad Sci.* 2005 Dec;1060:303-8.

The Timechart Company. *Timetables of Medicine.* New York: Black Dog & Leventhal, 2000.

Thie J. *Touch for Health.* Marina del Rey, CA: Devorss Publications, 1973-1994.

Thomas MK, Lloyd-Jones DM, Thadhani RI, Shaw AC, Deraska DJ, Finkelstein JS, et al. Hypovitaminosis D in Medical Inpatients. *NEJM.* 1998 March 19;338(12):777-783.

Thomas Y, Litime H, Benveniste J. Modulation of human neutrophil activation by "electronic" phorbol myristate acetate (PMA). *FASEB Jnl.* 1996;10: A1479.

Thomas Y, Schiff M, Belkadi L, Jurgens P, Kahhak L, Benveniste J. Activation of human neutrophils by electronically transmitted phorbol-myristate acetate. *Med Hypoth.* 2000;54: 33-39.

Thomas Y, Schiff M, Litime M, Belkadi L, Benveniste J. Direct transmission to cells of a molecular signal (phorbol myristate acetate, PMA) via an electronic device. *FASEB Jnl.* 1995;9: A227.

Thomas-Anterion C, Jacquin K, Laurent B. Differential mechanisms of impairment of remote memory in Alzheimer's and frontotemporal dementia. *Dement Geriatr Cogn Disord.* 2000 Mar-Apr;11(2):100-6.

Thompson D. *On Growth and Form.* Cambridge: Cambridge University Press, 1992.

REFERENCES AND BIBLIOGRAPHY

Tian FS, Zhang HR, Li WD, Qiao P, Duan HB, Jia CX. Study on acupuncture treatment of diabetic neurogenic bladder. *Zhongguo Zhen Jiu.* 2007 Jul;27(7):485-7.

Timofeev I, Steriade M. Low-frequency rhythms in the thalamus of intact-cortex and decorticated cats. *J Neurophysiol.* 1996 Dec;76(6):4152-68.

Ting W, Schultz K, Cac NN, Peterson M, Walling HW. Tanning bed exposure increases the risk of malignant melanoma. Int J Dermatol. 2007 Dec;46(12):1253-7.

Tiwari M. *Ayurveda: A Life of Balance.* Rochester, VT: Healing Arts, 1995.

Toomer G. "Ptolemy". *The Dictionary of Scientific Biography.* New York: Gale Cengage, 1970.

Triglia A, La Malfa G, Musumeci F, Leonardi C, Scordino A. Delayed luminsecence as an indicator of tomato fruit quality. *J Food Sci.* 1998;63:512-515.

Trivedi B. Magnetic Map" Found to Guide Animal Migration. *Natl Geogr Today.* 2001 Oct 12.

Tsong T. Deciphering the language of cells. *Trends in Biochem Sci.* 1989;14: 89-92.

Tsuei JJ, Lam Jr. F, Zhao Z. Studies in Bioenergetic Correlations-Bioenergetic Regulatory Measurement Instruments and Devices. *Am J Acupunct.* 1988;16:345-9.

Tsuei JJ, Lehman CW, Lam F, Jr, Zhu D. A food allergy study utilizing the EAV acupuncture technique. *Am J Acupunct.* 1984;12:105-16.

Tweed K. Study: Conceiving in Summer Lowers Baby's Future Test Scores. *Fox News.* 2007 May 9, 2007. (Study done by: Winchester P. 2007. Pediatric Academic Societies annual meeting.)

Udermann H, Fischer G. Studies on the influence of positive or negative small ions on the catechol amine content in the brain of the mouse following shorttime or prolonged exposure. *Zentralbl Bakteriol Mikrobiol Hyg.* 1982 Apr;176(1):72-8.

Ulett G. Electroacupuncture: mechanisms and clinical application. *Biological Psychiatry.* 1998;44(2):129-138.

Ulrich RS. Aesthetic and affective response to natural environment. In Altman, I. and Wohlwill, J. F. (eds) *Human Behaviour and Environment: Advances in Theory and Research. Volume 6: Behaviour and the Natural Environment.* New York: Plenum Press: 1983:85-125.

Ulrich RS. Influences of passive experiences with plants on individual wellbeing and health. In Relf, D. (ed) *The Role of Horticulture in Human Well-Being and Social Development: A National Symposium.* Portland: Timber Press, Portland. 1992:93 -105.

Ulrich RS. Natural versus urban scenes: some psychophysiological effects. *Environment and Behaviour.* 1981:523-556.

Ulrich RS. View through window may influence recovery from surgery. *Science.* 1984;224:420 - 421.

Ulrich RS. Visual landscapes and psychological well being. *Landscape Research.* 1979;4:17-23.

Unger RH. Leptin physiology: a second look. *Regul Pept.* 2000 Aug 25;92(1-3):87-95.

Vallance A. Can biological activity be maintained at ultra-high dilution? An overview of homeopathy, evidence, and Bayesian philosophy. *J Altern Complement Med.* 1998 Spring;4(1):49-76.

Van Cauter E, Leproult R, Plat L. Age-related changes in slow wave sleep and REM sleep and relationship with growth hormone and cortisol levels in healthy men. *JAMA.* 2000 Aug 16;284(7):861-8.

Van Cauter E. Slow wave sleep and release of growth hormone. *JAMA.* 2000 Dec 6;284(21):2717-8.

Vaquero JM, Gallego MC. Sunspot numbers can detect pandemic influenza A: the use of different sunspot numbers. *Med Hypotheses.* 2007;68(5):1189-90.

Vargha-Khadem F, Polkey CE. A review of cognitive outcome after hemidecortication in humans. *Adv Exp Med Biol.* 1992;325:137-51.

Vena JE, Graham S, Hellmann R, Swanson M, Brasure J. Use of electric blankets and risk of postmenopausal breast cancer. *Am J Epidemiol.* 1991 Jul 15;134(2):180-5.

Vescelius E. *Music and Health.* New York: Goodyear Book Shop, 1918.

Vgontzas AN. The diagnosis and treatment of chronic insomnia in adults. *Sleep.* 2005 Sep 1;28(9):1047-8.

Vierling-Claassen D, Siekmeier P, Stufflebeam S, Kopell N. Modeling GABA alterations in schizophrenia: a link between impaired inhibition and altered gamma and beta range auditory entrainment. *J Neurophysiol.* 2008 May;99(5):2656-71.

Vigny P, Duquesne M. *On the fluorescence properties of nucleotides and polynucleotides at room temperature.* In. Birks J (ed.). Excited states of biological molecules. London-NY: J Wiley, 1976:167-177.

Villani S. Impact of media on children and adolescents: a 10-year review of the research. *J Am Acad Child Adolesc Psychiatry.* 2001 Apr;40(4):392-401.

Viner RM, Cole TJ. Television viewing in early childhood predicts adult body mass index. *J Pediatr.* 2005 Oct;147(4):429-35.

Viola AU, James LM, Schlangen LJ, Dijk DJ. Blue-enriched white light in the workplace improves self-reported alertness, performance and sleep quality. *Scand J Work Environ Hlth.* 2008 Aug;34(4):297-306.

Volkmann H, Dannberg G, Kuhnert H, Heinke M. Therapeutic value of trans-esophageal electrostimulation in tachycardic arrhythmias. *Z Kardiol.* 1991 Jun;80(6):382-8.

Voll R. The phenomenon of medicine testing in elecroacupuncture according to Voll. *Am J Acupunct.* 1980;8:97-104.

Voll R. Twenty years of electroacupuncture diagnosis in Germany: a progressive report. *Am J Acupunct.* 1975;3:7-17.

von Schantz M, Archer SN. *Clocks, genes and sleep. J R Soc Med.* 2003 Oct;96(10):486-9.

Vyasadeva S. *Srimad Bhagavatam.* Approx rec 4000 BCE.

Wachiuli M, Koyama M, Utsuyama M, Bittman BB, Kitagawa M, Hirokawa K. Recreational music-making modulates natural killer cell activity, cytokines, and mood states in corporate employees. *Med Sci Monit.* 2007 Feb;13(2):CR57-70.

Walker M. *The Power of Color.* New Delhi: B. Jain Publishers. 2002.

Wang R, Jiang C, Lei Z, Yin K. The role of different therapeutic courses in treating 47 cases of rheumatoid arthritis with acupuncture. *J Tradit Chin Med.* 2007 Jun;27(2):103-5.

Wang XY, Shi X, He L. Effect of electroacupuncture on gastrointestinal dynamics in acute pancreatitis patients and its mechanism. *Zhen Ci Yan Jiu.* 2007;32(3):199-202.

Watson L. *Beyond Supernature.* New York: Bantam, 1987.

Watson L. *Supernature.* New York: Bantam, 1973.

Wayne R. *Chemistry of the Atmospheres.* Oxford Press, 1991.

Weaver J, Astumian R. The response of living cells to very weak electric fields: the thermal noise limit. *Science.* 1990;247: 459-462.

Wee K, Rogers T, Altan BS, Hackney SA, Hamm C. Engineering and medical applications of diatoms. *J Nanosci Nanotechnol.* 2005 Jan;5(1):88-91.

Weinberger P, Measures M. The effect of two audible sound frequencies on the germination and growth of a spring and winter wheat. *Can. J. Bot.* 1968;46(9):1151-1158.

Weinert D, Waterhouse J. The circadian rhythm of core temperature: effects of physical activity and aging. *Physiol Behav.* 2007 Feb 28;90(2-3):246-56.

Wertheimer N, Leeper E. Electrical wiring configurations and childhood cancer. *Am J Epidemiol.* 1979 Mar;109(3):273-84.

Wetterberg L. Light and biological rhythms. *J Intern Med.* 1994 Jan;235(1):5-19.

Weyandt TB, Schrader SM, Turner TW, Simon SD. Semen analysis of military personnel associated with military duty assignments. *Reprod Toxicol.* 1996 Nov-Dec;10(6):521-8.

Wharton B, Bishop N. Rickets. *Lancet.* 2003 Oct 25;362(9393):1389-400.

White AR, Rampes H, Ernst E. Acupuncture for smoking cessation. *Cochrane Database Syst Rev.* 2002;(2):CD000009.

White J, Krippner S (eds). *Future Science: Life Energies & the Physics of Paranormal Phenomena.* Garden City: Anchor, 1977.

White S. *The Unity of the Self.* Cambridge: MIT Press, 1991.

Whittaker E. *History of the Theories of Aether and Electricity.* New York: Nelson LTD, 1953.

WHO. How trace elements in water contribute to health. *WHO Chronicle.* 1978;32: 382-385.

Wilen J, Hornsten R, Sandstrom M, Bjerle P, Wiklund U, Stensson O, Lyskov E, Mild KH. Electromagnetic field exposure and health among RF plastic sealer operators. *Bioelectromag.* 2004 Jan;25(1):5-15.

Winchester AM. *Biology and its Relation to Mankind.* New York: Van Nostrand Reinhold, 1969.

Winfree AT. *The Timing of Biological Clocks.* New York: Scientific American, 1987.

Wolf, M. Beyond the Point Particle - *A Wave Structure for the Electron. Galil Electrodyn.* 1995 Oct;6(5):83-91.

Wolpowitz D, Gilchrest BA. The vitamin D questions: how much do you need and how should you get it? *J Am Acad Dermatol* 2006;54:301-17.

Wolverton BC. *How to Grow Fresh Air: 50 House Plants that Purify Your Home or Office.* NY: Penguin, 1997.

Wyart C, Webster WW, Chen JH, Wilson SR, McClary A, Khan RM, Sobel N. Smelling a single component of male sweat alters levels of cortisol in women. *J Neurosci.* 2007 Feb 7;27(6):1261-5.

Yamaoka Y. Solid cell nest (SCN) of the human thyroid gland. *Acta Pathol Jpn.* 1973 Aug;23(3):493-506.

Yan YF, Wei YY, Chen YH, Chen MM. Effect of acupuncture on rehabilitation training of child's autism. *Zhongguo Zhen Jiu.* 2007 Jul;27(7):503-5.

Yang HQ, Xie SS, Hu XL, Chen L, Li H. Appearance of human meridian-like structure and acupoints and its time correlation by infrared thermal imaging. *Am J Chin Med.* 2007;35(2):231-40.

Yeager RL, Oleske DA, Sanders RA, Watkins JB 3rd, Eells JT, Henshel DS. Melatonin as a principal component of red light therapy. *Med Hypotheses.* 2007;69(2):372-6.

Yeung JW. A hypothesis: Sunspot cycles may detect pandemic influenza A in 1700-2000 A.D. *Med Hypotheses.* 2006;67(5):1016-22.

Yu XM, Zhu GM, Chen YL, Fang M, Chen YN. Systematic assessment of acupuncture for treatment of herpes zoster in domestic clinical studies. *Zhongguo Zhen Jiu.* 2007 Jul;27(7):536-40.

REFERENCES AND BIBLIOGRAPHY

Yuan SY, Lun X, Liu DS, Qin Z, Chen WT. Acupoint-injection of BCG polysaccharide nuclear acid for treatment of condyloma acuminatum and its immunoregulatory action on the patient. *Zhongguo Zhen Jiu.* 2007 Jun;27(6):407-11.

Zaets VN, Karpov PA, Smertenko PS, Blium IaB. Molecular mechanisms of the repair of UV-induced DNA damages in plants. *Tsitol Genet.* 2006 Sep-Oct;40(5):40-68.

Zhang C, Popp, F., Bischof, M.(eds.). *Electromagnetic standing waves as background of acupuncture system. Current Development in Biophysics - the Stage from an Ugly Duckling to a Beautiful Swan.* Hangzhou: Hangzhou University Press, 1996.

Zimecki M. The lunar cycle: effects on human and animal behavior and physiology. *Postepy Hig Med Dosw.* 2006;60:1-7.

Zimmerman FJ, Christakis DA. Children's television viewing and cognitive outcomes: a longitudinal analysis of national data. *Arch Pediatr Adolesc Med.* 2005 Jul;159(7):619-25.

Zittermann A, Schleithoff SS, Koerfer R. Vitamin D insufficiency in congestive heart failure: why and what to do about it? *Heart Fail Rev.* 2006 Mar;11(1):25-33.

Index

absorption, 48, 154, 164, 180, 181, 222
accumbens, 140
acetylcholine, 79, 90, 93, 98, 161, 255
acrophobia, 83
acupressure, 151
acupuncture, 109, 110, 116, 118, 119, 120, 144, 147, 148, 150, 151, 226
adaptive power, 198
adenosine-diphosphate, 138
adenosine-triphosphate (ATP), 63, 72, 103, 129, 138
adipose cells, 103
adrenal glands, 80, 83, 90, 107, 146, 178
adrenal insufficiency, 161
adrenaline, 79, 93, 134, 167, 236, 255
adrenocorticotropic hormone, 93
aether, 21, 124, 142
aggression, 204, 236
air, 9, 12, 13, 26, 29, 34, 43, 52, 56, 61, 96, 121, 137, 141, 143, 159, 166, 185, 186, 209, 225, 226, 236, 244, 248, 253, 259
airspeed, 17
ajna, 139
alambusha, 144, 146
alcohol, 82, 189, 211
aldosterone, 93, 135
alkaloids, 206
allergies, 67, 167, 225, 236
allyl sulfides, 241
alpha waves, 73, 82, 83, 175
alveoli, 137, 138, 142
amino acids, 48, 52, 206, 241, 242

amplitude, 14, 15, 16, 18, 19, 33, 122, 148, 154, 216, 247, 252, 259
anahata, 137
androgen, 135
anesthesia, 83
angina, 163
angiotensin, 93
antioxidants, 233, 234, 241
anus, 134, 135, 142, 144, 146
anxiety, 82, 83, 157, 166, 178, 180, 183, 205, 250, 255
appetite, 92, 177, 178
arrhythmias, 51
arthritis, 147, 167, 217
artificial light, 41, 106, 156, 183
asthma, 160, 236
astronomy, 194
atherosclerosis, 87, 167, 241
atmosphere, 8, 10, 17, 18, 34, 35, 36, 39, 67, 94, 128, 131, 138, 153, 169, 177, 208, 209, 210, 225, 231, 234, 253, 254
atomic energy, 7, 22, 24, 170
auroras, 56
autoimmune disorder, 225
autoimmune-related diseases, 163
Ayurveda, 115, 116, 117, 118, 123, 125, 132, 135, 136, 142, 158, 171, 176, 177, 179, 228, 230
basophils, 97
behavior, 6, 35, 37, 55, 56, 82, 96, 137, 146, 154, 176, 179, 181, 204, 236, 239, 245
beta waves, 76, 82, 175, 176
beta-carotene, 241
bilirubin, 173
biofeedback, 72, 76, 77

Made in the USA
Lexington, KY
26 November 2012